THE GEOLOGIC SYSTEMS

GENERAL EDITOR
KALERVO RANKAMA

THE PRECAMBRIAN

VOLUME 3

THE GEOLOGIC SYSTEMS

THE PRECAMBRIAN

VOLUME 3

EDITOR

KALERVO RANKAMA

1967

INTERSCIENCE PUBLISHERS

A Division of John Wiley & Sons, Inc.

New York — London — Sydney

*Printed in Great Britain by Richard Clay (The Chaucer Press), Ltd.,
Bungay, Suffolk*

PREFACE

Among the five contributions printed in this volume, four deal with Precambrian areas in and around the western Indian Ocean. The immense and intricate Precambrian terranes in India have been painstakingly studied by generations of British and Indian geologists for more than a century. The Precambrian of the subcontinent has not only produced a marble for the construction of the Taj Mahal but has also provided the petrologist with charnockites—rocks now eagerly investigated in all the Precambrian Shield areas. The Precambrian of Peninsular India continues in Ceylon, where the Precambrian rocks occupying nine-tenths of the island area have been comprehensively studied for forty years. Ceylon is famous for the abundance and variety of gemstones and semiprecious stones, and for many rare minerals in her Precambrian crystalline rocks. The Seychelles Archipelago in the western Indian Ocean, a rugged group of islands rising steeply from the sea, is remarkable for the occurrence of Precambrian granites in an oceanic environment. The Precambrian of Madagascar, covering two-thirds of the island, has been exclusively surveyed and completely mapped in less than forty years. The Precambrian of the Republic of the Congo and of the two small adjoining states, Rwanda and Burundi, has been studied in great detail since the time the European geologists first penetrated the interior of the area. The present-day knowledge is largely a by-product of research in economic geology since the late 1870's. The contribution presented in this volume is partly based on still unpublished data.

I was fortunate enough to visit Madagascar in 1965, gaining some first-hand knowledge of the Precambrian during brief field trips under the expert guidance of Dr. Henri Besairie. The similarity between the metamorphosed Precambrian of Madagascar and of Finland is indeed astonishing.

It is a well-known fact that the Precambrian stratigraphic terminology is largely unsettled and that no internationally accepted stratigraphic classification exists. The Authors of the monographs printed in this volume have consequently used their own stratigraphic terminology, or the terminology currently adopted in their respective countries. The contributions in this volume afford ample evidence of the difficulties met when correlations are extended across geologic or geographic barriers and political boundaries.

In 1966, the Executive Committee of the International Union of Geological Sciences decided to set up a Subcommission on Precambrian

v

Stratigraphy operating as one of the subcommissions of the Commission on Stratigraphy. The main task of the Subcommission is to investigate the possibility of dividing the Precambrian globally into internationally acceptable units of System rank and, assumedly, of Supersystem (Erathem) rank. In due course, the Subcommission will certainly be able to submit a global stratigraphic classification for the scrutiny of Precambrian geologists and stratigraphers.

The Authors of the monographs printed in this volume have followed many rules set up, as a style guide, for the sake of uniformity of treatment of the subject matter. It is my privilege, as the Editor, to thank the Authors for their cooperation and patience in preparing their manuscripts for publication in *The Precambrian*. It is a pleasant duty to acknowledge the valuable help of the INTERSCIENCE–WILEY editorial staff in London and Chichester and of the Printers, especially their willingness to meet numerous suggestions and requests from the Authors and the Editor alike. Their co-operation is thoroughly appreciated. Finally, because the forthcoming volumes of *The Precambrian* will be handled by INTERSCIENCE–WILEY in New York, I take much personal pleasure in acknowledging the help, cooperation, and goodwill of the editorial and production staffs in London since the start of *The Geologic Systems* project in 1959.

"Nothing is so plentiful as Time".

KALERVO RANKAMA

Adelaide, S.A.
   September, 1967

CONTENTS

THE PRECAMBRIAN OF INDIA [1]

C. S. Pichamuthu

Department of Geology, Bangalore University, India

Contents

[1] Manuscript received April 25, 1962. Revised manuscript received April 28, 1964.

1. Introduction

1.1. *Physiography*

India may be geographically divided into three regions. First, there is the Peninsular region, which is the triangular area projecting into the Indian Ocean. The second region, i.e. the mountain belt of the Himalayas in the north, is called the Extrapeninsular region. The Indo–Gangetic alluvial region separates the first two. The geographical regions do not correspond to any stratigraphical boundaries. The part of the Extrapeninsular region which is known as the Lesser Himalaya should be considered as the outer fringes of the Peninsular region, because in the Kashmir, Simla, Darjeeling, and Assam areas there are representatives of the Cuddapah, Vindhyan, and Gondwana groups which became involved in the tectonic processes which produced the Himalayan ranges. The more important physiographical features, such as the river and mountain systems of India, are shown in Fig. 1.

Bordering the west coast of the Peninsula and stretching from the Tapti estuary to Cape Comorin, the Western Ghats constitute a conspicuous range of hills with an average height of about 1,200 m. The western side of this range is cut into a steep scarp by faulting and denudation for a length of nearly 1,600 km.

The Eastern Ghats join the Western Ghats in the Nilgiri Plateau, and the two ranges enclose between them the Mysore Plateau. The Eastern Ghats are too irregular and ill-defined really to be called a range. The average height of the hills is about 600 m. The Precambrian rocks present are charnockites and garnet-bearing schists and gneisses, and indicate a high grade of metamorphism.

The Satpura Hills separate the Narbada and Tapti Rivers, and consist mainly of basaltic traps. The Central Satpuras, apart from the traps, are also composed of Precambrian rocks.

The Vindhya Range, north of the Narbada, and its eastward continuation in the same direction north of the Son Valley, known as the Kaimur Range, are merely the southern scarps of the vast Malwa or Vindhyan Plateau to the west and of the Bundelkhand Plateau to the east.

The Aravalli Range is continuous from Ajmer southwestward through Rajputana up to Mount Abu (altitude, 1,700 m). It has probably extended farther to the southwest, because isolated peaks which are relics of the Aravalli range exist in Kathiawar and Cutch. Northeast of Ajmer the range is practically drowned by blown desert sand or alluvium, and is represented by scattered and isolated hills which can be traced as far as Delhi.

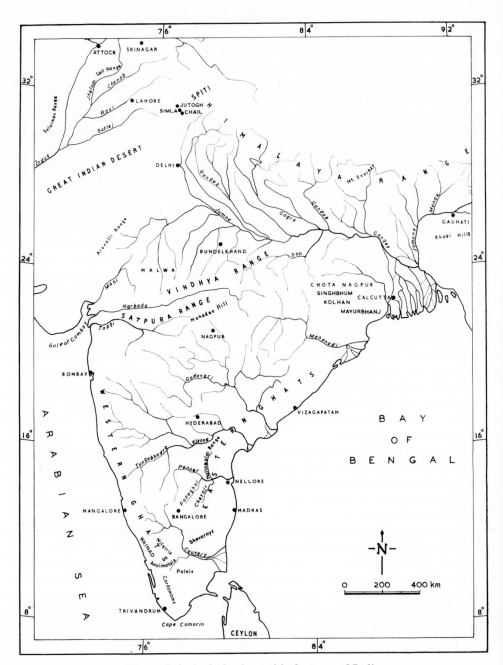

FIG. 1. Principal physiographic features of India.

1.2. *Nomenclature*

Captain T. J. NEWBOLD (1844–1850) was one of the earliest geologists to examine the Precambrian rocks of India, and his field of observation lay mainly in Mysore State, which later became a classic area. He recognized both schistose and gneissic types of rocks, and described the complex as being composed of "protogine schists and gneisses" intruded by various granites.

The Precambrian rocks of Madras State were later studied by W. KING, who grouped them into the "altered or transition rocks", and the "crystalline rocks". To the former he (KING, 1872, p. 36) gave the names "Kadapah" and "Karnul", and to the latter, the name "the gneissic series".

R. BRUCE FOOTE in 1886 proposed the name "Dharwar" for the "lower transition" group of schistose rocks, which he described as a "system" of sedimentogenic beds with intercalated traps. He chose the name "Dharwar" from the district (now in Mysore State) in which he first recognized the schistose rocks as a distinct and separate "system" (FOOTE, 1888, p. 41). He differed, however, from NEWBOLD in considering that the granitic gneiss complex, which was called the "fundamental granitoid gneiss", was the basement on which the Dharwar sediments were deposited.

One of the main principles of stratigraphical classification is based on the occurrence of unconformities in rock sequences. When Indian rocks were thus divided into groups it was found that the groups did not always correspond with those established in other parts of the world. There is, for instance, no unconformity in India between the Paleozoic and the Mesozoic. However, a well-defined break occurs at the base of the Permian–Carboniferous, a horizon which was correlated with the topmost stage of the Upper Carboniferous by HOLLAND (1909, p. 56), and which he used to demarcate the Aryan group above from the Dravidian group below.

The Dravidian group begins approximately from the base of the Cambrian. In the Peninsula this boundary is drawn by some geologists at the top of the Vindhyans. According to others, the Vindhyans belong to the Paleozoic.

Below the Dravidian is the Purana group. There is an unconformity between the two groups. The Purana group comprises the formations lying between the base of the Cambrian and the Archean. In the evolution of ideas it corresponds somewhat to the Animikian and the Keweenawan of Canada. Most of the Purana rocks were originally included in the "upper transition" group, which comprised comparatively much less metamorphosed rocks between which and the gneiss there is no such close connection and parallelism as there is in the rocks of the "lower transition" group.

The Archean rocks may be divided into two principal types, the one schistose and the other gneissose. The schistose rocks comprise the Dharwar group,[1] which was formerly known as the "submetamorphic series", or the

_____

[1] As a chronostratigraphical term, "system" and the corresponding geochronological

"lower transition" group. It is a succession of metamorphosed sediments, volcanic flows, tuffs, and minor intrusions. The gneissose group, which was formerly known as the "Fundamental gneiss", is a complex comprising plutonic and hypabyssal intrusions which were emplaced prior to the Eparchean interval; some of them are younger than, and intrusive into, the Dharwar schists. Because of their prevalence in Peninsular India, they are now called, without prejudice to their relative age, the Peninsular gneiss (SMEETH, 1916).

In many parts of India the oldest metasedimentary rocks, either because of their position in the local stratigraphical succession or sometimes because of certain lithological resemblance, have been called the Dharwars. Some of these ancient rocks differ considerably in age from one another and from rocks in the type area in the south. Structural studies and age determinations have shown that the real Dharwars in Mysore State are older than both the Eastern Ghats and the Satpura belts. It is, therefore, necessary to discontinue the use of the name "Dharwar" for schistose rocks outside the type area, because it is not possible to consider all the fossil-free rocks of sedimentary origin and associated intrusive rocks in Peninsular India as synchronous or even homotaxial, since lithologically similar rocks occur in younger orogenic cycles (PICHAMUTHU, 1962, 1963). In both the Archean and the Purana it is, therefore, extremely difficult to decipher stratigraphical relationships and to establish satisfactory correlations.

2. Mode of occurrence and origin

2.1. *Basement*

After the Archean rocks had been divided into the schistose and the gneissose groups, there arose considerable differences of opinion as to their relationship to one another.

R. BRUCE FOOTE was probably the first geologist who believed that the gneiss formed the basement on which the Dharwar sediments were deposited. Later R. D. OLDHAM accepted FOOTE's view. He referred to the relation of the Dharwars to the granitoid gneiss of Bellary as one of undoubted unconformity, because the bottom beds of the schists, wherever the contact is found, rest on an uneven eroded surface of the granitoid gneiss (OLDHAM, 1893, pp. 23–24). HOLLAND (1902, p. 74) generally agreed with FOOTE's view, even though he found it somewhat difficult to believe that the strongly

term "period", are totally inadequate to denote the Precambrian time during which certain formations were deposited. It must be stated, however, that the names "system" and "series" have been current in Indian geology for nearly a century to describe Precambrian formations. The name "group" has been used in this article instead of the name "system" as the stratigraphical equivalent of an "era". The writer proposes, however, to continue the usage of the name "series", because any change in nomenclature at the present time would lead to confusion.

folded Dharwar rocks of the Kolar schist belt in Mysore State could be younger than the much less deformed Peninsular gneisses of the region.

While examining the Gadag belt of Dharwar schists, MACLAREN (1906, p. 107) came to the conclusion that the gneisses were the fundamental rocks on which the Dharwars were laid down, even though he described some small and narrow gneiss intrusions along the cleavage planes of schist. MIDDLEMISS (1917, p. 197) also inclined to the view that the Dharwars were deposited unconformably on the gneisses. He explained the gneissic intrusions as being caused by local re-fusion or plastic deformation and penetration.

In 1899, along with H. K. SLATER and B. JAYARAM, W. F. SMEETH made a detailed examination of the Kolar schist belt in Mysore State, and arrived at some very important conclusions regarding the age relationships of the Precambrian formations. He and his colleagues found that the granites and gneisses associated with the schists were intrusive into the schists and did not form the basement rocks on which the material of the schists was laid down. SMEETH (1901, p. 19) believed that no rocks older than the Dharwars could be definitely recognized anywhere in Mysore State. FERMOR (1909, p. 998) found evidence of intrusive contacts along the boundaries of some of the Dharwar outcrops and consequently agreed with SMEETH that the Dharwars are the oldest rocks wherever they occur and that the associated gneisses are intrusive into the Dharwars.

The relationship between the Dharwar schists and the gneisses offered no problem regarding the basement until work in Mysore State and elsewhere showed that the Peninsular gneiss, which was formerly known as the "Fundamental gneiss", was definitely intrusive into the Dharwars and therefore was younger. But if the Dharwars are older than the Peninsular gneiss, on what solid base were they laid down? As PASCOE (1950, p. 62) has stated: "to be asked to regard the Dharwar sediments and lavas as everywhere the oldest rocks present is like being asked to look at a picture with no wall to support it". Do the Lower Dharwars, which are composed of silicic and mafic volcanic flows, represent the first-formed rocks of the preaquatic period [1] of the Earth's history, or were they extravasated on a very ancient granitic floor which represents the primeval crust?

In southern India no rocks have been definitely proved to be older than the Dharwars. The greater part of these ancient formations was either removed by denudation or modified by granitization, but thick sections were preserved because they were tightly folded prior to being invaded. There is, however, no conclusive evidence for the recognition of any basement, because the presumed foundation rocks have probably been repeatedly granitized.

In the oldest mafic volcanic rocks pillow structures exist which indicate that the flows are of submarine origin. Associated with the oldest volcanic rocks there are thin bands of ferruginous cherts and dark siliceous schists

[1] The time before the assumed condensation of water vapor.

which represent the earliest formed sediments that have been preserved in a metamorphosed state. The Lower Dharwars cannot, therefore, be basement formations.

The oldest known gneissic rock in Mysore State is the Champion gneiss, which is considered by some geologists to be older than the Dharwars and, hence, probably the floor on which the Dharwar sediments were deposited. In support of this view it has been stated that the intrusive relationship between the Dharwars and the Champion gneiss is not as conclusive as that between the Dharwars and the Peninsular gneiss, that these two formations are always found adjacent to each other, often with parallel strikes, and that many of the conglomerates are associated with outcrops of the Champion gneiss. Unfortunately, there is great difference of opinion as to what the Champion gneiss exactly is, and this has caused considerable confusion. It has also been suggested that the use of the name "Champion gneiss" should be discontinued, and in the classification of the Precambrian of Mysore proposed by RAMA RAO (1940, p. 83) there is no mention of the Champion gneiss. It is necessary that the type area should be reexamined carefully, and if possible dated, before finally discarding the name "Champion gneiss" for a group of rocks which possesses certain characteristic features.

The Lower Dharwars are composed mainly of silicic and mafic volcanic flows and dikes. The overlying Dharwars commence with conglomerates which contain pebbles of quartzite, indicating that the Lower Dharwars, just as the Keewatin rocks in North America, were formed not only of igneous rocks but also of typical sedimentary rocks. The occurrence of quartzite beds indicates the preexistence of a terrain composed of quartz-bearing silicic rocks by the disintegration of which the arenaceous sediments were derived.

There are pebbles of gneiss in the Kalavararanganbetta conglomerates in the Shimoga schist belt and in the Talya conglomerates of the Chitaldrug schist belt. Pebbles of these pre-Dharwar gneisses are probably the only fragmentary evidence that exists of the Dharwar basement in southern India.

Somewhat similar is the history of research on the Precambrian rocks occurring in the northern parts of Peninsular India. As early as 1893, R. D. OLDHAM was of the opinion that the more pronouncedly foliated gneisses were younger than the massive gneisses such as the Bundelkhand gneiss of central India. Later A. M. HERON came to the conclusion that the Rajputana equivalents of the Dharwars were deposited or poured out on an old floor of Bundelkhand gneiss. He did not believe that all the granitic rocks in the former State of Hyderabad were of intrusive origin, because it was difficult to distinguish between a primary intrusive contact and a depositional contact which had been blurred by the subsequent strong metamorphism.

In Rajputana the Bundelkhand granite when traced westward passes into a highly foliated gneiss upon which the Aravalli schists appear to rest with an erosional unconformity. The Aravalli rocks are considered by some geologists to belong to the Dharwar System, and thus the Bundelkhand granite has sometimes been regarded as a relic of the old igneous floor on which the Dharwar sediments were deposited. Work by R. C. MISRA, M. N. SAXENA, and P. C. MATHUR (see JHINGRAN, 1958, p. 17), however, showed that even though mainly a granitic rock without conspicuous foliation, the Bundelkhand granite is locally migmatitic and contains recognizable xenoliths of older schistose rocks in various stages of granitization. It cannot, therefore, be the "oldest rock of India", as has commonly been supposed on the double assumption that it is pre-Aravalli and pre-Dharwar. According to HOLMES (1955, p. 95), the genuine floor-rocks of the Aravalli geosyncline, viz. the Banded gneiss complex and the Bundelkhand gneiss, must be dated before their precise positions in the Precambrian sequence can be discussed.

2.2. *Igneous* vs. *sedimentary origin*

One of the problems which seriously confronted the workers who were concerned with the study of the Precambrian of India was the mode of origin of many of the component rocks.

The early geologists, such as R. BRUCE FOOTE, P. BOSWORTH SMITH, and E. W. WETHERELL, were of the opinion that many of the Dharwar rocks were of sedimentary origin. W. F. SMEETH, who in 1900 became State Geologist in Mysore, also held this view, but later he (SMEETH, 1910, pp. 13, 35) concluded that the Dharwar conglomerates in Mysore were not normal sedimentary rocks, but autoclastic, i.e. crush conglomerates formed by subsequent pressure. He was also reluctant to admit the sedimentary origin of any of the Dharwar rocks. The quartzites were supposed to represent crushed vein quartz, felsite, or quartz porphyry; the limestones were considered to be either highly calcified parts of mafic traps or metasomatic replacements of the silicic Champion gneisses; the ferruginous quartzites were believed to be derived by the alteration of amphibolites; and the kyanite–staurolite schists, sillimanite–cordierite gneisses, and similar rocks were believed to have been formed by the contact metamorphism of mafic igneous rocks.

L. L. FERMOR also inclined to the view that most, but not all, of the Dharwar conglomerates were autoclastic. With the hornblende schists and such other rocks as were then accepted to be of igneous origin, he associated certain quartzites, potstones, and other magnesium-rich schists in Singhbhum and certain mica schists in Chhindwara, as having a similar origin. He, however, believed that the majority of the slates, phyllites, mica schists, and quartzites of the Dharwars (in which he included the highly crystalline limestones and the calcium-rich gneisses of Madhya Pradesh) were metamorphosed sediments.

MIDDLEMISS (1917) opposed the view that the Dharwars do not include sediments. In support of his opinion he drew attention to the fact that the Dharwar outcrops of southern India occur as comparatively narrow strips in the gneiss, a relationship which indicates that the schist bands are remnants of an old sedimentary sequence which was deposited on the gneiss and was later folded along with the gneiss.

In Mysore State itself there were a few geologists who did not agree with SMEETH. SAMBASIVA IYER (1918) was one of them, and he advocated a sedimentary origin for some of the quartzites occurring in the Tumkur district.

B. JAYARAM succeeded W. F. SMEETH as Director of Geology in Mysore, and he (JAYARAM, 1925) stated that the limestones and the sillimanite- and cordierite-bearing rocks of the Sakarsanhalli area were of sedimentary origin. At about this time RAMA RAO (1927) also indicated his inclination toward a sedimentary origin for some of the Dharwar rocks, particularly for the crystalline graphitic schists, and for certain cordierite- and sillimanite-bearing rocks. He felt, however, that definite proof was lacking.

As the result of a detailed examination of some of the typical components of the Dharwar formations of Mysore, PICHAMUTHU (1935a, b) concluded that the conglomerates and grits, quartzites, and ferruginous quartzites were undoubtedly sedimentary in origin. Current bedding, graded bedding, ripple marks, and intraformational folding were also reported to occur.

Official opinion finally turned in favor of a sedimentary origin when RAMA RAO (1936), then the Director of Geology, announced that investigations in Mysore disclosed concrete evidence of sedimentation. The tardy recognition of the occurrence of sedimentary beds in the Dharwars hindered much of the progress which might have been made in the elucidation of the stratigraphy, structure, and tectonics of the Precambrian of Peninsular India.

3. Distribution, classification, and stratigraphy

3.1. *General*

The Precambrian rocks occupy about two-thirds of Peninsular India and parts of the Lesser Himalayas in the Extrapeninsular region. The outcrops in southern India occur generally as elongated belts in the gneiss.

After India became an independent nation in 1947, all the Native States were abolished, the nomenclature and boundaries of the former provinces and presidencies were revised, and a few new States were created. The spellings of many of the names of localities were also altered. All these changes will probably confuse readers who are not familiar with the geography of India. In order to clarify the position, two maps of India are presented. Figure 2 delineates the situation before independence and Fig. 3 shows the present-day distribution of the States.

The distribution of the Precambrian rocks in India is presented in Fig. 4. The broad expanse of the Deccan traps, and the Indo–Gangetic alluvium probably cover considerable parts of the Precambrian areas, and, con-

FIG. 2. Boundaries of the States of India before independence in 1947.

sequently, the structure and continuity of the Precambrian formations in certain areas become a matter of inference or conjecture.

The Precambrian rocks stretch from Cape Comorin in the extreme south of India to Madhya Pradesh and Bihar, and presumably continue beneath the Gangetic alluvium into the Assam Plateau. The Precambrian rocks of Mysore are probably connected with some of the outcrops in Gujarat and Rajasthan underneath the Deccan traps.

The important regions in Peninsular India where extensive complexes of Archean rocks occur are Mysore, Madras, Eastern Ghats, Jeypore–Bastar, Nagpur–Chhindwara, Rajasthan, Gujarat, Bundelkhand, Singhbhum, Gangpur, Bengal, and Assam. The Cuddapahs and their probable equivalents apart from the type area in Andhra Pradesh occur in Kaladgi, Chhattisgarh, Gwalior, Bijawar, and Delhi.

TABLE 1

Precambrian rocks in India

	Peninsula	Northern Himalayas	Kashmir–Hazara	Simla–Garhwal	Eastern Himalayas–Assam
Purana	Cuddapah and Delhi groups	Haimanta group	Dogra slates	Simla slates	Buxa series
Archean	Aravalli and Dharwar groups	Vaikrita group	Salkhala series	Chail series Jutogh series	Daling series Darjeeling series Shillong series
	Gneisses		Gneisses		Gneisses

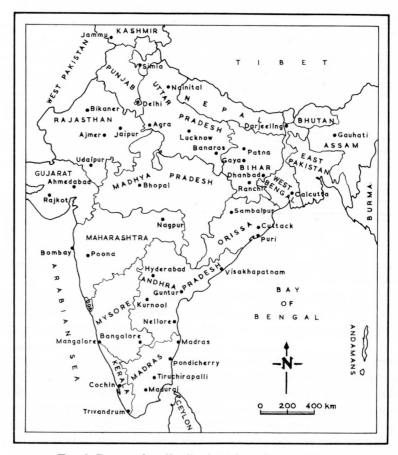

FIG. 3. Present-day distribution of the States of India.

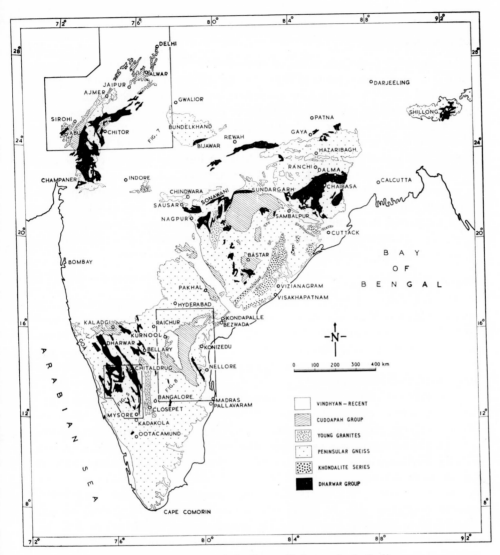

FIG. 4. Distribution of the Precambrian rocks in India.

In the Extrapeninsular region, Archean rocks exist in northwestern Himalaya, Spiti, Simla, Garhwal, Nepal, Sikkim and eastern Himalaya. Rocks resembling the Cuddapahs and Delhis occur in Kashmir, Punjab, North-West Frontier Province, Simla, Garhwal and Kumaon.

Table 1 gives a general classification of the important Precambrian rocks of India.

3.2. *Peninsular India*

3.2.1. Archean group

The Archean rocks are widely distributed in Peninsular India. Regional work done in different parts of India by the officers of the Central and State Geological Surveys resulted in numerous publications. Local names were necessarily used by individual workers to designate the various rock units and a general idea of the rock types may be obtained from Table 2. The placing alongside each other of units in Table 2 is based generally on certain lithological resemblances and does not indicate that they are similar or of the same age, for it is known that many are not.

In this account it will not be possible to go into detailed descriptions. It is proposed, however, to give the classifications and correlations which have been suggested for some of the important Precambrian regions of India. Since Mysore State is one of the areas where these rocks have been studied in some detail, it is appropriate to commence with this State.

Mysore State

Between 1899 and 1915, under W. F. SMEETH's direction, practically the whole of Mysore State was rapidly traversed and mapped. A geological map of the State, which embodied the work of the surveys conducted till then, was published in 1915. Figure 5, which is based on this map, presents the Precambrian geology of a part of Mysore State which includes the Shimoga and Chitaldrug schist belts.

The Dharwar schists of Mysore were classified by SMEETH (1916) on lithological grounds into two groups without any perceptible unconformity between them, viz. a lower division consisting of dark hornblende schists and amphibolites of igneous origin, associated with thin bands of quartz schists, ferruginous quartz rocks, and calcium pyroxene granulites, and an upper division composed mostly of greenstones, chlorite schists and mica schists, associated with quartzites, conglomerates, limestones, and ferruginous quartzites. All the rocks were considered to be of igneous origin. According to SMEETH, there were four separate granitic intrusions into the Dharwar schists, viz. the Champion gneiss, the Peninsular gneiss, charnockite, and the Closepet granite. The Champion gneiss was believed to be the earliest silicic intrusion into the Dharwar rocks and thus definitely younger than the Dharwar schists, the two rock sequences being separated by an eruptive unconformity.

Between 1915 and 1920 B. JAYARAM and P. SAMPAT IYENGAR extended the connotation of the name "Champion gneiss" and ascribed to the alteration and modification of this gneiss a wide range of Dharwar rocks such as schists, quartzites, conglomerates, limestones, and even ferruginous quartzites. In view of this, SAMPAT IYENGAR (1920) suggested that the Champion gneiss should be considered a member of the Dharwar "system", and that the eruptive unconformity should not be placed between the Dharwar

TABLE 2

Archean rocks of Peninsular India. No horizontal correlations are intended or implied

Mysore	Madras	Eastern Ghats and Bastar	Bihar and Orissa	Madhya Pradesh	Rajasthan	Assam
Closepet and Bellary granites	Hosur, Arcot, and other granites	Granite	Singhbhum granite Dome gneiss?	Amla granite	Alkalic syenite?	Mylliem granite
Peninsular gneiss	Peninsular gneiss	Granite gneiss	Chota Nagpur or Bengal gneiss	Granite gneiss	?	Granite gneiss
Upper Dharwars (shales, grits, etc.)	?	Kopayi stage?	Kolhan series?	?	Raialo series?	?
Middle Dharwars (banded ferruginous rocks, quartzites, etc.)	Magnetite—quartz and hematite—quartz schists, etc.	Bailadila iron-ore series	Iron-ore series	Sakoli and Chilpi Ghat series	Aravalli group, Champaner series	Shillong series
Lower Dharwars (chlorite schists, hornblende schists, mica schists, etc.)	Chlorite schists, etc.	Bengpal series, khondalites, kodurites	Gangpur series (gondites, marbles, etc.)	Sausar and Sonawani series (gondites, marbles, etc.)	Bijawar and Gwalior series?	Granulites, calcium silicate gneisses, etc.
Oldest Archean rocks (represented only by pebbles in conglomerates)	?	?	?	?	Banded gneiss?	?

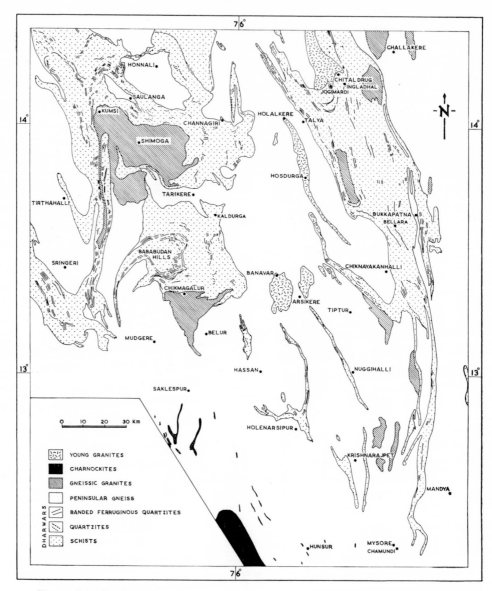

Fig. 5. Distribution of Precambrian rocks in a part of Mysore State, a type area.
Published with the permission of the Director of Mines and Geology, Mysore State.

"system" and the Champion gneiss, but between the Champion gneiss and
the Peninsular gneiss. SMEETH (1926, pp. 43, 51) agreed with this view. The
writer considers it more probable that the Champion gneiss dates from the
Lower Dharwar time, because it is associated with the hornblende schists of
the Kolar gold belt and has contributed opalescent grains of quartz to some
of the quartzites of the Middle Dharwars. A Lower Dharwar age would also

explain the frequent association of the Champion gneiss with conglomerates.

The generalized succession of Precambrian rocks in Mysore is presented in Table 3.

In Mysore the Dharwars, as do similar formations in many other parts of the world, start with an igneous complex of mafic, intermediate, and silicic lava flows and intrusives. The Lower Dharwars contain extensive areas

TABLE 3

Precambrian rocks in Mysore State

		Mafic dikes Felsite and porphyry dikes Closepet granite Charnockite series Peninsular gneiss complex
Dharwar group	Upper	Cherty, ferruginous, and calcareous shales, quartzites, and conglomerates
	Middle	Granitic rocks, granite porphyry Mafic and ultramafic intrusives Ironstones, limestones, argillites, quartzites, and conglomerates
	Lower	Champion gneiss Rhyolites, felsites, quartz porphyry Mafic volcanic flows and intrusions

of mafic rocks. The Lingadhalli traps in the Shimoga schist belt are epidiorite flows with spilitic affinities. Quartz keratophyres also occur in association with the mafic lavas. Massive and schistose greenstones are among the oldest rocks of the Chitaldrug schist belt.

After the above-mentioned epoch of igneous activity, the Middle Dharwar cycle of sedimentation commenced. The closing phases of this cycle were marked by extensive igneous activity as evidenced by batholiths and stocks of silicic rocks. This orogenic phase was followed by the emplacement of minor intrusives and volcanic flows of mafic rocks. In the Shimoga schist belt the banded ferruginous quartzites are intruded by sills and dikes of quartz dolerites which now occur as epidiorites. As the result of the intrusion of the epidiorites in the Bababudan Hills, sodium amphiboles, such as bababudanite, formed in the ferruginous quartzites. The mafic intrusives and flows in the Chitaldrug schist belt have been described under various names, e.g. the Bellara trap, the Jogimardi trap, the Chitaldrug gray trap, and the trappoidal hornblende schist. The Jogimardi trap and the dark hornblende traps of Chitaldrug are very low in potassium and relatively high in sodium, which is characteristic of spilitic rocks. Typical pillow structures also occur in the Chitaldrug traps (see Fig. 6). PICHAMUTHU

(1957) gave an account of the pillow lavas associated with the Dharwar schists in various parts of Mysore State.

The Upper Dharwar sediments were subsequently deposited, and almost the same sequence of events as in the first cycle was repeated, ending again with a period of igneous activity. The deeper-lying rocks were intensely metamorphosed and migmatites were formed. The granite batholiths,

FIG. 6. Pillow lava of Dharwar age. Maradihalli, Chitaldrug district, Mysore State. In spite of the great age of the rock, the shape of the pillows, the arrangement of the vesicles, and the glassy outer skin are clearly seen. Photo, C. S. Pichamuthu.

which are now identified as parts of the Peninsular gneisses, and some of the mafic dikes are evidence of the third phase of volcanism which marked the close of the second cycle of Dharwar sedimentation.

In the classification proposed by RAMA RAO (1935a) the Champion gneiss and a part of the Peninsular gneisses were considered to be older than the conglomerates, quartzites, argillitic schists, dolomitic limestones, and banded hematite quartzites. He (RAMA RAO, 1936) divided the Dharwars of the Shimoga and Chitaldrug schist belts into three groups which were separated by conglomerates. The name "Champion gneiss" was dropped in this classification. Later he (RAMA RAO, 1940, p. 81) postulated only two epochs of granitic intrusion: the intrusion producing the Closepet granite, and the intrusion producing all the other older granites. This suggestion implied that what had hitherto been considered as separate intrusions of the

Champion gneiss and of the Peninsular gneiss belonged to a single period. Acceptance of this view raises several difficulties.

The oldest Dharwar conglomerates in Mysore contain gneiss pebbles (see p. 8). Again, the Kaldurga conglomerates contain pebbles derived from a suite of rocks characterized by the presence of albite. This eruptive stage comprising the spilitic suite of rocks predated the formation of the Kaldurga conglomerates and occurred at the close of the cycle of sedimentation of the Middle Dharwars. The next eruptive interval was at the end of the Upper Dharwar time and, consequently, is separated from the earlier intrusion by the time necessary for the deposition of the Upper Dharwars. It has already been stated that the Champion gneiss was presumably formed toward the end of the Lower Dharwar time (see p. 16). Thus, apart from the probable existence of a pre-Dharwar granite, there were four separate epochs of granite formation, one each at the closing stages of the Lower and the Middle Dharwars, another at the end of the Upper Dharwar time, and a fourth, a much later one, comprising the Closepet granite, the Chitaldrug granite, the Arsikere and Banavar granites, the Chamundi granite, and other similar young granites, which are generally pink and often porphyritic.

Madhya Pradesh

Two main sedimentary divisions, viz. an older Bengpal series and a younger Bailadila series, were recognized by CROOKSHANK (1963) in Bastar State, in addition to granites, gneisses, greenstones, and islands of charnockite.

The Bailadila series comprises banded hematite quartzites and iron ores, banded hematite–chlorite and hematite–grunerite rocks, ferruginous shales and conglomerates, calcium silicate schists, and amphibolites. It is strongly reminiscent of the Iron-ore series of Singhbhum. The Bengpal series consists of hornblende schists, andalusite- and garnet-bearing schists, banded grunerite quartzites, anthophyllite–cordierite gneisses and such other rocks, and corresponds to a part of the Gangpur series. Granites, pegmatites, and dolerites have intruded the sedimentary formations. According to GHOSH (1941), the charnockites of this region owe their origin to hybridism between granites and calcium silicate schists.

In the southern part of the Chhindwara district the Sausar series was studied in considerable detail and was subdivided into stages, the uppermost of which may be the equivalent of the lowermost Sakoli beds (FERMOR, 1931, p. 108). The succession, never complete in any one section, is presented in Table 4.

The rocks of the Sausar series as a whole are more strongly metamorphosed than the bulk of the Dharwars of Mysore or Madras, the metamorphic group comprising such rocks as, among others, hypersthene granite gneiss, hornblende gneiss, and amphibolite.

Southeast of Nagpur there occurs the Sakoli facies. With a general N.E.–S.W. strike, the Sakoli beds are parallel to the Sausar rocks in the

TABLE 4

Stratigraphical and lithological classification of the Sausar series in
Chhindwara District

Stage	Lithological description
Bichua stage	White dolomitic marbles, forsterite-, spinel-, chondrodite-, and serpentine-bearing marbles; diopsidites; tremolite, anthophyllite, and wollastonite schists; scapolite granulites; scapolite–diopside marbles
Junewani stage	Muscovite–biotite schists, with small crush "pebbles"; staurolite, kyanite, and sillimanite schists; garnetiferous biotite gneiss
Chorbaoli stage	Quartzites; feldspar-bearing muscovite–quartz schists, sometimes garnetiferous
Mansar or Gondite stage	Muscovite–biotite–sillimanite schists, often garnetiferous, with manganese ore bodies
Lohangi stage	Pink calcitic marbles; banded calciphyres; black manganiferous marbles; piedmontite marbles; some manganese ores; banded calcium silicate granulites; hornblende–biotite granulites; magnetite–biotite granulites

north. In the Sakoli succession manganese ores, manganese silicate rocks, calcium silicate granulites, and marbles are entirely absent.

The Sakoli series comprises muscovite–chlorite schists; feldspar-bearing muscovite–quartz schists with vein quartz containing wolframite; quartzites (some highly ferruginous); phyllites and slates (sometimes with magnetite and garnet); rocks containing kyanite, tourmaline, rutile, occasional dumortierite, topaz, and roscoelite; and sillimanite rocks. Among the Sakoli metasediments occur thick bodies of epidiorite.

Bihar and Orissa

Parts of southern Bihar State, especially Singhbhum and its neighborhood, have been investigated in some detail with respect to Precambrian geology. The rocks are of two facies, an unmetamorphosed one on the south, and a metamorphosed one on the north, separated by a major thrust zone which marks the overfolded limb of a geanticline. Mafic igneous rocks, both intrusive and extrusive, and large masses of granite are present. The Singhbhum region is economically one of the most important in India because it contains some of the richest and most extensive deposits of iron ore in the world.

JONES (1922) gave the name "Iron-ore series" to the group of rocks of sedimentary and extrusive origin among which the iron ores occur. Later work by DUNN (1940) disclosed that two formations had been included in the iron-ore series. He retained the name "Iron-ore series" for the older of the two, and proposed the name "Kolhan series" for the younger.

The relationships among the various Precambrian rocks of the Bihar and Orissa region are represented by the provisional classification given in Table 5.

The Newer dolerites occur as dikes in the Arkasani granophyre and thus cannot be the intrusive phase of the Dhanjori lavas. According to DUNN (1940, p. 363), they could be of post-Gondwana age, and probably coeval with the Deccan traps (PASCOE, 1950, p. 231). However, they have nowhere been seen to penetrate the Kolhan beds, and, hence, probably are of pre-Kolhan age.

DUNN and DEY (1942) believed that the lower Chaibasa stage and the upper Iron-ore stage occur on either side of a major thrust zone (Copper Belt thrust). The studies of SARKAR and SAHA (1959) in Singhbhum and adjacent areas indicated that the Iron-ore stage in the south represents an older orogenic belt, the closing stages of this orogeny being represented by the

TABLE 5

Precambrian rocks in Bihar and Orissa

Kolhan series
———————— (Unconformity) ————————
Newer dolerites
Arkasani granophyre
Chakradarpur gneiss
Singhbhum granite
Chota Nagpur gneiss
Dalma and Dhanjori lavas
Dhanjori sandstone-conglomerate
———————— (Unconformity) ————————

Iron-ore series	Iron-ore stage	Phyllites and tuffs, conglomerates and quartzites Banded quartzites, often hematite-bearing Phyllites and mafic igneous rocks
	———————— (Possible overlap) ————————	
	Chaibasa stage	Mica schists, hornblende schists, quartz granulites, quartz schists; tuffs and cherts in less strongly metamorphosed areas

emplacement of the Singhbhum granite complex. Moreover, they suggested that the sediments and lavas of the Chaibasa stage and of the Iron-ore stage of DUNN (Dhalbhum stage) in the north were deposited in the active belt adjoining the already stabilized continent to the south. Table 6 presents the revised correlation suggested by them for the Precambrian of Singhbhum and neighboring areas.

In Gangpur State (now called the Sundargarh district), which lies west of the Singhbhum district, there is an anticlinorium which has an E.N.E.–W.S.W. axial direction, in the core of which there is a manganese-bearing horizon containing gondite. Apart from the manganese-bearing rocks, the

Gangpur series comprises carbonaceous phyllites, calcitic and dolomitic marbles, and certain older metamorphic rocks. It is separated by a shear zone from the overlying Iron-ore series.

Rajasthan

Rajasthan is important both structurally and stratigraphically. The chief formations of pre-Vindhyan age are as follows:

> Malani suite of igneous rocks
> Delhi group
> Raialo series
> Aravalli group
> Banded gneiss complex and Bundelkhand gneiss

TABLE 6

Correlation of the Precambrian rocks in Singhbhum and the adjacent areas.
According to SARKAR and SAHA (1962)

South of the Copper Belt thrust zone	North of the Copper Belt thrust zone
Newer dolerite	Newer dolerite
Granophyre, biotite granite	Ultramafic sills and dikes
Ultramafics of Jojohatu (? Ultramafic bodies associated with the Singhbhum granite)	Sodium granite, granophyre, Kuilapal granite, Chakradharpur granite gneiss
———— Singhbhum orogeny ————	———— Singhbhum orogeny ————
	(934 Myr–905 Myr)
Dhanjori ⎰ Dhanjori lava	Dalma lava
group ⎱	———— Overlap ————
Quartzite and conglomerate	Singhbhum series ⎰ Dhalbhum stage [Iron-ore stage of DUNN and DEY (1942)] ⎱ Chaibasa stage
? Kolhan series (1,584 Myr)	
———— Unconformity ————	
Singhbhum granite	
——— Iron-ore orogeny (2,038 Myr) ———	
Gabbro, anorthosite, epidiorite	
Iron-ore series ⎰ Upper shales with sandstones and volcanics ⏐ Banded hematite jasper ⏐ Lower shales ⏐ Lavas ⎱ Sandstones and conglomerates	
———— Unconformity ————	
Older metamorphic rocks: mica, sillimanite, hornblende, chlorite, and quartz schists	

The Aravalli chain and its subordinate ranges are situated in this area, and it was here that HERON (1936, p. 9; 1953, pp. 21–22) came to the conclusion that in both the Bundelkhand gneiss and the Banded gneiss complex there are probable remnants of the old floor on which were laid down the sediments considered to be equivalent to the lower part of the "Dharwar" group.

The distribution of the Precambrian rocks is shown in Fig. 7. The general stratigraphical sequence in this region, according to PASCOE (1950, p. 247), is given in Table 7.

The Aravalli group, even though more argillaceous, has a general resemblance to the Dharwars. According to HERON (1917, p. 110), the unconformity at the top of the sequence represents the great Eparchean interval. The Aravallis have been intruded by granite which is older than the Raialo and the Delhi metasediments. The Aravalli rocks show a general decrease

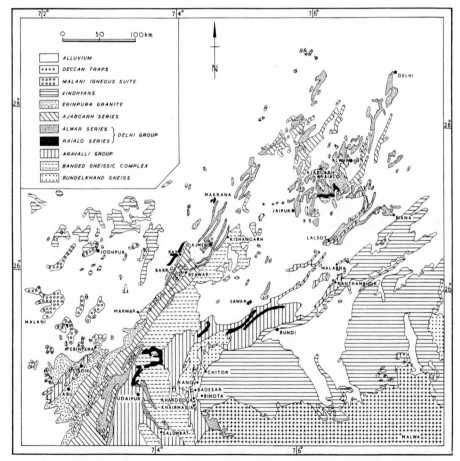

FIG. 7. Precambrian rocks of a part of Rajasthan. According to HERON (1935). Published with the permission of the Director, Geological Survey of India.

in the degree of metamorphism from the northwest toward the southeast, i.e. away from the axis of the Aravalli range.

The disposition of the quartzite bands indicates that the folding of the Aravallis was very complex and was affected by shearing and thrust faulting. Although repeated by isoclinal folding, a very thick sequence of sediments is represented by the Aravalli group.

TABLE 7

Precambrian rocks in Rajasthan. According to PASCOE (1950)

Aravalli group	Ranthambhor or Mandalgarh quartzite	Kanoj grits Badesar quartzites	Khardeola grits Khairmalia amygdaloid
	(Conformable passage)	(? Unconformity)	(? Unconformity)
	Thick succession of shales, slates, phyllites, and mica schists, with local quartzites and limestones		
	Thin ferruginous limestones		
	Thin basal quartzite or conglomerate, often with arkose		
	Volcanic beds (local)		

———————————————— Unconformity ————————————————

Pre-Aravalli rocks	Bundelkhand granite Berach granite	Quartz veins Pegmatites and aplites Amphibolites Biotite granite Biotite schists, chlorite schists, and quartzose bands	Banded gneiss complex

The Aravalli rocks are chiefly argillaceous, varying according to the degree of metamorphism from shales in the southeast, through slates and phyllites, to mica schists containing garnet, staurolite, andalusite (chiastolite), and kyanite along the northwestern margin.

The basal member of the Aravallis in Mewar is supposed to mark the position of one of the most ancient shore lines in India. It varies from a fine-grained quartzite to a coarse pebbly grit or conglomerate, and is frequently separated from the gneissic granite by a layer of arkose. The quartz grains of the arkose also display the purple opalescence of the quartz in the granite.

The gritty or conglomeratic quartzite is, when feldspar-bearing, very similar to the granite. The pebbles, all of them of quartz or quartzite, may be angular or subangular and are sometimes rounded. At Beawar the base of the Aravallis is a coarse conglomerate of subangular cobbles of quartzite set in a matrix made up of angular quartz grains derived from the granite floor. Blunt wedges of granite sometimes project into the conglomerate. In the lower part of the conglomerate lie spheroidal boulders of granite. The erosional unconformity at the base of the Aravalli beds is observed not only at their junction with the Berach (Bundelkhand) granite but also where they lie upon the Banded gneiss complex.

HERON (1936, p. 5) believed that the Berach granite, even though it is about 270 km away, is only a westward extension of the Bundelkhand granite. According to him, the Berach granite is pre-Aravalli and, therefore, pre-Dharwar in age. According to other geologists, the Banded gneiss complex resulted from the granitization of the Aravalli schists, of which the Bundelkhand granite is the end product. This interpretation implies that the Bundelkhand granite is definitely of post-Aravalli age (SHARMA, 1953).

3.2.2. Eparchean interval

Significance of the interval

The ancient crystalline schists and gneisses of Peninsular India are generally separated from the next oldest rocks by a profound unconformity. Such a break between the Archean rocks and the subsequent rock groups has been noticed in all parts of the world, but this does not mean that the limits of the Archean, or the interval of denudation which followed it, were of the same magnitude everywhere. The break separates the crystalline schists and gneisses below from a series of generally nonfoliated and little altered sediments and lavas above. Foliation and intense metamorphism are not confined only to the rocks below this widespread unconformity. The Delhi rocks, for instance, which HERON (1953, pp. 22–23) placed above this unconformity, are extensively metamorphosed in the central and southern parts of Rajputana and are comparable in the degree of metamorphism to the underlying Aravalli rocks.

The Eparchean gap is made narrower from time to time by the discovery of rock sequences which have to be added either to the top of the Archean or to the bottom of the succeeding Purana group, or else given a place in the Eparchean interval itself. Much of the so-called Fundamental gneiss is now considered to be post-Dharwar in age. The "Dharwar" metasediments of Rajputana, however, are believed to lie upon a basal granite which in places appears to have intruded into much older sediments. The deposition of these sediments was followed by several periods of igneous intrusion, all of them assignable to the Archean.

After the addition below the Eparchean interval of much of the so-called Fundamental gneiss and of some of the igneous intrusions, one rock sequence appears to fit somewhere in the gap itself. This is the Raialo formation in the Aravalli Hills, which occurs definitely below the Delhi group and is separated therefrom by a pronounced unconformity. If the Delhi rocks are regarded as members of the Purana, because they lie stratigraphically below the Lower Vindhyan and are younger than the Aravalli rocks, then the Raialo formation must be either an older part of the Purana group or a part of a group older than the Purana and intermediate between the Purana and the Archean. The second conclusion is more probable, because the unconformity with the overlying Delhi beds is almost as pronounced as the unconformity with the underlying Aravalli rocks. The Eparchean interval in India has thus been reduced in size by the insertion of six or seven consecu-

B

tive intrusions at the bottom and by the introduction into its midst of the sedimentary Raialo series. As HOLMES (1955, p. 97) said, the name "Eparchean interval" only connotes the mental telescoping of several intervals and has no more claim to significance than the name "Archean", which itself has no stratigraphical meaning.

Raialo series

The Raialo series consists principally of a white limestone bed about 600 m thick, with a thin basement bed of quartzite or sandstone which is sometimes conglomeratic. Frequently the basal quartzite or sandstone is absent, and the limestone then rests unconformably upon the Aravalli rocks, the Bundelkhand granite, or the Banded gneiss complex, as the case may be. Some of the best exposures of the Raialos are observed in the State of Mewar, north of Udaipur City (see Fig. 7), where they occur in an intricately folded syncline. The basement boulder conglomerate is up to 9 m thick. The Raialos as a whole are less altered than the Aravalli rocks, but at certain places they exhibit a degree of metamorphism similar to that in the Aravallis. The limestone is extensively marmorized. It varies from a pure calcite rock in the northwest of the Aravalli range to a virtually pure dolomite rock in the southwest. The Makrana marble is celebrated because it is the material used in the construction of the beautiful Taj Mahal and many other Moghul buildings of northern India.

3.2.3. Purana group

General

After a long period of continental conditions parts of the Indian continent composed of metamorphosed, steeply dipping, and greatly eroded Archean sedimentary strata sank below a shallow sea. The marine deposits that were formed then lie with a profound unconformity upon the Archean rocks. They are generally little disturbed except in the Aravalli region, where rocks supposed to belong to the Purana group have suffered metamorphism and plication like those of the Dharwars. There was widespread volcanic activity during the Purana time, as evidenced by the occurrence of flows and dikes of mafic rocks. In spite of the fact that many of the Purana beds are undisturbed and consequently well adapted for the preservation of remains of organisms, no undoubted fossils have so far been definitely identified. The Purana rocks are generally spread over large areas with gentle dips and, hence, except in the Aravalli region, are in marked contrast to the strip-like belts of the Dharwars.

The Purana rocks of southern India were deposited in more or less isolated basins under similar conditions. A land barrier appears to have separated the water tracts of southern India from waters covering areas in the north, including, probably, those now occupied by the southern slopes of the Himalayas. The so-called Satpuran protaxis of FERMOR (1914, p. 164) is a broad ridge of gneiss which served as a barrier between the Son Valley basin and the Aravalli basin, on the one side, and the Chhattisgarh or upper Mahanadi basin, on the other side. It is possible that this rock barrier running from the east to the west was an ancient Archean hill range. North of this mountain range it is extremely difficult to identify with any certainty the equivalents of the Cuddapahs.

Cuddapah group

One of the best known and largest outcrops of the Purana rocks is the crescent-shaped Cuddapah basin in Andhra Pradesh (see Fig. 8). The distance from the tip of the northeastern horn of the crescent in the Palnad to the southern termination at the Tirupati Hill is about 340 km, and the maximum width is about 150 km. The western edge of the basin is a precipitous gorge, with cliffs which are often 150 m–200 m high. More than a third of the area in the Cuddapah basin is concealed by the overlying Kurnool series.

The Cuddapah group is essentially a succession of sandstones or quartzites and slates or shales, the latter frequently associated with limestones. The

TABLE 8

Stratigraphical succession in the Cuddapah group. According to KING (1872)

Series	Thickness, m	Lithological units
Kistna series	600	Srisailam quartzites Kolamnala shales Irlakonda quartzites
───────── Unconformity ─────────		
Nallamalai series	1,000	Cumbum shales Bairenkonda quartzites
───────── Unconformity ─────────		
Cheyair series	3,200	Tadpatri (Pullampet) shales Pulivendla (Nagari) quartzites
───────── Unconformity ─────────		
Papaghni series	1,400	Vempalle shales and limestones Gulcheru quartzites

succession is not as simple and uniform as in the overlying Kurnools but is complicated by unconformity and overlap, and, in the eastern parts of the basin, by frequent and sometimes severe folding and crushing (KING, 1872, p. 126). The prevalent dip of the Cuddapahs is toward the east. The stratigraphical succession, according to KING (1872), is given in Table 8.

The base of the Papaghni series contains some conglomerate beds, the pebbles in which are mainly derived from the brecciated quartz veins and the banded jaspery hematite beds of Dharwar age. Pebbles of granite or gneiss

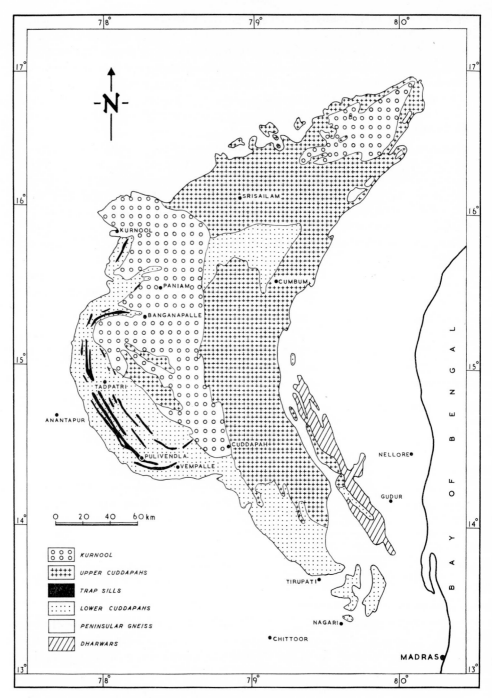

FIG. 8. Geological sketch map of the Cuddapah basin in Andhra State. According to
KING (1872). Published with the permission of the Director, Geological Survey
of India.

are rare, a fact which is probably due to the tendency of these rocks to disintegrate readily.

Mafic igneous intrusions are plentiful in the Cheyair series. The sills are sometimes 100 m thick. The rocks are similar to the Newer dolerites of Singhbhum. No such intrusives exist in the Cuddapahs younger than Cheyair or in the Kurnools. The agglomerate neck at Wajrakarur is probably one of the volcanic foci from which the Cuddapah traps were emitted.

Kaladgi series

Rocks of the Kaladgi series, somewhat similar to the Cuddapahs, occur along the southern border of the Deccan trap. They stretch from the east to the west continuously for more than 150 km, and if the outliers are also taken into account the basin from the east to the west is more than 250 km long. The Kaladgis rest unconformably on the gneisses and schists. They are feebly metamorphosed and are considered to belong to the Cuddapahs because of lithological resemblance, although the particular subdivisions of the Cuddapah rocks cannot be recognized. The conglomerate beds at the base contain pebbles, often subangular, of the adjoining crystalline rocks or of the jasper-bearing hematite schists of the Dharwar bands.

The Kaladgis and the Cuddapahs lie only about 200 km apart. Oolitic chert bands occur in both of them. Intrusive mafic rocks characterize both areas, even though they are rare in the Kaladgis. In both basins the older formation is unconformably associated with a younger one, namely, the Kurnool in the Cuddapah basin and the Bhima in the Kaladgi basin.

Pakhal series

A large tract of Cuddapah rocks extends up the Godavari Valley and is split into two outcrops by a broad N.W.–S.E.-striking band of younger rocks which include the Sullavais (Vindhyan) and the Gondwanas. The bottom beds, lying upon the gneiss, are nearly always coarse pebbly sandstones grading to conglomerates with pebbles of quartzite and slate, and scarcely ever of gneiss.

The Pakhal series is divided into two well-marked stages, viz. a lower, more or less slaty, sequence with thick sandstone beds and at least two bands of limestone, and an upper stage which is essentially arenaceous with some conglomerates and in which slate beds are few and limestones are absent. The Pakhals exhibit about the same degree of induration as do the Cuddapahs in the type area and a similarity in their stratigraphical relation to the Archean gneisses and schists.

Delhi group

The Delhi group of Rajasthan differs from the Puranas of other parts of the Peninsula in its more intense folding and in the amount of igneous intrusions. The rocks are sometimes so metamorphosed as to resemble the underlying Aravallis.

There are many similarities between the Delhis and the Cuddapahs. The general facies is similar, namely, quartzites below passing upward into slates. The thickness of the Delhis is comparable with the total thickness of 6,000 m of the Cuddapah group. Both groups are characterized by mafic lava flows and intrusions. However, the Cuddapahs of the type area are for the most part gently inclined, whereas the Delhis are strongly disturbed. Also, granite and pegmatite intrusions are common in the Delhis but are completely absent in the Cuddapahs, as indeed they are in all the Purana rocks of Peninsular India outside Rajputana and Gujarat.

The distance between the Delhi and the Cuddapah basins is about 1,300 km, and a land barrier separates them. Consequently, any lithological resemblances between their outcrops must be more or less accidental. The Delhi rocks are considered to belong to the Puranas because of their position in the stratigraphical sequence and also because of the profound unconformity between the Delhi and the Aravalli groups (or the Raialo series where it is present), which is reminiscent of the unconformity between the Cuddapahs and the Dharwar schist or Archean gneiss.

Accepting the Erinpura granite as an intrusion belonging to the Delhi time, the Purana age of the Delhi group is confirmed by some datings of uraninite from Bisundni in Ajmer-Merwara, and of monazite from Soniana in Mewar State, minerals which occur in pegmatites derived from the Erinpura granites. The uraninite gave a crude age of 725 Myr, and the monazite, 610 Myr. The Erinpura pegmatites are thus much younger than the Archean pegmatites of Gaya (the Satpura belt), the crude age of which lies between 900 Myr and 960 Myr.

Obviously the Delhis have been more involved in orogenic movements than any other Purana formations such as the Cuddapah but, as a whole, not to the same extent as were the Dharwars.

The break between the Aravalli beds and those which succeed them, whether Raialos or Delhis, is, according to HERON (1917, pp. 10–11), a violent and very distinct unconformity which has been traced for a distance of nearly 500 km from Alwar in the north to Idar in the south. It is marked by a great discordance in dip, strike, and lithological character between the rocks above and below it. The basal bed of the Delhi group is often composed of arkose, grits, and conglomerates derived from the granitic rocks in the pre-Aravalli complex.

Mafic sills and flows, now altered to epidiorite and hornblende schist, granitic bosses, and pegmatite veins are the types of igneous rocks found in the Delhis. The granites include the Erinpura granite suite, which, even though post-Delhi in age, was intruded before the Vindhyans. The Malani granite which intrudes the Delhis is of Lower Vindhyan age. The epidiorites and hornblende schists originated as mafic rocks during the Lower Vindhyan but were later metamorphosed.

Like the Aravallis, the Delhi beds also display a general decrease of tectonic activity and degree of metamorphism away from the central fold axis of the old mountain system.

In northeastern Rajputana and in adjacent districts the Delhi group is divided into two series, viz. a lower arenaceous sequence, the Alwar, and an upper, more argillaceous sequence, the Ajabgarh.

The chief igneous intrusive in the Delhi sedimentary sequence is the Erinpura granite suite. It is younger than the group of mafic intrusives and occurs in bodies ranging from bosses to sills. Unlike the later Malani suite, it has no effusive equivalent.

3.3. *Extrapeninsular India*

3.3.1. General

The Lesser Himalaya is formed of a thick sequence of fossil-free meta-sediments whose exact age is unknown but which could range from Archean, Purana, or Early Paleozoic to Late Paleozoic. Their correlation has been attempted only on a lithological basis and from their relative stratigraphical position and degree of metamorphism. Several individual sequences have been established, each with a local name, and many of them may prove to be more or less equivalent. Other formations thought to be coeval may turn out to be of very different ages. The complicated tectonics of the Himalayas, intrusions of granite, and metamorphic effects have obliterated the stratigraphical succession and structure, thereby rendering any correlation extremely difficult. Among the many possible schemes that have been suggested for the correlation of the Precambrian rocks of the Himalayas, one which appears reasonable is that of PASCOE (1950, p. 432) given in Table 9.

3.3.2. Kashmir

WADIA (1931, p. 196) gave the name "Salkhala series" to the oldest sedimentary rocks of northwestern Himalaya, which comprise carbonaceous schists and limestones, quartzites, quartz schists, and mica schists. They are associated with a gneissic complex which includes granulites, biotite gneiss, and hornblende gneiss. The Salkhala rocks form a huge hairpin bend round the northwestern end of the Kashmir Valley. The lithology and the degree of metamorphism favor a correlation of the Salkhala series with the Jutogh series of Simla.

The Dogra slates rest often on the Salkhalas. They consist of a thick series of black and green phyllitic slates interbedded with chloritized contemporaneous trap flows. They are correlated with the Simla slate series, which they resemble lithologically. The Dogra slates are also the equivalent of the Attock slates and the Hazara slates.

In one or two places WADIA (1931, p. 202) recorded an apparently conformable passage from the Salkhalas through the Dogra slates into virtually fossil-free sediments assigned to the Lower Cambrian.

TABLE 9

Precambrian formations of Extrapeninsular India

Kashmir–Punjab	Simla–Garhwal		Chakrata	Spiti	Eastern Himalaya
Dogra and Attock slates	Simla slates	Chail series	Chandpur series	Middle and Upper Haimanta and Vaikrita	Daling series and Darjeeling gneiss
Salkhala series	Jutogh series				

3.3.3. Simla

The name "Jutogh series" pertains to some quartzites, carbonaceous slates, and limestone beds at Jutogh near Simla. Like all the strongly metamorphosed rocks of India, these rocks have been considered to be the equivalents of the "Dharwars"; also, no other rocks in the neighborhood are older. Their anomalous position above less altered rocks is caused by inversion, overfolding, recumbency, and overthrusting. The beds underlying the Jutoghs are almost everywhere Chails, which in their turn have been thrust over younger beds. According to PILGRIM and WEST (1928), the Jutogh series could be more strongly metamorphosed rocks of the neighboring Chail series and the Simla slates, both of which are provisionally assigned to the Purana.

The Chor granite, probably of Late Paleozoic age, intrudes the Jutogh beds, and a metamorphic aureole surrounding the granite body is present.

With the exception of the Jutoghs, the Chail beds are the oldest in this part of the Himalayas, and are invariably bounded at their base by the Chail thrust. The upper limit of the Chail series has also, with few exceptions, been mapped as a thrust plane. There is neither paleontological nor reliable stratigraphical evidence as to the relative age of the series. According to PILGRIM and WEST (1928), epigrade metamorphism in this area has affected the Chail series, which consequently differs from the Jutogh beds which everywhere display a mesograde metamorphism. The two facies of different degrees of metamorphism were brought into juxtaposition by thrusting.

In the western Himalayas and in their continuation through the districts of Hazara and Attock in West Pakistan, a thick series of slates is present. In the Simla Himalayas the sequence is called the Simla slates. They are stratigraphically equivalent to the Attock slates, the "slate series" of Hazara, and the Dogra slates of Kashmir. The Simla slates, although overlain by the Jutogh beds because of overthrust, are considered to be the younger of the two (WEST, 1939). They have been assigned a late Purana age, and their nearest match in the Peninsula would be the argillaceous Ajabgarh series in Rajputana.

3.3.4. Garhwal

The schists in the Lesser Himalaya of Garhwal, although lithologically resembling the Dharwars, i.e. being strongly metamorphosed, are probably very much younger. These schists, like those occupying a somewhat similar position in the Kulu region in the northwest, and in Nepal and Darjeeling in the southeast, contain copper mineralizations.

AUDEN (1935, pp. 134–136) described from the Garhwal region a varied assemblage of schists, phyllites, and granulites, intruded by gneissose granite and granite pegmatite. These rocks rest upon slightly metamorphosed shales, phyllites, limestones, and quartzites, from which they are separated by a thrust plane. At Badrinath the rocks become calcareous and are reminiscent of the Salkhalas. In the Badrinath area the rock sequence includes pyroxene granulites, marbles, diopside calciphyres, biotite schists, granulites, amphibolites, and gneiss.

3.3.5. Chakrata

The Chandpur series in the Chakrata district is an intimately banded association of quartzite and phyllite, with abundant green beds (metamorphosed tuffs). It is sometimes about 1,400 m thick. In the Mussoorie area the Chandpurs display different grades of metamorphism, and the rocks vary from banded slates to schists. The Chandpur rocks are said to have much in common with the Daling series of Sikkim. It is likely that the Chandpurs, Chails, and Simla slates are approximately equivalent.

3.3.6. Spiti

GRIESBACH (1891, p. 41) distinguished a thick rock sequence called the Vaikrita, varying much in lithological composition but consisting largely of schists and phyllites, which lie upon the gneiss. There appears to be no clearly defined boundary between the Vaikrita group and the overlying series of slates, phyllites, and quartzites which GRIESBACH called the Haimanta. Both groups take part in the complicated flexures of the Himalayan range.

AUDEN (1936) showed that some of the Vaikritas of Garhwal, consisting of garnet–biotite granulite, garnet–biotite schists, staurolite schists, and kyanite schists, pass with decreasing degree of metamorphism into epigrade Haimanta rocks which he correlated with the Simla slates and Chandpur beds.

3.3.7. Eastern Himalaya

The name "Daling series" was given by MALLET (1874, p. 12) to a slate sequence which, as a result of overthrust, lies above Gondwana (Damuda) beds. It consists predominantly of slates and phyllites, passing into silvery mica schists at the boundary with the Darjeeling gneiss. Chalcopyrite is in several places disseminated in the slates and the hornblende schists, and has in some instances been worked.

The Darjeeling gneiss is a crystalline complex comprising metamorphosed igneous and sedimentary rocks, the former consisting chiefly of varieties of biotite gneiss, and the latter principally of quartzites, limestones and marbles, calciphyres and calcium silicate granulites, mica–quartz schists, and hornblende schists.

3.4. *Stratigraphical position of the Vindhyans*

The Vindhyans are devoid of fossils except for a few obscure and doubtful impressions which cannot be definitely identified. For this reason they have sometimes been considered to belong to the Precambrian. The absence of fossils, however, is a common and inexplicable feature in India, even in rocks which are much younger than the Vindhyans. It is therefore difficult to determine the exact stratigraphical position of the Vindhyans. OLDHAM (1893) included the Vindhyans in the Paleozoic. PASCOE (1950, p. 31) followed this practice, but said that it must be clearly understood that the evidence for either alternative is most meagre. The present writer is also inclined toward assigning the Vindhyans a Lower Paleozoic age, and, hence, only a very brief account of them will be given here.

The unconformity between the uppermost Purana beds and the Lower Vindhyans is usually not very great. The Upper Vindhyans especially look younger than the Purana rocks, because they have suffered less disturbance and alteration. The Vindhyan beds are generally horizontal or nearly so and rarely dip at high angles.

The Vindhyans include two more or less distinct rock sequences, viz. the Lower Vindhyans (Semris), which are predominantly calcareous and probably marine, and the Upper Vindhyans, which are arenaceous and largely fluviatile or deltaic.

The Kurnool formation of Andhra Pradesh is correlated with the Lower Vindhyans. The Bhima beds, which outcrop from below the southeastern margin of the Deccan trap, are considered to be their equivalents. The Cuddapahs are represented along the southern edge of the Deccan trap, but there is no direct evidence to show that the strata of these two areas were once continuous, even though FOOTE (1876, p. 164) favored the view that the Bhima and the Kurnool rocks once formed a continuous outcrop.

The Lower Vindhyans, compared with the Upper Vindhyans or with the Puranas, are much less in thickness, even though widely distributed and constant in lithological character. The absence or extreme scarcity of definitely recognizable fossils in these beds was construed by some as suggesting a fresh-water origin, and the red color of the sandstones was considered evidence of deposition in a closed basin. However, their great lateral extent and the small lithological variations from the Son Valley to the neighborhood of Bijawar, a distance of 1,100 km, suggest a marine origin. A volcanic suite of rocks varying from rhyolites to quartz andesites, known as the Malani rhyolites, is associated with the Lower Vindhyan metasediments.

The Upper Vindhyans do not often show any discordance with the Lower

Vindhyans; there is, however, extensive overlap. They consist chiefly of fine-grained, hard, red sandstones, which from the days of KING ASOKA (273 B.C.–232 B.C.) have been used in Indian architecture. The Upper Vindhyans are confined to the region extending from Bihar to the Aravalli Hills and differ greatly in their distribution from the Lower Vindhyans. The persistent red color of the sandstones and the area of deposition suggest that they may have been laid down in a land-locked basin. That they are shallow-water deposits is indicated by the frequent occurrence of ripple marks. No contemporaneous igneous rocks are associated with the Upper Vindhyans.

The Aravalli Range completely separates the Vindhyan rocks of the Marwar basin from those of the main basin which lies east of the range. The north-westerly limits of the Marwar basin are not known, because the rocks are concealed under the Jurassic strata of Jaisalmer and the sands of the Thar or the Great Indian Desert.

4. Structure, tectonics, and correlation

4.1. *Introduction*

There is a marked contrast in structure between Peninsular India and the Extrapeninsular region. The greater part of the Peninsula has been a land surface since the Vindhyan time, whereas the Extrapeninsula is a region of strongly folded lofty mountains of Tertiary age.

The Western Ghats, which run almost parallel to the west coast, are the most important hill range of the Peninsula. North of about 16° N. the Ghats consist of nearly horizontal flows of basalt (the Deccan traps), but south of it the traps disappear and the range is composed of Precambrian rocks whose foliation directions often correspond to the trend of the hills. The range continues up to Cape Comorin, the southernmost point of India.

The Eastern Ghats join the Western Ghats north of the Palghat Gap. There is a distinct parallelism between the northeast–southwesterly orientation of the Godavari–Mahanadi section of the Eastern Ghats and the strike of the Precambrian folds.

The Satpura Range is situated south of the Narbada River and stretches from the west to the east. The Central Satpuras, which comprise the Pachmarhi or Mahadeo Hills, are composed partly of Precambrian rocks, and there is some correspondence between the strike of the foliation of the metamorphic rocks and the trend of the hill ranges.

The Vindhya Range also has a W.–E. trend and is situated north of the Satpuras. The general directions of the Vindhyan scarp and of the Narbada and lower Son Rivers are roughly parallel to tectonic features exhibited by the Vindhyan rocks.

The Aravalli Range is composed of strongly disturbed Precambrian rocks and trends in a northeast–southwesterly direction from Delhi to Gujarat.

Here there is a swing first to the south-southeast and, finally, to the south-east.

SMEETH and WATSON (1918, pp. 206–214) were probably the first geologists in India to study the radioactivity of Precambrian rocks with a view to distinguishing the various groups from one another. FERMOR (1936) made an attempt to correlate the different Precambrian rock sequences scattered over Peninsular India, and demarcated the charnockitic from the noncharnockitic region. The degree of metamorphism and occurrence of special types of rocks of sedimentary origin such as iron ores and manganese ores were among the criteria he used for correlation. These, however, are not reliable criteria, since lithology, mineralogy, ore deposits, chemical composition, orogeny, igneous activity, and unconformities are not often distinctly recognizable, identical in character, or synchronous over widely separated regions (HEDBERG, 1961). Rocks like the banded ferruginous quartzites which were once considered characteristic deposits of the Precambrian occur in the Paleozoic also (O'ROURKE, 1961, 1962).

The advances in the knowledge of the age of the Precambrian rocks of India are mainly due to the work of HOLMES (1949, 1950, 1955). He threw considerable light on the Precambrian geochronology of India and, for the first time, related radiometric ages with the orogenies that have produced the characteristic regional strikes of the Archean structural provinces. However, for a large country like India, where the Precambrian is widespread, reliable ages are still all too few. Comparisons and correlations, therefore, are only provisional.

There are a few main characteristic regional trends in the Precambrian of Peninsular India as represented by the Dharwar schist belt (N.N.W.–S.S.E.), the Eastern Ghats belt (N.E.–S.W.), the Satpura belt (W.S.W.–E.N.E.), and the Aravalli and Delhi belts (N.E.–S.W.). A tectonic map of the Precambrian orogenic belts of Peninsular India is presented in Fig. 9, in which the main structural trends and the reliable ages so far obtained are given. The Deccan traps cover a considerable part of mainly Precambrian terrain, leaving one to surmise as to the mutual relationships of the Dharwar, Aravalli, and Satpura strike directions, because the critical regions where they could have been investigated lie hidden under the volcanic flows. Correlations are therefore almost entirely dependent on the evidence provided by dating radioactive minerals.

Among the noteworthy structural studies made in the Precambrian, mention may be made of the classic work of HERON (1917, 1953) in Rajasthan, which proved the existence of northerly-plunging folds in both the Aravalli and the Delhi systems; the identification by WEST (1936) of a nappe structure in the Nagpur district; the elucidation of the complex structure of the manganese-ore belt in Madhya Pradesh by STRACZEK and his co-workers (1956), NARAYANASWAMI (1959), and VEMBAN (1961); the detailed work in the Bhandara–Drug–Balaghat region by SARKAR (1957, 1958); the recognition of a system of large-scale folds in Singhbhum and Manbhum by

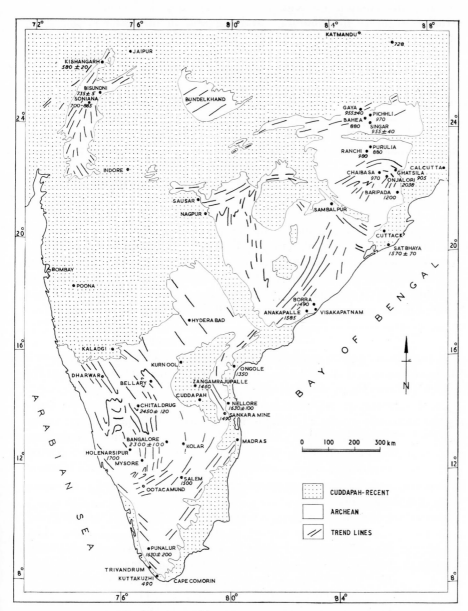

FIG. 9. Structural map of Peninsular India showing the main trends of the
Archean orogenic belts. The figures indicate ages in Myr.

DUNN (1929) and DUNN and DEY (1942); the identification of an anticlinorium in Gangpur by KRISHNAN (1937); and the elucidation of the
intricate structure in Dhalbhum and Singhbhum by NAHA (1955, 1956,
1965) and SARKAR and SAHA (1959, 1962).

4.2. *The Dharwars*

The Dharwars of southern India are usually considered to occur as
somewhat isolated well-defined bands. Such a geographical grouping has
certain advantages for descriptive purposes, but it gives unnecessary
individuality to each of the belts, and even the proposed classifications of
Dharwar rocks are influenced by such regional considerations. In Mysore
State there is a prominent ferruginous quartzite band which contains manganese and is often associated with limestones. Using it as a marker bed, a
structural synthesis was attempted between the well-developed Shimoga
and Chitaldrug schist belts (PICHAMUTHU, 1951, pp. 117–119). This marker
band is disposed in a huge anticlinorium with minor anticlines and synclines
and has a general N.N.W. plunge. That the iron–manganese–limestone
band is a definite stratigraphical zone is indicated by the fact that the
Dharwar quartzites in Mysore State are all older, because no outcrops of
quartzite occur in the wide schist areas in the western part of the Shimoga
belt and in the whole of the Chitaldrug belt east of the marker bed.

The general trend of the Dharwars in Mysore State varies from N.N.W.–
S.S.E. to N.W.–S.E. In southern Mysore the trend becomes N.–S., and
then turns S.W. and W.S.W., thus aligning with the trend in the Eastern
Ghats of Salem and the Nilgiris. In the region south and southeast of the
Nilgiris the trend is N.W.–S.E.

The Dharwars are now divided into three divisions, of which the lower
is predominantly volcanic, and the middle and the upper divisions each
include a major sedimentary cycle. The Dharwars represent an enormous
span of time and comprise several orogenies with their attendant igneous
intrusions. Considering the vastness of its geological history, the Dharwar
time is still most inadequately investigated, especially regarding the dating
of its component rock units.

The dating of a monazite from a pegmatite near Yadiur in the Bangalore
area yielded a $^{207}Pb/^{206}Pb$ age of $(2,300 \pm 100)$ Myr (HOLMES, 1955,
pp. 85–86). By using the lead–alpha method, VENKATASUBRAMANIAN and
KRISHNAN (1960, p. 96) obtained 2,200 Myr as the age of the same monazite.
The age of the Yadiur monazite would go up to 2,605 Myr if corrected for
daughter-isotope diffusion (NICOLAYSEN, 1957, p. 50). The age for the Yadiur
monazite published by HOLMES is in agreement with the age of the Ingladhal
galena from the Chitaldrug schist belt of Mysore State, viz. $(2,320 \pm 120)$
Myr (RUSSELL and others, 1954, p. 306). When this conventional age is read
from diagrams prepared by F. G. HOUTERMANS and J. GEISS (HOLMES,
1955, p. 86), it is found to be $(2,450 \pm 120)$ Myr.

A biotite from the Bundelkhand granite of Chattarpur, Madhya Pradesh, yielded an age of 2,500 Myr–2,510 Myr (S. N. SARKAR, personal communication), which makes this granite coeval with the Dharwars. Until the Banded gneiss complex of Rajasthan has also been dated, it is not possible to say anything definite regarding the position of the Bundelkhand gneiss in the Precambrian of India.

4.3. *The Eastern Ghats belt*

Parts of the Nilgiri Mountains and the districts of Coimbatore and Salem exhibit an E.N.E.–W.S.W. strike. West of the Nilgiris N.N.W.–S.S.E. and N.–S. strikes are observed. East of the Nilgiris the E.N.E.–W.S.W. strike continues for some distance but gradually assumes a strike from N.E.–S.W. to N.N.E.–S.S.W. in the Salem and Trichinopoly districts. North of Madras it curves parallel to the coast, the southern part of the curve being parallel to the trend of the Dharwar schists into which the Nellore mica-bearing granite pegmatites are intrusive. The strike then becomes N.E., but curves westward with a N.N.E. direction near the northern border of Orissa until it runs athwart the Satpura strike of the Gangpur–Singhbhum region. In the western part of northern Orissa the iron-ore ranges of Keonjhar and Bonai have a N.N.E.–S.S.W. strike. It is probable that there is a bifurcation of the Eastern Ghats near Bezwada, one part going south toward Madras or Ceylon and the other bending round to the southwest through the Arcot and Salem districts to the Nilgiris.

The eastern margin of the Cuddapah basin displays crushing and overthrusting. Some rocks near the Singareni coalfield are folded and strongly metamorphosed. Granitic rocks are associated with the folding, and HERON (1949, pp. 118–121) correlated them with the Pakhals, which are considered to be Cuddapahs.

The Eastern Ghats consist largely of charnockites, khondalites, and kodurites accompanied by some granitic intrusives. FERMOR (1936, p. 48) was of the opinion that they constitute a belt of block uplift with faulted margins. That is how he accounted for the high-grade metamorphism of the rocks which he thought was acquired by deep burial. CROOKSHANK (1938, pp. 399–404), however, could not trace any such fault.

The ages obtained on dating a detrital monazite from near Satbhaya in the Cuttack district, Orissa (HOLMES, 1955, p. 90), are so discordant as to suggest not only that lead and uranium have been lost from the monazite but also that much ^{208}Pb has been preferentially lost. The ^{207}Pb/^{206}Pb age is $(1,600 \pm 40)$ Myr, and the adopted age is $(1,570 \pm 70)$ Myr.

There has been some doubt as to whether the Nellore schist belt, which trends N.N.W.–S.S.E. with local irregularities, belongs to the Eastern Ghats cycle or to the Dharwar cycle. The schist sequence is dominantly biotitic, and includes garnet-, kyanite-, and staurolite-bearing schists, interbanded with quartzites, and associated with hornblende schists and talc schists. Overlying this is a volcanic sequence composed of hornblende schists and chlorite schists, representing mafic lavas and tuffs, with associated quartzites. The strike corresponds to the strike of the Dharwars, and the lithological association suggests a metamorphic grade which is lower than that which generally pertains in the Eastern Ghats belt. There is a marked resemblance to the Holenarsipur schist belt in Mysore State.

The eastern strip of the Nellore schist belt has been intruded by numerous granite pegmatite lenses and veins usually along, but sometimes across, the foliation of the schists. Samarskite samples from pegmatites of the Nellore mica belt have been dated, and they gave reasonably comparable un-corrected ages (HOLMES, 1955, p. 92), which may be collectively expressed as (1,630 ± 100) Myr. This age agrees very well with the $^{207}Pb/^{206}Pb$ age of (1,570 ± 70) Myr for the Satbhaya monazite and thus supports the view that the Nellore pegmatites belong to the Eastern Ghats orogeny rather than to the Dharwar orogeny. Further evidence in favor of this interpretation was obtained by ASWATHANARAYANA (1956, p. 25), who for allanite from a granite pegmatite near Anakapalli in Andhra State obtained an age of 1,585 Myr, and for samarskite from the Nellore pegmatites an age of (1,625 ± 75) Myr.

VENKATASUBRAMANIAN and KRISHNAN (1960) determined alpha–helium ages for several rocks and minerals from the Eastern Ghats, but many of the ages are low because of the leakage of helium. The ages of magnetite quartzites from Ongole and Konizedu in Andhra State are 1,350 Myr and 1,290 Myr, respectively. The age of a magnetite quartzite from Kanjimalai, Madras State, is 1,500 Myr, and a pyroxenite from the same area yielded an age of 1,300 Myr.

VENKATASUBRAMANIAN (1953) determined the rubidium–strontium age of a lepidolite from Borra, near Visakhapatnam, as 1,490 Myr. VENKATA-SUBRAMANIAN and KRISHNAN (1960, p. 96) dated a specimen of cyrtolite from the Sankara mica mine in the Nellore district, Andhra State, by the lead–alpha method, and obtained an age of 1,490 Myr, which corresponds fairly well with many of the ages of minerals from the Eastern Ghats belt.

The rubidium–strontium age of phlogopite from a pyroxenite dike near Punalur, in Kerala State, is (1,630 ± 200) Myr (VENKATASUBRAMANIAN, 1953). The strike here corresponds to that of the Dharwar schist belt, but the age is that of the Eastern Ghats cycle. Punalur is situated in the Western Ghats section of the former State of Travancore (now Kerala) and lies within the "charnockitic region" (in the Travancore–Ceylon province) of FERMOR (1936, p. 42), as does his Eastern Ghats province. More reliable ages on this region are necessary before it is possible to decide whether it should be included in the Eastern Ghats cycle.

The ages of minerals and rocks from the Eastern Ghats belt, which is the longest structural belt of the Precambrian of Peninsular India, obtained by various workers and by different methods, range between 1,490 Myr and 1,640 Myr, a samarskite age being as high as 1,765 Myr. The average age of the Eastern Ghats cycle may be taken as 1,600 Myr.

The age of metamorphism and granitization of the Bengpal series (and of the Bailadila Iron-ore series) in Bastar, as indicated by muscovite from the granite gneiss, is 2,090 Myr (S. N. SARKAR, personal communication). According to him, the Iron-ore series of Bastar may be correlated with the Iron-ore series of Singhbhum–Keonjhar–Mayurbhanj, because the age of crystallization of the Singhbhum granite (post-Iron-ore series) is 2,020 Myr–2,038 Myr (SARKAR and SAHA, 1962). These ages suggest the probable existence of an Iron-ore cycle intermediate in age between the Dharwar cycle and the Eastern Ghats cycle. Biotites from the charnockites of Visakhapatnam and Kondapalli and from the coarse-grained granites and pegmatites of Visakhapatnam have been dated by the rubidium–strontium and potassium–argon methods (U. ASWATHANARAYANA, personal communication). The four potassium–argon ages and the four rubidium–strontium "whole rock"–biotite intersection ages obtained are mutually consistent within experimental limits and may be collectively expressed as (500 ± 20) Myr. This age indicates the period of metamorphism and homogenization (and uplift?) which the rocks of the Eastern Ghats, in general, experienced during post-Cuddapah time.

4.4. *The Satpura belt*

The Satpura Range has a pronounced E.N.E.–W.S.W. strike. The range is composed of Deccan traps between the Narbada and Tapti Rivers in Gujarat, and the trend continues through the Mahadeo Hills, the Maikal Range, the Mampat Hills, and the northern part of the Chota Nagpur Plateau to the Rajmahal region in the Ganges Valley. The Precambrian rocks are exposed mainly from Jubbulpore eastward. The same strike is also observed in the Nagpur–Chhindwara–Balaghat region of Madhya Pradesh and in the Gangpur–Singhbhum region. The same trend continues into the Garo Hills in the western part of the Shillong Plateau.

The Satpura orogeny was studied by DUNN and his associates (1929, 1940, 1942). A major thrust zone separates the strongly metamorphosed northern area from the unmetamorphosed southern part. This thrust zone runs roughly E.N.E.–W.S.W. and E.–W. for nearly 160 km, turning to the southeast near the eastern end. Because of its association with copper mineralization, it is known as the Singhbhum Copper Belt. There are two nearly parallel thrust zones to its north. All the thrust zones are parallel to the Satpura trend. South of the main thrust zone the same rock sequences are virtually unmetamorphosed but have been affected by the Eastern Ghats strike (N.N.E.). The thrust zone continues westward into Gangpur through the northern border of the Gangpur anticlinorium, which contains rocks considered by KRISHNAN (1937) to be older than those of Singhbhum.

The major structural units in this belt, as recognized by DUNN and DEY (1942), are the Singhbhum anticlinorium of strongly metamorphosed schists which continues east from North Singhbhum and turns southeast beyond Jamshedpur; the north-dipping arcuate Copper Belt thrust zone formed along the overfolded southern limb of the anticlinorium; and, north of the anticlinorium, the Dalma syncline, which has been traced for about 200 km from the Ranchi district to Dhalbhum and Bankura in the east. The northern limb of this syncline is inverted and has in places been overthrust (Dalma thrust) by the rocks from the north.

DUNN and DEY (1942, p. 439) correlated the rocks of the Iron-ore stage north of the Copper Belt thrust with those in the south, using the banded hematite quartzite as a datum. SARKAR and SAHA (1959, p. 130; 1962, p. 128) did not agree with this correlation (see Table 6) because of several lithological contrasts which suggest that the Iron-ore stage north of the thrust and the Iron-ore stage south of it probably belong to separate orogenic episodes.

The general stratigraphical sequence in the Satpura belt, which trends E.N.E.–W.S.W., is given in Table 10.

The swarm of granite pegmatites in the Gaya and Ranchi districts of Bihar is well known as the world's leading source of high-grade muscovite. A specimen of monazite from Gaya district was dated by T. C. SARKAR (1941, p. 247), and of allanite from Ranchi by P. B. SARKAR (see HOLMES, 1955, p. 93). The apparent ages range from about 830 Myr to 980 Myr, and the average of four crude ages is 950 Myr. The age of a uraninite from Singar

TABLE 10

General stratigraphical succession in the Satpura belt

Pegmatites and quartz veins	
Orogeny and granitization	Migmatites and granites, including the Chota Nagpur (or Ranchi), Singhbhum, and "Dome" gneissose granites
Sakoli series?	Iron-ore series
Sausar series	Gangpur series

(24° 34′ N.; 85° 30′ E.) is likely to be less than 995 Myr and more than 912 Myr, i.e. (955 ± 40) Myr (HOLMES, 1950, p. 22). This dating is sufficient, however, to show that the Satpura belt represents the orogenic cycle immediately preceding that of the Delhi belt.

S. N. SARKAR (personal communication) has thrown further light on the tectonic history of the Satpura belt. The age of metamorphism and granitization of the Amgaon series in the Bhandara–Drug district is 1,434 Myr–1,490 Myr (biotite ages). The Sakoli series, which is post-Amgaon (S. N. SARKAR, 1957, 1958) has a complex metamorphic history, with a first stage of metamorphism at 1,330 Myr (muscovite age), and a later stage at 950 Myr (muscovite age). The ages (mica ages) of metamorphism of the Sausar series (864 Myr–950 Myr), the Gangpur series (940 Myr–993 Myr), the Singhbhum series (934 Myr–940 Myr), and the Ranchi–Muri belt (890 Myr–970 Myr) indicate that all these rock sequences belong to the Satpura cycle.

Two samples of magnetite from the Singhbhum area yielded ages of 970 Myr and 1,200 Myr (ASWATHANARAYANA, 1956, pp. 26, 28). The sample which gave the higher age is a vanadian magnetite from the large lopolithic intrusion of gabbro, north of Baripada, which is the equivalent of the gabbro–anorthosite bodies of northern Mayurbhanj and eastern Singhbhum. The other sample of magnetite is from Chaibasa, but its exact locality or the formation to which it belongs is not known. The two magnetite ages are somewhat lower than the ages of radioactive minerals along the Eastern Ghats belt, but do not differ very much from the age of 1,350 Myr of the Ongole magnetite, which is also from the Eastern Ghats belt.

Although the available ages do not definitely indicate that the rocks south of the Copper Belt thrust zone belong to the Eastern Ghats orogenic cycle, they support the view that these rocks are older than the rocks in the north which belong to the Satpura orogenic belt.

4.5. *The Aravalli and Delhi belts*

The Aravalli belt in Rajasthan has a general N.E.–S.W. trend which is very marked from Delhi to Champaner in Gujarat. Toward the south the trend swings round to a N.–S. direction in the Champaner series of Gujarat, which contains gondites and manganiferous marbles. The trend gradually becomes N.N.W.–S.S.E. as the Deccan traps are approached. Continued under the Deccan trap cover, this direction would appear to link up the Aravallis with the dominant N.N.W.–S.S.E. strike of the Dharwars of the type region in Mysore State. It is also likely that this trend, which becomes south-easterly farther east in Gujarat, gradually turns round and merges with the Satpura strike. FERMOR (1950, p. 141) favored this view and suggested that the Aravallis of Jhabua State with their enclosed gondite rocks may be the western stratigraphical continuation of the gondite rocks of the Sausar series. HOLMES (1955, p. 94) also felt that if the orogenic belt to which the Aravallis belong must be either Dharwar or Satpura the latter is the more probable alternative.

The Aravalli strike continues northward into Garhwal in the Himalayas, and the rocks appear to have retained their original trend unaffected by the Tertiary orogenic movements.

Three major cycles may be recognized in the Aravalli region, viz. the Delhi cycle, the Aravalli cycle, and the gneiss complex cycle.

The Delhi orogenic belt with a N.E.–S.W. trend comprises the Raialo, Alwar, and Ajabgarh sequences of sedimentary rocks and their metamorphic equivalents, with associated mafic igneous rocks. Orogeny and metamorphism are evidenced by the Erinpura granites and by formation of migmatites. Pegmatite and quartz veins are present. There is a major unconformity between the Delhi cycle and the Aravalli cycle.

The Aravalli orogenic belt has a somewhat similar rock sequence. The

Aravalli orogeny is accompanied by granites and migmatites, with younger pegmatite and quartz veins. The prevailing N.E.–S.W. trend becomes N.–S. and changes to N.N.W.–S.S.E. as the Deccan traps are approached.

Below another major unconformity lies the gneiss complex consisting of paragneisses, amphibolites, schists, granites, and migmatites, traversed by pegmatite and quartz veins.

Pegmatites occur in all the three cycles, and because it is difficult to assign them definitely to their proper orogeny, there is a certain amount of uncertainty about dating the different belts. Pegmatites are distributed along a broad belt from Gujarat to Delhi, but so far only pegmatites thought to be of Late Delhi age have been dated (HOLMES, 1949). Because some of them traverse the schists and quartzites of the Delhi group, the whole suite has been regarded as belonging to a late stage in the Delhi cycle, despite the fact that many of the pegmatites, including the dated ones, occur in the Aravalli belt.

Uraninite from a pegmatite in biotite gneiss at Bisundni, Ajmer-Merwara, and monazite from a pegmatite at Soniana, Mewar State, were dated by HOLMES (1949), who found the RaG/U and AcD/U ages to be in perfect agreement (733 Myr). The AcD/RaG age was estimated as 740 Myr. According to HOLMES, the age assigned to the Bisundni uraninite, viz. (735 ± 30) Myr, is one of the very few acceptable as being of first-class reliability. The age of the monazite lies between 700 Myr and 865 Myr, and HOLMES pointed out that this conclusion is at least consistent with the reliable age of 735 Myr of the uraninite. ASWATHANARAYANA (1959) dated the samarskite from a pegmatite near Kishangarh, Rajasthan, and obtained a closely spaced age spread ($^{207}Pb/^{206}Pb$, 578 Myr; $^{206}Pb/^{238}U$, 587 Myr; $^{207}Pb/^{235}U$, 578 Myr). This gives a reliable age of (580 ± 20) Myr. The existence of a pegmatite younger than those of Bisundni and Soniana supports the view of HERON (1953, p. 368) that pegmatite intrusions did not take place at the same time all along the immense synclinorium. The possibility of there being two sets of similar pegmatites of two distinctly different ages should not be lost sight of, and one of them may be pre-Delhi (HOLMES, 1955, pp. 96–97), a contingency which was envisaged by CROOK-SHANK (1948, p. 109), when he found that the pegmatites in Mewar, Ajmer-Merwara, and Jaipur often were more foliated than those near Delhi.

It is significant that the potassium–argon age of (728 ± 12) Myr of the detrital muscovite from the mica quartzite of the Nawakot nappe in the Nepal Himalayas (KRUMMENACHER, 1961) is of the same order as that of the post-Delhi pegmatites. This fact indicates a Precambrian metamorphism in the Himalayan region.

4.6. *The Cuddapah group*

The Cuddapah group is separated by unconformities from the Dharwars below and the Kurnools above. The Delhi group is separated by unconformities from the Aravallis below and the Vindhyans above. The Delhis have therefore been correlated with the Cuddapahs on the assumption that the Aravallis and the Dharwars are of the same age, and that the intervening unconformities in both areas represent the same Eparchean interval. That these assumptions may not be correct is indicated by the fact that the Delhi group has been affected by orogeny, with consequent emplacement of granites and pegmatites, whereas no such evidence is available from the Cuddapah basin.

Again, if the Aravallis were deposited on the ancient floor of a gneiss complex which can be correlated with the Peninsular gneiss, then the Eparchean interval would have to be placed between the base of the Aravallis and the gneiss complex. If this is the case, then the Cuddapahs would be contemporaneous with the Aravallis and older than the Delhis. The strata in the Cuddapah basin are fairly undisturbed, but on the eastern side they have been folded along axes roughly parallel to the Eastern Ghats strike. HOLMES (1955, p. 98) suggested that the Cuddapahs may belong to the end of the Eastern Ghats cycle and the period immediately following, a conclusion which would make the Cuddapahs older than the rocks of the Satpura and Delhi belts.

DUBEY (1930) made an attempt to estimate the age of a Purana rock by determining the helium indexes of three basaltic rocks from the Gwalior series. The ages ranged from 200 Myr to 500 Myr. These ages must not be taken at their face value, for even the highest age would make these rocks post-Cambrian in age.

U. ASWATHANARAYANA (personal communication) determined in 1963 the whole-rock potassium–argon ages of five dolerites (lower age limit, 1,160 Myr) from the lower Cuddapahs and of two slates (530 Myr and 590 Myr) from the Cumbum horizon of the Nallamalai series. A "model" age of 1,400 Myr was obtained for the galena from the Cumbum shales (ASWATHANARAYANA, 1962). These radiometric ages suggest that the Cuddapahs were deposited after the Eastern Ghats orogeny and that they were subsequently metamorphosed about 500 Myr ago. The potassium–argon age of the shales is essentially the age of their metamorphism, and corresponds to the date of formation of muscovite and chlorite from the clay sediments.

The radiometric age of the Cuddapahs generally indicates that the comparatively undisturbed Cuddapahs are older than the much disturbed Satpura and Delhi belts. Such apparently anomalous age relationships have been noticed in the Precambrian of British Guiana (SNELLING, 1963) and of South Africa (McDOUGALL, 1963).

4.7. *Young pegmatites*

Monazite has long been known to occur along with ilmenite, zircon, garnet sillimanite, and rutile in the beach sands of Travancore, now part of Kerala and Madras States. Monazite occurs in the pegmatites, leptynites, and charnockites of the region.

The uncorrected age of 625 Myr of a monazite concentrate from Travancore compares fairly well with its lead-isotope age. According to HOLMES (1955, p. 103), the exact age of the monazite is probably about 600 Myr. The concentrate is a mixture of monazites of different types and, hence, of different ages, and if, as is likely, a part of them are derived from the old leptynites and charnockites, the remaining monazites would be only about 500 Myr old, or even younger, an age which corresponds to the ages of thorianites and associated monazites of Ceylon. Some support for this idea is furnished by the uncorrected age of 490 Myr calculated for a cheralite, a green thorium-rich member of the monazite group, from a kalolinized pegmatite at Kuttakuzhi, about 37 km east-southeast of Trivandrum in southern Travancore, Kerala State[1] (HOLMES, 1955, pp. 102–103).

4.8. *Geochronology*

The Precambrian orogenic sequence in India, as determined by radiometric age data, is supported by structural evidence. On the basis of mutually consistent age determinations for the several structural belts, the general succession of the main orogenic cycles is given in Table 11. The position of

TABLE 11

Precambrian orogenic cycles in India

Orogenic cycle	Age, Myr
Balangoda cycle	520 ± 20
Delhi cycle	735 ± 30
Satpura cycle	950 ± 50
Eastern Ghats cycle	1,600 ± 70
Iron-ore cycle	2,020 ± 80
Dharwar cycle	2,400 ± 100

the Aravalli belt in this sequence is still uncertain, even though there is a single age of 1,020 Myr for the mica schists of Zawar (S. N. SARKAR, personal communication), which is comparable to the age of the Satpura cycle.

The young pegmatites of Travancore, Kerala State,[1] are about (520 ± 20) Myr old and probably correspond to the pegmatites of similar age in Ceylon (see p. 115; VITANAGE, 1959, p. 57), East Africa (CAHEN, 1961, p. 543), and Antarctica (NICOLAYSEN and others, 1961, pp. 96–97; STARIK and others, 1961, pp. 578–581).

Single mineral ages indicate the probable existence of the following orogenic cycles, but more age determinations are necessary before they can be confirmed: Kishangarh cycle (580 ± 20) Myr; Cuddapah cycle (1,400 ± 60) Myr.

[1] After the recent reorganization of the Indian States, Kuttakuzbi is situated in Madras State. The name "Travancore" is no longer used, because northern Travancore is now part of the newly formed Kerala State, and the southern part is merged with Madras State (see Figs. 2 and 3).

4.9. *Gravity measurements*

It was on the basis of investigations in India that AIRY (1855) and PRATT (1855) proposed their hypotheses of isostatic compensation. BURRARD (1912), HAYDEN (1913), OLDHAM (1917), GLENNIE (1932, 1951), AUDEN (1949), GULATEE (1952, 1955, 1956), and KAILASAM (1958) studied gravity anomalies in India for geodetic as well as geological purposes.

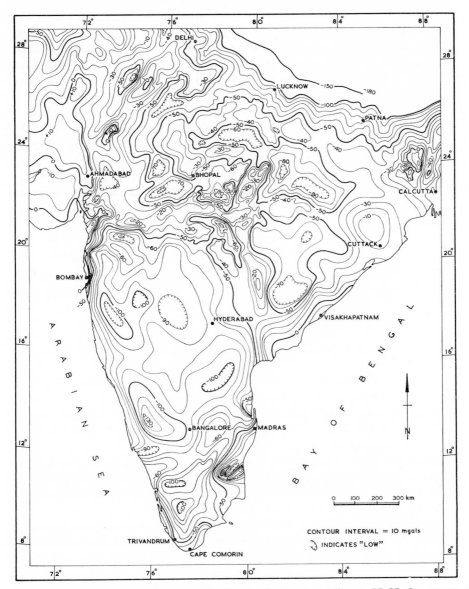

FIG. 10. BOUGUER anomaly map of Peninsular India. According to M. N. QURESHY (personal communication).

In 1963 Dr. M. N. QURESHY (personal communication) correlated regional geology and gravity anomalies in India. In the BOUGUER anomaly map produced by QURESHY (see Fig. 10) the gravity anomaly pattern generally portrays the major structural trends of Peninsular India. The map also affords some evidence that prongs of the Peninsular Shield extend at depth into the Indo–Gangetic alluvial plain, and that the Aravalli Range is a horst, as suggested by FERMOR (1930, pp. 402–405).

The uplifted charnockite massifs of the Nilgiri Mountains and the charnockite–khondalite region of the Eastern Ghats display gravity maxima which indicate their horst-like character. It is remarkable that the large triangular region bounded by the Satpuras, the Nilgiris, the Eastern Ghats, and the Western Ghats, which is occupied predominantly by the Deccan traps and the Dharwars, is an area of relatively low BOUGUER anomaly values. The gravity low extends in a north-northwest direction in Mysore State and corresponds to the axial trend of the plunging Dharwar anticlinorium (PICHAMUTHU, 1951). The gravity minima may also result from the general tilt of the Peninsula to the northwest, as postulated by FERMOR (1936, p. 48). The general picture which emerges from the BOUGUER anomaly map is that within the Indian shield large crustal blocks have moved vertically in relation to one another. According to GULATEE (1956, p. 12, Chart II), the large negative anomalies in southern India with the HAYFORD reference standard of 113.7 km do not connote an extra deficient mass or a greater thickness of Sial underneath but the fact that the MOHOROVIČIĆ discontinuity is at a depth of the order of 15 km.

5. Petrography and petrology

5.1. *Conglomerates*

Whereas OLDHAM (1893, p. 49) stated that conglomerates were of frequent occurrence at or near the base of the Dharwar group, FERMOR (1936, pp. 69–70) was of the opinion that basal conglomerates are rare in the Dharwars. According to PASCOE (1950, pp. 85–86), OLDHAM's statement merely implies that a conglomerate often appears to be the lowermost member of a local "Dharwar" sequence, and that it loses none of its significance by being separated from the eroded floor on which the sediments lie by a small but appreciable thickness of finer-grained material. Uncertainty as to what is meant by the base of the "system" is heightened by the fact that the Dharwar succession was affected by later granitizations, and that nowhere is there undisputed evidence of the existence of basement rocks older than the first granitization.

Conglomerates have been described from many parts of Peninsular India. Their pebbles are made up of schists, vein quartz, quartzite, grit, and gneiss. In some conglomerates the pebbles were rolled out and elongated into rods or flattened into disc-like bodies because they were involved in the protracted and severe deformation which subsequently affected these rocks (see Fig. 11). The existence of such crush conglomerates led SMEETH (1910, pp. 15–18; 1912, p. 38; 1915, p. 25) and SAMPAT IYENGAR (1917; 1920, p. 7) to postulate an autoclastic origin for all the Dharwar conglomerates in Mysore State. Later work (PICHAMUTHU, 1935a; RAMA RAO, 1936) has shown that many of the conglomerates are of true sedimentary origin, and that

FIG. 11. A steeply dipping bed of Dharwar conglomerate. Bisanattam, Kolar schist belt, Mysore State. Photo, C. S. Pichamuthu.

they, because of their great age, were subjected to shearing subsequent to their formation, during which process the pebbles were drawn out or distorted in various ways.

5.2. Schists

The schistose rocks of the Dharwars are composed chiefly of chlorite schists and hornblende schists. Their present-day metamorphosed state often makes it difficult to determine whether they were originally igneous rocks or sediments. There is evidence of extensive igneous activity, but it is probable that a large part of the chlorite schists were originally ferruginous marls. The bulk of the hornblende schists, however, were derived from mafic igneous rocks.

The hornblende schists are tough, coarse- or fine-grained dark greenish-gray rocks. The hornblende, which is the predominant mineral, may be tufted, fibrous, or granular. Under the microscope the hornblende is bluish-green or yellowish-green. Granular aggregates of plagioclase and quartz are present. Epidote, chlorite, and some ilmenite (more or less altered to leucoxene) are common accessory minerals. Zoisite and calcite are usually present in the more altered varieties. Pyroxene, biotite, and almandine occur near igneous contacts.

According to the kind and grade of metamorphism which the schistose rocks have undergone, albite–chlorite schists, mica schists, tremolite–actinolite schists, kyanite–staurolite schists, talc schists, graphite schists, cordierite–sillimanite schists, and other schists are present in the Precambrian terrain of India.

5.3. *Quartzites*

Well-defined outcrops of quartzite can be traced for long distances in schistose areas. They are generally dirty white, and sometimes light blue or gray. Some are feldspar-bearing and others contain sericite. The sedimentary origin of the Dharwar quartzites was doubted because some of the beds are

FIG. 12. A slab of Dharwar quartzite with ripple marks. Dodguni, Mysore State. Photo, C. S. Pichamuthu.

obviously crushed and granulated quartz reefs, and some are metamorphosed and silicified quartz porphyries. Recent investigations in Mysore
show that many of the quartzites are typical sedimentary rocks, often
ripple-marked (see Fig. 12) and current-bedded. Graded bedding also exists
in some of the gritty beds (PICHAMUTHU, 1935a, pp. 264–265).

The quartzites sometimes contain opalescent quartz grains. This feature
has been adduced as evidence that such rocks are only the crushed phase of
the Champion gneiss. This is not an acceptable explanation, because these
quartzites are undoubtedly sedimentary. If the Champion gneisses were older
than those quartzites they could possibly have furnished the opalescent
blebs.

The fuchsite quartzite of Mysore, because of its deep green color and
compact texture, makes an exceedingly pretty ornamental stone.

5.4. Ferruginous quartzites

Banded ferruginous quartzites are characteristic rocks which, because
of their resistance to weathering, form the backbone of many of the hill
ranges of Peninsular India. They constitute a folded series of rocks and often,
e.g. in the Bababudan Hills of Mysore State, present steep escarpments
(see Fig. 13). The iron-bearing quartzites are finely banded with alternate
parallel layers of granular quartz and hematite or magnetite. The silica
layer is often cherty or jaspery. In many exposures the individual layers are
rarely more than 1 mm–2 mm in thickness but are regular and persistent

FIG. 13. An escarpment showing a folded outcrop of banded ferruginous quartzite. Near Kemmangandi on the Bababudan Hills, Mysore State. Photo, C. S.
Pichamuthu.

over long distances. Intraformational folding and brecciation are sometimes present (see Fig. 14).

In Mysore the banded ferruginous quartzites were previously considered to have been formed by the decomposition and reconstruction of cummingtonite schists and other amphibole-bearing rocks of igneous origin. However, even though some quartzites may have been formed by the metasomatic

FIG. 14. Intraformational folding in a banded ferruginous quartzite of Dharwar age. Lingadhalli, Mysore State. The scale is in inches. Photo, C. S. Pichamuthu.

alteration of sheared igneous rocks, most are of typical sedimentary origin, as witnessed by their rock associations, stratigraphical disposition, and structural behaviour (PICHAMUTHU, 1935b).

Dark acicular amphibole crystals, such as cummingtonite and bababudanite, have originated in some of the ferruginous quartzites as a result of metasomatism associated with mafic igneous intrusion (PICHAMUTHU, 1950a). Amphiboles, pyroxenes, and garnets occur in these rocks when subjected to higher grades of metamorphism, e.g. in the southern parts of Mysore State.

5.5. *Limestones*

As in the case of the other members of the Dharwars, doubt has been expressed about the sedimentary origin of the limestones. Calcification of traps, modification of the Champion gneiss, and contact alteration of mafic schists were some of the explanations proposed for the origin of the limestones in Mysore. Their close association and sometimes interstratification with typical sedimentogenic rocks such as quartzites and ferruginous quartzites indicate that the limestones also must be of sedimentary origin.

The majority of the Dharwar limestones are magnesian. They are generally coarsely crystalline and vary in color from light to dark gray. Quartz, chlorite, and phlogopite are frequently associated, and in metamorphosed limestones garnet, cummingtonite, rhodonite, and other minerals are present. Scales of graphite are sometimes present. The so-called tarurites of Mysore, which are composed of diopside, epidote, and other calcium silicate minerals, are also metamorphosed calcitic or dolomitic limestones.

5.6. *Mafic intrusions*

Dikes and sills of mafic igneous rocks are common in the Precambrian. As a result of metamorphism, they are generally represented by epidiorites and hornblende schists or chlorite schists.

The "Newer dolerites" of Singhbhum have been regarded as being of Cuddapah age, but it is possible that they may be of any age up to that of the Deccan traps. There are many resemblances to the Cuddapah dikes, but it is likely that there is more than one generation of mafic dikes in the Singhbhum region.

There is an exactly similar group of dikes in the Bundelkhand granite area. The dikes are pre-Vindhyan, but the granite is believed to be much older than any of the granites of Singhbhum. Mafic dikes of Lower Vindhyan age occur in the Son Valley and in parts of Rajputana. Dikes probably identical with the "Newer dolerites" occur in Bastar.

The dike rocks vary from a fine-grained to a coarse-grained dolerite, and some dikes are gabbro or norite. The texture is ophitic, and the common minerals are plagioclase and titanian augite. Quartz is sometimes present in micropegmatitic intergrowth with the plagioclase. Ilmenite, partly altered to leucoxene and sphene, is abundant, but olivine is rare. In the porphyritic dolerites there are stout phenocrysts of altered feldspars.

Mafic sills and dikes, originally dolerites but now epidiorites and hornblende schists or amphibolites, occur in the Aravallis. Some of the dikes are fine-grained basalts or coarse-grained gabbros. According to HERON (1935, p. 26), some of the epidiorite sills and dikes traversing the Aravallis and the Bundelkhand granite may be hypabyssal equivalents of the Khairmalia vesicular lava, which occupies a position between the Aravalli slates and the Khardeola grits.

Just below the base of the Delhi group, epidiorites are abundant in the Banded gneiss complex. Some of them are probably post-Aravalli basalts and dolerites, and others are older than the Aravallis. In northern and central Rajasthan there occurs a post-Delhi dolerite. Even though all these mafic rocks are of different ages, they are often indistinguishable from one another; they can, however, be distinguished from the much younger Deccan traps.

There are numerous linear mafic dikes in the Bundelkhand area. They traverse the great quartz reefs, but none of them penetrates the Gwalior or Bijawar metasediments bordering the granite. There is some resemblance to the Cuddapah dikes, but the mafic dikes could be the feeders of the sills of trap in the Gwaliors and Bijawars, from which they are petrologically indistinguishable.

Mafic igneous intrusions are plentiful in the Cheyair section of the Cuddapahs. The commonest type is a coarse-grained mafic dolerite, but some rocks approach basalt, and some are porphyritic. Olivine is sometimes present. The intrusions, which are sometimes 100 m thick, are generally concordant with the bedding. In certain places the sheets are connected by dikes. It is possible that some of the sheets may be contemporaneous flows. No mafic intrusives are known to occur in strata younger than the Tadpatri in the Cuddapah formation, and such mafic intrusive rocks are also absent in the overlying Kurnools.

The only intrusive rocks observed in the Kaladgi area are four dikes of diorite, somewhat different from the older diorites of the gneiss area.

The lower strata of the Alwars contain numerous large masses of epidiorite. Some are contemporaneous lava flows, and others are intrusives occurring in the form of lenticular phacoliths and thick sills. The epidiorites are homogeneous granulitic rocks consisting chiefly of hornblende with interstitial quartz and plagioclase.

In the northwestern parts of Jaipur sills, laccoliths, veins, and minute *lit-par-lit* injections of epidiorite invade the Ajabgarhs and the Alwars. Biotite, apatite, garnet, ilmenite, and sphene occur as accessories. Whereas the neighbouring Erinpura granite is typically foliated, the epidiorites are seldom schistose, being generally recrystallized into granulitic rocks. They occur as inclusions in the granite.

In Sirohi the amphibolitic rocks, even though older than the Erinpura granite, invade both the Delhis and the older Aravalli rocks. Most of them are sills, but some may be contemporaneous flows. The rocks vary from epidiorites to amphibolites and actinolite schists; some are highly epidotized, some contain abundant scapolite, and tourmaline may occur near the Erinpura granite.

There are a few mafic intrusives present only in Sirohi and in its neighborhood, which comprise coarse-grained gabbro-like rocks, dolerites, and granulites. They are veined by fine-grained dolerites and basalts resembling the Cuddapah dikes, and by a red pegmatite which is usually associated with the Erinpura granite.

5.7. *Volcanic rocks*

Volcanic activity is recognized at various stages in the Dharwars of Mysore. There are the Santaveri and Lingadhalli flows in the Shimoga belt; the Jogimardi, Chitaldrug, and Bellara flows in the Chitaldrug belt; and the dark hornblende-bearing traps in the Kolar belt.

The Lingadhalli and Santaveri flows of Shimoga are epidiorites. The original augite is never seen, but the ophitic texture is sometimes discernible. The plagioclase is sodic, epidote is abundant, and ilmenite is generally altered to leucoxene. The vesicles are filled with minerals such as celadonite, delessite, penninite, actinolite, epidote, zoisite, quartz, calcite, pyrite, and magnetite. In metamorphosed amygdales plagioclase is present, probably a product of alteration of the original zeolites.

The Chitaldrug volcanics are less metamorphosed than those in the Shimoga belt. They are often variolitic. They vary from compact aphanitic rocks with skeleton crystals to coarser varieties exhibiting ophitic or subophitic texture. The augite is generally altered into amphibole and chlorite; where this change is incomplete, relict augite grains are surrounded by hornblende. Epidote, clinozoisite, chlorite, and leucoxene are common secondary minerals, and sphene and ilmenite are the usual accessories.

The Kolar flows represent a more strongly metamorphosed mafic lava, and occur now as dark hornblende schists often associated with bands of amphibolite.

PICHAMUTHU (1950b) noticed pillow lavas in the Chitaldrug area. Since then similar rocks have been observed in the schist belts in other parts of Mysore State, especially in the Tumkur, Shimoga, and Kolar districts. Although the pillow lavas are not rich in Na_2O, they are comparable with spilites from other parts of the world.

In northern Singhbhum the top of the Iron-ore series contains intercalations of contemporaneous lava flows, tuffs, and agglomerates. The lava is fine-grained, but has been almost entirely recrystallized to a hornblende rock in which the original amygdales and even the radial structure of the zeolites, now altered to epidote, are preserved.

South of the shear zone the Dalma volcanics extend without interruption for more than 150 km and give rise to precipitous hills, in places attaining a height of 3,500 m above the sea level, i.e. 1,000 m above the level of the Ranchi Plateau. The flows and sills, which were originally basalt or dolerite, now consist mainly of varieties of epidiorite and of hornblende schists. On shearing, the schists give rise to sericite–chlorite rocks or talc schists.

Volcanic breccias and agglomerates indicate the proximity of volcanic foci. Typically, the agglomerates and breccias comprise large angular and subangular fragments of epidiorite in a matrix of a different texture.

About 40 km from the western edge of the main Cuddapah outcrop, and 16 km south of Guntakal, there is a volcanic neck near Wajrakarur, which is probably one of the centers from which the Cuddapah trap erupted. The neck is filled with an agglomerate which strongly resembles the Kimberley "blue ground". It is soft and friable, and, consequently, the site of the neck has been eroded into a hollow. In a matrix of matted chlorite, rounded and subangular fragments of gneiss, granite, hornblende schist, amphibolite, and epidote are present. The agglomeratic neck itself has yielded no diamonds, even though Wajrakarur has long been noted for the diamonds found in its neighborhood.

5.8. *Ultramafic intrusions*

Amphibolites, pyroxenites, peridotites, harzburgites, serpentinites, talc schists, talc–chlorite schists, and dunites are associated with Precambrian rocks in many parts of Peninsular India. Because many of the ultramafic bodies are intruded and cut out along with the schists by the granites, they are included in the Precambrian.

In Mysore State it is noteworthy that almost all the chief chromite-bearing ultramafic rocks occur in a comparatively narrow N.N.W.–S.S.E.-trending band extending for about 160 km. This ultramafic zone occupies an axial position between the two limbs of a N.N.W.-plunging anticlinorium into which the Dharwars have been folded (PICHAMUTHU, 1956). This intrusion is of the Alpine type and contains valuable chromite deposits (see pp. 38, 83). Corundum and vermiculite are often observed in the amphibolites along their contact with the gneiss.

Olivine rocks are present in the Salem district, the best-known occurrence being the "Chalk Hills" and the neighboring tract near the foot of the Shevaroys. The rocks are strongly altered and are replaced by abundant veins of magnesite.

The occurrence of anorthosites in Bengal was first recognized by HOLLAND (1900, p. 208), and detailed work on the petrography of these rocks was done by CHATTERJEE (1936). According to CHATTERJEE (1959b), the anorthosite body was intruded as an elongated sheet-like mass into the gneisses.

The mineralogy and petrology of a completely metamorphosed and reconstituted layered complex of anorthosites with associated gabbro and chromite facies in the Salem district was described by SUBRAMANIAM (1956), who interpreted the complex as a metamorphosed gravity-stratified sheet. Of special interest is the highly calcic plagioclase (An_{80}–An_{100}) in the anorthosites.

Ultramafic rocks are associated with the Iron-ore series, particularly in Dhalbhum and Mayurbhanj, where they are intruded by the Singhbhum granite. They contain small deposits of vanadium-bearing titaniferous iron ore.

About 15 km west-southwest of Chaibasa there are three thick laccolithic intrusions consisting of strongly serpentinized peridotite, with associated saxonite, dunite, subordinate pyroxenite, and, in one instance, lherzolite. Bands of chromite 20 cm–25 cm thick occur in both dunite and saxonite.

In Rajasthan there is an extensive group of talc–serpentine–chlorite rocks which are considered to be metamorphosed intrusions of peridotite or pyroxenite. They are composed of talc, serpentine, and chlorite in varying proportions. Steatite and magnesite occur as alteration products. The soapstone from which were made the small ornaments and utensils found in the ancient city of Taxila in the extreme north of the Punjab may have come from these ultramafic bodies.

Ultramafic intrusives occur among the Aravalli phyllites but not in the true Delhis, and, hence, are presumably pre-Delhi in age. They have produced some contact effects in the surrounding rocks: phyllite was converted into mica schist, limestone into marble, and the grayish-white quartzites into violet or bluish rocks.

5.9. *Khondalite series*

The name "khondalite" was given by WALKER (1902) to an unusual series of rocks in the Eastern Ghats belt. The name was derived from the Khonds, one of the aboriginal tribes of India, in whose country the series is well developed. It occurs as well-defined bands which are mainly composed of metamorphosed sediments.

The khondalites are essentially garnet–sillimanite schists containing varying amounts of graphite and some quartz and orthoclase. They are grayish or reddish in color, usually foliated, with abundant reddish-brown almandine in a strongly crushed groundmass. They are susceptible to decomposition, and so it is rarely possible to collect fresh specimens. Sillimanite occurs in hair-like needles (fibrolite) or as broken crystals, graphite forms nests or pockets, and calcite, biotite, and rutile are generally present. Orthoclase and oligoclase–andesine are common in small quantities.

DUNN (1942, p. 237) considered the khondalites "dry" metamorphic rocks, because their typical minerals do not contain water and other volatile constituents.

Khondalites are often accompanied by beds of crystalline limestone, schists containing much hematite, and bands of a granular garnet–magnetite rock in which hypersthene may be present. When strongly metamorphosed, as they are in Kalahandi State, the impure limestones associated with the khondalites are converted into aggregates of a colorless pyroxene outwardly resembling wollastonite, diopside, spinel, almandine, and, sometimes, scapolite. Khondalites extend in a S.W.–N.E. direction from the Guntur district in Andhra State into Orissa State, some of the most northerly occurrences being situated on the border of Sambalpur district, and along the banks of Mahanadi River. Rocks resembling khondalite occur near Ranchi in Bihar, Coimbatore in Madras, and in parts of Mysore State.

5.10. *Kodurite series*

The name "kodurite series" is derived from the Kodur manganese mine near Visakhapatnam, where the typical rock is well exposed (FERMOR, 1909, pp. 243–271). The kodurites are hybrid rocks formed by the addition of granitizing material to manganese-ore bodies and to manganese silicate rocks corresponding to the gondites (MIDDLEMISS, 1915, pp. 103–104). Kodurites differ from gondites in containing potassium. Koduritic rocks are unique in the world because of the high percentage of manganese they contain. The typical kodurite is composed of potassium feldspar, manganese garnet and apatite, usually accompanied by manganese-bearing pyroxenes (such as schefferite and rhodonite) and quartz. The garnet is intermediate between

C

spessartite and andradite and was called "spandite" by FERMOR (1909, p. 164). Biotite is a rare constituent.

Kodurites are generally extremely altered. They decompose and give rise to irregularly shaped manganese-ore bodies derived from the manganese silicates, and masses of lithomarge from the feldspars, the other secondary products being chert, ochres, and wad.

The name "kodurite", like the name "charnockite", was used by FERMOR (1909) for what he thought was an igneous rock suite ranging from silicic to ultramafic, the rock types varying from quartz kodurites to pyroxene kodurites. The rocks are generally granular in texture. A pegmatitic variety is sometimes seen. CROSS (1914) did not agree with FERMOR's view that the kodurites constitute a petrographic province, and considered them only hybrid rocks.

Some rocks occurring near Sakarsanhalli in Mysore State contain spessartite and rhodonite. They grade into various pyroxenites, pyroxene gneisses, calciphyres, and marbles. The crystalline limestones resemble the black manganiferous limestones of the Chhindwara and Nagpur districts (the Lohangi stage of the Sausar series), the similarity going so far as to include the presence of black manganese oxide along the cleavage planes of the calcite. One of the manganese garnets from Sakarsanhalli is a calcium-rich spessartite intermediate between the calcium-poor garnets of the gondite series and the calcium-rich garnets of the kodurite series.

5.11. *Gondite series*

The name "gondite series" was given by FERMOR (1909, pp. 306–353) after the aboriginal tribe of the Gonds, in whose country in central India typical rocks of the series occur, to a sequence characterized by the presence of the manganese silicates spessartite and rhodonite. These rocks are considered to be metamorphosed manganese-bearing sediments. Economically important manganese deposits are associated with the gondites, and the ore bodies consist of braunite and psilomelane, sometimes accompanied by hollandite, vredenburgite, and sitaparite. The typical gondite of Madhya Pradesh is a spessartite–quartz rock, often containing a little apatite, but usually nearly devoid of potassium feldspar.

The gonditic rocks are associated with schists of sedimentary origin, and, hence, may be inferred to be of a similar origin. According to FERMOR (1909), some of the ore was formed by the compression of the purest original manganese hydroxide and oxide sediments. Under deep-seated metamorphism, such sediments combined with the associated arenaceous and pelitic sediments to form the gondite group of rocks, the mixture of manganese ore and clay minerals forming spessartite. The banding of the gondites represents original layers of different composition.

5.12. *Granites and gneisses*

5.12.1. Bundelkhand gneiss, Berach granite, Banded gneiss complex

There are several granites and gneisses in the Precambrian of India. They are of different ages and petrological types, but correlations and sequences are difficult to arrive at because of lack of chronological data. To commence with the Rajasthan area, because it has been suggested that certain gneisses there could be the oldest rocks of India, there are the Banded gneiss complex, the Bundelkhand gneiss, and the Berach granite.

The Bundelkhand and Berach rocks appear to be the same even though they are separated by an area, more than 400 km wide, of younger rocks. They are traversed by prominent quartz reefs and numerous dolerite dikes. In both areas there are both gneissic and granitic rocks. In Bundelkhand there is a pink porphyritic granite, weathering concentrically like the "Dome gneiss" of Bihar into large spheroidal masses, and resembling the Closepet or the Bellary granite. It is medium-grained or coarse-grained and consists chiefly of quartz, orthoclase, hornblende, and some plagioclase. Orthoclase is red or pink and occurs in crystals sometimes more than 5 cm long. In the Berach Valley the granite is pink, medium-grained, and non-foliated. The chief minerals are quartz, orthoclase, subordinate microcline, biotite, and hornblende. The quartz has a faint violet opalescence. Transitions exist from the reddish unfoliated granite to a gray foliated rock until it finally becomes a greenish-gray, slabby gneiss which is greasy to the touch. In the greasy character, the opalescence of the quartz, and the usually decomposed condition of the ferromagnesian minerals and feldspars, these gneisses sometimes resemble the Champion gneiss of Mysore State (see below).

The Banded gneiss complex is an intimate association of granite with various types of schists, gneisses, quartzites, and limestones. Some geologists believe that it is the granitized representative of the Aravalli schists. According to HERON (1953, p. 21), however, there is a distinct unconformity between the gneiss complex and the overlying Aravallis. If this interpretation is accepted the gneiss complex would be a basement complex and the schistose inclusions in it would be metamorphosed ancient sediments which might represent some of the oldest rocks in India.

5.12.2. Champion gneiss

The Champion gneiss was first recognized as an irregular band enclosed in the hornblende schists of Kolar in Mysore State, and was named after the Champion Lode in the Kolar goldfield. It is intrusive into the schists, but is itself intruded by Peninsular gneiss. It is a comparatively fine-grained, strongly crushed, micaceous granitic gneiss, a typical feature of which is the presence of grains or blebs of opalescent quartz often containing acicular and dusty inclusions.

The Champion gneiss is the oldest known gneiss in Mysore, and there is

some speculation as to whether it could form a part of the old floor on which
the Dharwar sediments were deposited. Unfortunately, there are wide
differences of opinion as to what exactly is the Champion gneiss. Confusion
in nomenclature and correlation was caused in Mysore when certain metasedimentary rocks, such as conglomerates, grits, and quartzites, and some
silicic igneous porphyries, were designated as Champion gneiss.

According to RAMA RAO (1935b, pp. 85–86), there are granitic types of
the Champion gneiss which are dull gray or pale pink in color, generally
fine- or medium-grained, and with a strikingly greasy appearance. Micas
(muscovite and biotite) are subordinate constituents. The plagioclase (mostly
oligoclase and andesine, rarely labradorite) is intensely sericitized. Biotite
is altered to chlorite. Apatite, magnetite, zircon, and tourmaline are common accessories but idocrase and allanite are rare. The granitic varieties
often grade marginally into microgranites and granite porphyries; by
intense crushing the porphyritic types are transformed into augen gneisses.
The larger bodies of the Champion gneiss are traversed by thin veins of
aplite or quartz, but pegmatites are very rare.

The gold-bearing quartz veins of Kolar are regarded as being genetically
related to the closing phases of the Champion granite intrusion. The
minerals associated with gold are galena, arsenopyrite, pyrrhotite, pyrite,
chalcopyrite, ilmenite, magnetite, tourmaline, scheelite, sphalerite, and
minor quantites of telluride minerals.

5.12.3. Peninsular gneiss

The Peninsular gneiss was originally called the Fundamental gneiss because it was considered to be the floor on which the Dharwar sediments and
lavas were deposited. In view of the uncertainty regarding its being really
the basement, the more general name "Peninsular gneiss" suggested by
SMEETH (1916, pp. 16–17) is now used to denote the gneissic complex of
Peninsular India.

The Peninsular gneiss contains inclusions of diverse sizes of the Dharwar
rocks in many stages of granitization. Agmatites are frequently present
(see Fig. 15). The various gneisses differ markedly from the Champion
gneiss in the following properties. They are not greasy-looking; the feldspars
and micas are much less altered; they do not grade into hypabyssal types
nor are they intimately associated with the Dharwar conglomerates; pegmatites and quartz veins are common.

The Peninsular gneiss is generally banded and often strongly contorted.
The rock types vary from a coarse-grained gneissic granite to a strongly
foliated migmatitic gneiss (see Fig. 16). They are essentially biotite gneisses,
but granitic, syenitic, and dioritic types also occur. They are generally poorer
in SiO_2 and richer in Al_2O_3 than the Champion gneiss, and they are richer
in accessory minerals.

The plagioclase is mostly andesine or oligoclase, rarely labradorite, and
there are varying proportions of microcline or orthoclase. Biotite is usually

Fig. 15. Agmatite in Peninsular gneiss. Bangalore, Mysore State. Photo, C. S. Pichamuthu.

fresh, hornblende is present in the neighborhood of mafic inclusions, and muscovite and chlorite are rare. Apatite and zircon are common accessories.

The Peninsular gneiss complex represents a long period of time and affords evidence of several episodes of intrusion, injection, granitization, and tectonics. It is extremely difficult, therefore, to differentiate the component types and to determine the sequence of their formation.

The Peninsular gneiss is of batholithic dimensions and is intrusive into the Dharwars. It cuts across the strike of the schists and has also forced itself between the members of the Dharwar schists as sills or sheets.

5.12.4. Dome gneiss

The Dome gneiss of Bihar is a pink alkalic gneissose biotite granite which gives rise to dome-shaped hummocks of bare rock, reminiscent of the Closepet granites. The rock is sometimes porphyritic. It consists of quartz and microcline (with some oligoclase), biotite, hornblende, and accessory sphene, apatite, and zircon. There is no definite banding caused by alternating layers of different minerals, but the rock has generally a faint gneissose structure caused by the parallel disposition of the minerals.

The Dome gneiss occurs as large lenticular bosses or as thin sheets intruded into the schists. There are xenoliths of quartzite and schist. The contact zone with the schists is of varying width and is characterized by hornblende- and garnet-bearing granulitic rocks. The mode of occurrence of the gneiss suggests intrusion similar to that of a salt dome.

FIG. 16. Migmatitic Peninsular gneiss cut by a forked pegmatite vein. Bangalore, Mysore State. Photo, C. S. Pichamuthu.

5.12.5. Erinpura granite

The Erinpura granite is the chief igneous intrusive in the Delhi sedimentary sequence and is younger than the epidiorites and hornblende schists of the area. Mount Abu is a big batholith composed of the Erinpura granite, but the granite occurs also as small bosses and sills. The intrusion of the Erinpura granite reached its maximum intensity northwest of the main Aravalli Range, where it obliterated much of the northwestern flank of the great Delhi synclinorium. Its intrusive relationship to the Aravalli schists is indicated by the included fragments of the schists, and in some instances by the alteration of the rocks along the contact. Inclusions of the granite occur in the younger Malani granites.

The Erinpura granite varies widely in texture, grain size, and degree of foliation, but is fairly constant in mineral composition. The granite itself is a biotite granite with subordinate hornblende, and the coarse pegmatites related to it contain tourmaline and muscovite. Both granite and pegmatite are connected with aplite and microgranite veins.

The Mount Abu massif contains large crystals of microcline or orthoclase, sometimes perthitic. The common accessories are fluorite, iron ore, sphene, and zircon. There is sometimes a well-marked gneissic banding. In Idar bands of idocrase occur in the contact zone in the calcium schists bordering the granite. A porphyritic variety is present only in this area. Phenocrysts of quartz, microcline, orthoclase, plagioclase, and biotite vary in relative abundance. In the groundmass, which is often cryptocrystalline, micropegmatite is prevalent as a shell around the phenocrysts, a feature which links the porphyries to the microgranites and granophyres.

The Erinpura granite contains sometimes axinite, kyanite, and thulite (zoisite). Cassiterite and gadolinite occur in some pegmatites. North of Ajmer City the pegmatites contain huge crystals of beryl, some of them 2 m long.

It is probable that the intrusion of the Erinpura granite suite was spread over a considerable period of time covered by the tectonic history of the Aravalli Range.

5.12.6. Closepet (Bellary) granite

The main exposure of the Closepet granite, a characteristic young granite of Peninsular India, is a belt about 15 km–30 km wide which stretches with a general Dharwarian trend for about 400 km, passing through Mysore and Andhra States into the Kaladgi basin, where it occurs as isolated inliers within the Kaladgis, the Bhimas, and the Deccan traps. The main belt in Mysore is a range of bold precipitous hills often exceeding 1,200 m in height, with rugged disconnected peaks, forming isolated rounded bosses or domes which are steep-sided and more or less bare of vegetation. RADHAKRISHNA (1956) gave a detailed account of the occurrence, petrography, metamorphic history, and manner of origin of the Closepet granite.

The granite contains numerous intercalated elongated patches of gneiss, schists, quartzites, and ferruginous quartzites. Porphyroblasts of microcline are present in both the granite and the mafic schist inclusions, indicating that the narrow and elongated granite band represents a former Dharwar schist belt, of which only isolated remnants are now left in various stages of granitization.

The typical Closepet granite is a pink or gray coarse-grained porphyritic rock. There are, however, variations in texture which may be fine-, medium-, or coarse-grained, or porphyritic. The rock is essentially granitic in texture, but the margins are fine-grained, and the more uniform parts are distinctly foliated and even-banded, and the porphyritic parts exhibit a parallel arrangement of the constituent minerals.

The Closepet granite is composed of quartz, microcline, oligoclase, biotite, and hornblende. Sphene, apatite, and zircon are common accessories. Fluorite is rare, but epidote is generally present.

5.13. *Charnockite series*

The name "charnockite" was given by HOLLAND (1900) to certain hypersthene granites, and the name "charnockite series" to a group of rocks genetically related to charnockite and to one another, varying from silicic charnockite to ultramafic pyroxenite. The characteristic features of this sequence are the invariable presence of hypersthene and granulitic texture. Since HOLLAND published his classic memoir on the charnockites, similar rock types have been reported from virtually all the Shield areas of the world. The minerals commonly present are blue quartz, bluish-green feldspars (microcline, microperthite, plagioclase, antiperthite), hypersthene, diopside, garnet (rich in almandine and pyrope molecules), brownish hornblende, biotite, zircon, apatite, magnetite, ilmenite, pyrite, and pyrrhotite.

HOLLAND believed that the charnockite series constitutes a petrographic province and that the different rock types originated by magmatic differentiation. Some of the arguments in favor of an igneous origin are the form and structure of the great massifs, the presence of intrusive tongues and dikes, contact metamorphic phenomena, occurrence of included fragments of foreign rocks, correspondence of chemical composition to igneous rock series, porphyritic texture, evidence of magmatic differentiation and assimilation, and the association of magnetite and chromite ores, which suggests magmatic segregation.

After HOLLAND many geologists in India and elsewhere expressed the opinion that the charnockites were formed as the product of metamorphism of preexisting igneous or sedimentary rocks. The association of charnockites with khondalites, the absence of intrusive relationships, the rapid variations in texture and in the SiO_2 content, the occurrence of the charnockites only in regions affected by high-grade metamorphism, the metamorphic origin of their component minerals, and the absence of gradations from silicic to ultramafic types are among the reasons given by those who support a metamorphic origin.

It is probable that there are charnockites and charnockites, and that they originated in more than one way. There are two distinct types in Mysore State, namely one which is granulitic, often foliated and sometimes mylonitized, and another which is granitic, coarse-grained, and sometimes porphyritic (PICHAMUTHU, 1953). The first type is generally conformable to the regional strike of the Peninsular gneisses, and instances of transgression are observed in the second type. The gneissic or granulitic type is older and is formed by high-grade regional metamorphism of preexisting rocks. Much later there was palingenetic fusion and widespread metasomatism when the granitic, frequently intrusive, type of charnockite was generated (see Fig. 17). The two periods of metamorphism which were responsible for the formation of the two different charnockite types were separated by a period during which numerous mafic dikes intruded. In the charnockite region the plagioclases of the mafic dikes are "clouded", probably as a result of the regional thermal metamorphism that took place at the time when the second type of charnockite was formed (PICHAMUTHU, 1959).

The silicic and intermediate charnockites of southern Kerala State were considered by PAULOSE (1956) to be the result of assimilation of a preexisting, deep-seated, mafic rock of either igneous or sedimentary origin and a coexisting aluminous sediment, by influx of granite.

5.14. *Alkalic rocks*

5.14.1. Sivamalai series

The name "Sivamalai series" was given by HOLLAND (1901b) to a rock sequence in Coimbatore, Madras State, comprising nepheline syenites and corundum syenites, which he considered to be a suite of igneous rocks.

The nepheline syenites of Sivamalai and adjoining hills form lenticular masses in the gneisses. The linear arrangement of their mineral constituents is parallel to the general W.N.W.–E.S.E. foliation of the surrounding rocks. The common rock type is even-grained and granulitic. The chief constituents are nepheline, feldspars, biotite, graphite, magnetite, and ilmenite. Some

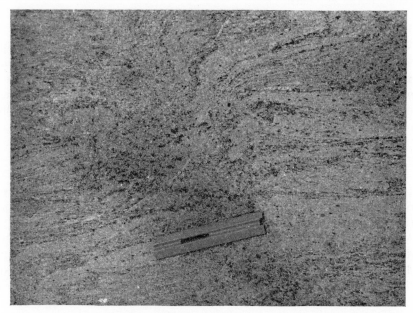

FIG. 17. Transformation of Peninsular gneiss into charnockite. The darker and coarser patches are charnockite. The Peninsular gneiss is highly contorted. Kabbaldurga, Mysore State. Length of scale, 15 cm. Photo, C. S. Pichamuthu.

of the feldspar is oligoclase, but the greater part is orthoclase or anorthoclase with a microperthitic structure. The coarse-grained pegmatitic rock is composed chiefly of nepheline and microperthite in crystals sometimes 10 cm–12 cm across. The granulitic varieties are devoid of graphite but contain nepheline, microcline, perthite, apatite, magnetite, and biotite. The lenticular mafic schlieren are composed chiefly of hornblende, with subordinate calcite, nepheline, and other minerals. Olivine-bearing augite syenite rocks similar to the larvikites of Norway, and a feldspar rock containing corundum, spinel, and other minerals, are often associated. A remarkable feature of these rocks is the freshness of the nepheline.

The corundum syenites which occur in large quantities in the area were considered by HOLLAND (1901b) to be genetically related to the nepheline syenites and augite syenites. The corundum-bearing rock is nonfoliated, composed mainly of an intergrowth of albite and orthoclase and nests of platy biotite. It is virtually devoid of quartz. Corundum occurs in large, well-preserved, hexagonal crystals which are sometimes 15 cm–20 cm across.

In the Sivamalai area SUBRAMANIAM (1950) described nepheline syenite, aplite syenite, biotite– and hornblende–nepheline syenites, nepheline syenodiorite, aegirine–augite syenite, and microperthitite. According to him, the presence of xenoliths of diopside granulite and the association of charnockite, pyroxene syenite, and nepheline syenite suggest a syntectic origin for this alkalic sequence.

5.14.2. Sodium syenites of Kishangarh

Northeast of Kishangarh (see Fig. 7) there are intrusions of sodium syenites into the pre-Aravalli beds composed of micaceous quartzites, quartz–mica schists, and mica–sillimanite schists (HERON, 1924). None of these syenites penetrates the Delhis (HERON, 1953, p. 331). The sodium syenites are themselves metamorphosed and intruded by amphibolite, granite, and pegmatite. They differ somewhat from the nepheline–sodalite syenites of Sirohi (COULSON, 1933, p. 13), but resemble the Sivamalai nepheline syenites, the chemical composition of which agrees very closely with that of the normal Kishangarh sodium syenites (see Table 14). Primary cancrinite and calcite are associated with the feldspars. Nepheline occurs in two generations, viz. as small rounded phenocrysts and as allotriomorphic grains in the matrix.

According to NIYOGI (1960), several lenticular bodies of granitoid, foliated, and banded syenites lie within the Aravalli hornblende-bearing quartzites and calcareous amphibole schists. The syenites grade often into calcareous schists with an intermediate nepheline-free diorite gneiss. There is structural concordance between the lenticular syenite plutons and the country rock, which suggests *in situ* transformation of calcareous amphibole–biotite schists into nepheline syenite (SEN, 1952; NIYOGI, 1960).

The pegmatites traversing the syenite contain very large crystals of nepheline in a finely granular aggregate of sodalite, nepheline, and some cancrinite. One of the varieties of pegmatites in the Kishangarh area consists of white albite and microcline veined with deep blue sodalite, bright yellow cancrinite, and black biotite. Another variety of pegmatite contains large idiomorphic pale pink grossularite in cancrinite and albite, with biotite, apatite, sphene, sometimes calcite, and rarely molybdenite. There are also small veins of melanite.

5.15. *Felsite dikes and porphyry dikes*

The intrusion of dikes of different types of porphyry and felsite is considered to be one of the final phases of the Precambrian history of southern

India. Such dikes are common in Mysore State. They range from a few meters to about 7 km in length and trend more or less in two directions perpendicular to each other, viz. N.N.W.–S.S.E. and E.N.E.–W.S.W. The dikes vary in texture, ranging from hornstone with some small phenocrysts to a rock crowded with large phenocrysts in a scanty fine-grained matrix.

Idiomorphic plagioclase, generally strongly altered, is the chief porphyritic mineral. Hornblende phenocrysts, often twinned or zoned, are common, and allanite, sphene, and apatite occur as accessories. Some of the quartz–monzonite porphyries contain well-developed orthoclase crystals. Abundant dissemination of hematite dust has imparted a red color not only to the feldspars but also to the matrix of the porphyry dikes.

5.16. *Young granite pegmatites*

A series of pegmatite veins of economic importance occurs immediately west of Nellore on the east coast of the Peninsula. They are lens-shaped bodies, sometimes arranged *en echelon* or occurring as long irregular masses, more often disposed along, but also across, the foliation of the schists. The veins average 3 m–5 m in thickness and sometimes swell to more than 70 m; in length they average about 10 m, but have sometimes been traced for distances exceeding 400 m. The pegmatite veins are often associated with bosses of quartz. Big crystals of muscovite, sometimes as much as 3 m across the basal planes, occur in the pegmatites, even though the average crystal size is much smaller. Samarskite, allanite, cyrtolite, and beryl occur in some pegmatites.

The Bihar pegmatites are well known because they contain ruby mica, a muscovite so-called because of its color, which is highly valued for its electrical properties. The pegmatites were introduced into the schists, usually as sheets and lenses parallel to the foliation, and less frequently as cross-cutting dikes. The most valuable mica-bearing pegmatites tend to occur in the mica schists and contain a large and varied assortment of minerals, among which the following species may be mentioned: amazonite, moonstone, lepidolite, automolite (gahnite), tourmaline, indicolite (blue tourmaline), fluorite, garnet, eucryptite, löllingite, cassiterite, beryl, columbite, torbernite, triplite, uraninite, samarskite, gadolinite, and monazite.

5.17. *Petrochemistry*

In a large Precambrian terrane such as India, composed of tectonic belts which differ greatly in age from one another, and of rock sequences which have been metamorphosed to varying degrees of intensity, it is difficult to compare and contrast rocks from a chemical point of view. Some chemical characters have been noted in describing the petrography and petrology of Precambrian rocks. Attention will now be drawn only to a few selected areas where detailed chemical work has been done. As for the rest, chemical analyses of some important representative rock types will be given.

Mafic rocks, whether they were originally sills or flows, occur at various stages in the Precambrian. The chemical composition of representative types of some of the rock types is given in Table 12. Some of the oldest mafic rocks, which include pillow lavas, constitute the Kolar schist belt. RAMACHANDRA RAO (1937) made a chemical study of the schists and amphibolites of this belt and showed that they were metamorphosed basalts and pyroxenites. The mafic rocks in the Chitaldrug schist belt which exhibit pillow structures are spilites characterized by a low K_2O content and a comparatively high Na_2O content (PICHAMUTHU, 1938). The sills in the Lower Cuddapahs of the type area, according to VEMBAN (1946), are essentially basaltic in nature with only a limited range of differentiation, and derived from a tholeiitic magma.

SUBRAMANIAM (1956) made a petrochemical investigation of a metamorphosed layered complex of anorthosites with associated gabbroic and chromitic facies from Sittampundi, Salem district, Madras State. The complex consists of a sequence of meta-anorthositic gneisses and eclogite gabbros, the former with layers of chromitite and perknite, and is interpreted as a gravity-stratified sheet. The plagioclases in the anorthosite series are very calcic (An_{75}–An_{100}). One of the plagioclases contained An_{98}, and thus is, perhaps, the nearest approach in Nature to pure anorthite. The chemical composition of some anorthosites and almost pure anorthites is given in Table 13.

Alkalic rocks occur in several parts of Peninsular India, and the chemical composition of some of them is given in Table 14. SUBRAMANIAM (1949) made a petrochemical study of the nepheline syenites and associated rocks in the neighborhood of Sivamalai, Coimbatore district, Madras State, which HOLLAND (1901b) had considered to be a suite of igneous rocks. SUBRAMANIAM suggested a syntectic origin for this rock sequence. WALKER (1907) recognized alkalic rocks near Koraput, Orissa State, and described them as similar to miaskites and theralites. SATHAPATHI (1953) analysed the different types of rocks from this area chemically and determined their minor constituents by spectrochemical analysis. He concluded that the nepheline-bearing gabbros and syenites of Koraput were formed by fractional crystallization from a basaltic magma that had assimilated some calcareous sediments.

RAJAGOPALAN (1947) made a petrochemical investigation of the charnockite series of St. Thomas Mount near Madras and came to the conclusion that the rocks are igneous in origin, the diversity of the types being caused by magmatic differentiation. A similar study was made by SRIRAMARAO (1947) on the charnockites of Kondapalle near Bezwada, Andhra Pradesh. According to him, the charnockites are the differentiation products of an original mafic magma which had assimilated some khondalitic material. HOWIE (1955) examined the charnockites from the type area near Madras with particular reference to their chemistry and chemical mineralogy. He came to the conclusion that the charnockites, though they have subsequently undergone high-grade regional metamorphism, were originally calc-alkalic

TABLE 12

Chemical composition of mafic rocks

Constituent	1	2	3	4	5	6	7	8	9
	Uralite diabase	Metabasalt	Meta-dolerite	Epidiorite	Pillow lava	Hornblende schist	Dolerite sill	Dolerite sill	Newer dolerite
	Kolar schist belt, Mysore State	Jogimardi, Chitaldrug district, Mysore State	Bellara, Tumkur district, Mysore State	Chitaldrug, Mysore State	Maradihalli, Chitaldrug district, Mysore State	Sheopura, Ajmer, Rajasthan	Cuddapah trap, Chinnakudala, Andhra State	Cuddapah trap, Vemula, Andhra State	Keonjhar, Orissa
SiO_2	52.80	48.52	47.53	52.60	51.94	47.85	46.14	48.64	49.85
Al_2O_3	13.89	13.80	19.97	10.12	15.63	17.28	12.75	14.05	15.80
TiO_2	0.68	1.04	1.93	1.12	0.95	0.55	1.24	1.50	1.20
Fe_2O_3	2.57	3.65	2.86	3.84	2.12	1.78	3.86	2.84	0.23
FeO	10.03	9.83	8.74	12.73	5.40	9.12	11.52	11.75	11.60
MnO	0.40	0.14	0.30	0.03	0.03	0.25	n.d.	0.34	0.24
MgO	5.86	5.88	2.14	6.17	3.39	8.26	5.48	6.43	5.60
CaO	10.00	10.92	12.59	9.36	18.18	11.75	12.10	9.52	10.02
Na_2O	2.56	3.70	1.53	2.27	1.78	1.96	4.03	2.23	2.78
K_2O	0.39	0.32	0.18	tr.	0.70	0.19	1.02	0.69	0.94
P_2O_5	–	0.10	–	–	tr.	tr.	0.08	0.14	0.16
H_2O+	0.68	2.12	2.03	1.60	0.44	0.80	2.17	1.79	1.58
H_2O-	–	–	–	–	–	0.10	0.21	0.43	0.22
CO_2	–	–	–	–	–	–	–	–	0.16
Total	99.86	100.02	99.80	99.84	100.56	99.89	100.60	100.35	100.38

1. RAMACHANDRA RAO (1937, p. 27). Analyst, E. R. TIRUMALACHAR.
2, 3, 4. PICHAMUTHU (1930, pp. 24, 28, 26). Analyst, E. R. TIRUMALACHAR.
5. PICHAMUTHU (1957, p. 12). Analyst, B. S. RAJU.
6. HERON (1953, p. 334). Analyst, W. H. HERDSMAN.
7. MURTHY (1950, p. 690). Analyst, P. B. MURTHY.
8. VEMBAN (1946, p. 362). Analyst, N. A. VEMBAN.
9. PASCOE (1950, p. 233). Analyst, P. C. ROY.

tr., trace.
n.d., not determined.

TABLE 13

Chemical composition of anorthosites and anorthites

Constituent	1	2	3	4	5	6	7
	Anorthite–edenite gneiss	Anorthite–clinozoisite–garnet rock	Anorthite–anthophyllite–edenite rock	Anorthosite	Anorthosite	Anorthite	Anorthite
	Sittampundi, Salem district, Madras State	Konasamudram, Salem district, Madras State	Karungalpatti, Salem district, Madras State	Dalki Valley, Mayurbhanj, Orissa State	Bara Bantha, Mayurbhanj, Orissa State	Konasamudram, Salem district, Madras State	Konasamudram, Salem district, Madras State
SiO_2	44.58	41.61	44.89	56.64	54.30	43.74	43.88
Al_2O_3	30.81	33.17	31.53	25.13	23.65	36.40	36.18
TiO_2	0.06	0.06	0.05	tr.	tr.	–	–
Fe_2O_3	0.94	1.78	0.38	0.79	1.09	0.10	0.08
Cr_2O_3	0.02	–	–	–	–	–	–
FeO	1.77	0.22	2.66	1.75	1.19	–	–
MnO	0.04	0.02	0.05	n.d.	0.03	–	–
MgO	2.72	0.23	3.68	tr.	0.21	–	–
CaO	17.05	20.96	14.88	9.59	10.78	19.38	19.37
Na_2O	1.35	0.32	1.35	4.62	5.87	0.24	0.22
K_2O	0.07	0.05	0.03	0.66	0.80	0.04	–
P_2O_5	–	0.01	0.01	0.32	0.76	–	–
H_2O+	0.58	0.97	0.68	0.49	1.31	0.37	0.28
H_2O-	0.06	0.20	0.11	0.33	0.08	0.04	0.08
CO_2	–	0.51	–	–	–	–	–
Total	100.05	100.11	100.30	100.32	100.07	100.31	100.09

1, 2, 3. SUBRAMANIAM (1956, p. 368). Analyst, E. K. OSLUND.
4. CHATTERJEE (1945, p. 275). Analyst, S. C. CHATTERJEE.
5. DUNN and DEY (1937, p. 123). Analyst, MAHADEO RAM.
6. SUBRAMANIAM (1956, p. 333). Analyst, S. S. GOLDICH.
7. SUBRAMANIAM (1956, p. 333). Analyst, E. K. OSLUND.

tr., trace.
n.d., not determined.

TABLE 14

Chemical composition of alkalic rocks

Constituent	1	2	3	4	5	6	7
	Sodalite syenite	Nepheline syenite	Nepheline syenite	Nepheline syenite	Nepheline syenite	Biotite-nepheline syenite	Aegirine-augite syenite
	Mundwara, Sirohi State, Rajasthan	Kishangarh, Rajasthan		Koraput, Orissa State		Sivamalai, Madras State	
SiO_2	49.88	55.32	54.52	55.13	52.85	52.71	55.65
Al_2O_3	17.95	23.78	24.32	20.55	25.97	20.41	16.47
TiO_2	2.54	–	–	0.05	0.02	0.51	0.79
Fe_2O_3	2.42	} 4.73	} 6.62	1.57	0.29	1.42	4.86
FeO	5.33			4.32	3.02	6.03	7.01
MnO	0.24	–	–	0.03	0.03	–	–
MgO	2.37	1.07	0.43	0.84	0.61	1.83	2.48
CaO	4.14	1.18	1.71	2.45	2.56	5.04	2.58
Na_2O	8.47	8.46	10.62	6.87	8.68	7.21	6.83
K_2O	4.55	4.50	1.60	7.93	5.33	4.25	3.74
P_2O_5	1.24	–	–	0.18	0.22	tr.	–
H_2O+	0.07	–	–	} 0.71	} 0.51	} 1.24	} 0.16
H_2O-	0.73	–	–				
Cl	–	0.64	0.99	–	–	–	–
CO_2	–	–	–	0.21	0.49	–	–
Total	99.93	99.68	100.81	100.84	100.58	100.65	100.57

1. Coulson (1933, p. 88). Analyst, F. Raoult.
2, 3. Heron (1924, p. 186). Analyst, B. C. Gupta.
4, 5. Sathapathi (1953). Analyst, N. Sathapathi.
6, 7. Subramaniam (1949, p. 86). Analyst, A. P. Subramaniam.

tr., trace

TABLE 15

Chemical composition of charnockites, khondalite, and leptynite

Constituent	1	2	3	4	5	6	7	8	9	10
	Hypersthene granite	Hypersthene gabbro	Charnockite	Hypersthene diorite	Charnockite	Pyroxenite	Charnockite	Charnockite	Khondalite	Leptynite
	St. Thomas Mount, Madras State		Trisul Hill, Meenambakkam, Madras State	Pallavaram, Madras State	Kondapalle, Andhra State		Cape Comorin, Madras State	Myladi, Madras State	Pallavaram, Madras State	
SiO_2	74.99	50.09	71.97	51.55	73.82	50.22	69.49	50.28	75.88	77.93
Al_2O_3	13.21	16.52	13.30	13.86	14.03	7.81	13.36	13.91	11.03	10.65
TiO_2	1.09	1.49	0.40	1.12	0.38	0.56	0.36	0.91	0.58	0.31
Fe_2O_3	0.03	1.97	1.29	1.51	0.05	1.87	2.36	3.21	2.46	0.99
FeO	1.99	11.35	2.30	11.63	1.08	7.05	4.63	11.57	6.27	2.50
MnO	0.12	0.45	0.04	0.23	0.10	0.25	0.09	0.24	0.11	0.04
MgO	1.05	5.88	0.58	5.80	1.01	27.28	0.34	4.98	1.51	0.18
CaO	1.09	9.03	2.10	10.28	0.91	2.96	2.76	10.54	0.18	0.40
Na_2O	3.51	2.64	2.78	3.08	4.05	0.63	2.73	2.36	0.59	2.19
K_2O	3.19	0.51	4.24	0.54	3.97	0.10	3.85	1.28	0.11	4.54
P_2O_5	–	0.35	0.14	0.23	–	0.06	0.08	0.11	0.03	tr.
H_2O+	0.19	–	–	0.25	0.26	0.61	0.42	0.49	0.85	0.08
H_2O-	0.13	0.06	0.27	0.12	0.09	0.04	–	–	0.17	0.16
Total	100.59	100.34	99.41	100.20	99.75	99.44	100.47	99.88	99.77	99.97

1, 2. RAJAGOPALAN (1947, p. 238). Analyst, C. RAJAGOPALAN.
3, 4. HOWIE (1955, pp. 732, 733). Analyst, J. H. SCOON.
5, 6. SRIRAMARAO (1947, pp. 141, 149). Analyst, M. SRIRAMARAO.
7, 8. PAULOSE (1956, p. 28). Analyst, C. V. PAULOSE.
9. HOWIE and SUBRAMANIAM (1957, p. 572). Analyst, T. KATSURA.
10. HOWIE (1955, p. 732). Analyst, R. A. HOWIE.

tr., trace.

plutonic rocks, since their chemical composition falls on reasonably smooth curves on both the triangular and the LARSEN (1938) variation diagrams, which could not be the case for any random series of sediments. The distribution of the trace elements, which generally obeys GOLDSCHMIDT's (1954) rules, also pointed to the same conclusion.

PICHAMUTHU (1953) noticed that enderbites high in Na_2O and low in K_2O are common in Mysore State. HOWIE and SUBRAMANIAM (1957) showed that the charnockites in the type area near Madras are also akin to enderbites because there is a dominance of Na_2O over K_2O. A petrochemical study of the rocks and minerals of the charnockite series from Pallavaram near Madras was made by SUBRAMANIAM (1959), who suggested that the silicic sequence is an igneous suite which has undergone metamorphic reconstitution and recrystallization; that the rocks of the mafic sequence are essentially pyroxene granulites and other rocks which are not genetically related to the charnockites proper; and that the rocks of the intermediate sequence are hybrids resulting from partial assimilation of pyroxene granulites by the charnockite magma. The chemical composition of some representative silicic and mafic rocks of the charnockite series is given in Table 15. Since khondalites and leptynites are generally associated with charnockites, the chemical composition of these rocks is also given in Table 15.

Gneisses and granites cover the major part of the Precambrian terrane in Peninsular India. Migmatitization and granitization are widespread, and, hence, it is often difficult to determine the original lithological nature of the rocks. "Peninsular gneiss" is only a convenient term for grouping together a variety of silicic rocks of different age and composition. Some petrochemical work has been done on isolated exposures, but no generalizations are possible. Table 16 gives the chemical composition of some principal types of granites and gneisses.

6. Metamorphism

6.1. *General*

The Precambrian rocks of Peninsular India occupy such an immense area and are so varied in their petrographical character, stratigraphical disposition, and intensity of alteration that it is difficult to give a coherent account of their metamorphic history and to classify them into graded zones of metamorphism. Probably the earliest attempt in this direction was by FERMOR (1936), who tried to correlate the ancient fossil-free rocks. He noticed large terranes affected by very high-grade metamorphism of presumably deep-seated origin, and so adopted the principle of depth zones in his description.

The Archean nucleus in Mysore State, which contains the Dharwar schists, affords a good example of progressive regional metamorphism. The

TABLE 16

Chemical composition of gneisses and granites

Constituent	1	2	3	4	5	6	7	8	9	10
	Champion gneiss	Peninsular gneiss	Peninsular gneiss	Pre-Aravalli gneissic granite	Bundelkhand gneiss	Berach granite	Erinpura granite	Mount Abu granite	Singhbhum granite	Closepet granite
	Mysore State	Mysore State	Mysore State	Darwal, Mewar, Rajasthan	Chitor, Mewar, Rajasthan	Mandalgarh, Merwara, Rajasthan	Sendra, Merwara, Rajasthan	Mount Abu, Sirohi, Rajasthan	Singhbhum	Mysore State
SiO_2	75.16	73.33	63.06	73.44	71.78	65.90	73.10	71.48	73.02	72.84
Al_2O_3	11.45	14.78	15.68	5.50	13.75	16.63	13.60	13.35	13.33	11.99
TiO_2	0.84	n.d.	0.70	tr.	tr.	0.15	0.15	0.59	0.19	0.35
Fe_2O_3	1.00	0.46	2.07	3.40	0.78	1.00	0.14	0.06	0.35	0.46
FeO	0.92	0.84	5.56	5.92	5.60	4.11	2.95	3.83	1.54	1.93
MnO	0.06	0.10	0.02	0.04	0.05	–	tr.	0.09	0.02	tr.
MgO	0.72	0.40	1.49	2.20	0.22	1.70	0.39	0.33	0.06	0.69
CaO	0.96	1.72	4.30	1.68	0.90	1.40	2.00	1.40	1.38	2.68
Na_2O	4.18	3.94	4.06	1.60	2.65	2.70	2.56	2.73	3.82	2.63
K_2O	3.50	4.89	1.89	3.83	3.66	4.38	4.71	5.43	5.12	5.23
P_2O_5	n.d.	0.04	0.27	0.29	0.07	0.10	tr.	0.07	0.07	0.75
H_2O+	n.d.	n.d.	0.59	0.82	0.12	1.55	0.30	0.22	0.46	0.36
H_2O-	n.d.	n.d.	n.d.	0.14	0.33	0.25	–	0.57	0.12	0.24
CO_2	0.36	n.d.	n.d.	1.18	–	tr.	–	tr.	–	n.d.
Total	99.15	100.50	99.69	100.04	99.91	99.87	99.90	100.15	99.48	100.15

1, 2, 3. RAMA RAO (1940, p. 94). Analyst, E. R. TIRUMALACHAR.

4. HERON (1953, p. 87). Analyst, S. K. CHATTERJEE.

5. HERON (1953, p. 56). Analyst, R. DUTTA ROY.

6. HERON (1953, p. 56). Analyst, W. H. HERDSMAN.

7. HERON (1953, p. 363). Analyst, W. H. HERDSMAN.

8. COULSON (1933, p. 50). Analyst, F. RAOULT.

9. IYER (1932). Analyst, L. A. N. IYER.

10. RAMA RAO (1940, p. 95). Analyst, E. R. TIRUMALACHAR.

tr., trace.

n.d., not determined.

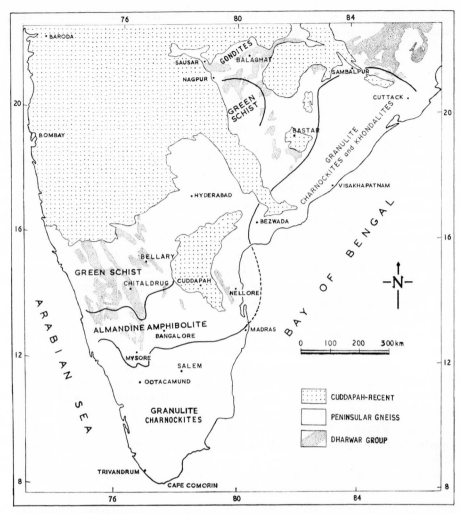

Fig. 18. General pattern of metamorphic facies in southern India. The isograds are approximate.

occurrence of N.–S.-trending linear bands of schistose rocks which include runs of quartzites, limestones, and ferruginous quartzites facilitates tracing the various changes which have taken place in those rocks with gradual increase in the strength of metamorphism.

Figure 18 is an attempt to demarcate in a broad manner the metamorphic facies of southern India. Although a fairly general picture of the progressive increase in the degree of metamorphism is obtained, the isograds are only approximations, because repeated deformation, variations in the intensity of tectonic disturbance in certain areas, the influence at different periods of intrusions of silicic and mafic igneous bodies, and retrogressive metamorphism all serve to complicate the metamorphic history of the Archean terrane in southern India.

6.2. *The Dharwar–Eastern Ghats region*

The Dharwar schist bands emerge from beneath the Deccan traps, Kaladgis, or Bhimas, and for nearly 300 km exhibit a low degree of metamorphism. Argillites, clay schists, jasper limonite, and similar rocks represent very feebly metamorphosed sediments. The schists in this low-grade zone are characterized by muscovite, chlorite, tremolite, actinolite, epidote, quartz, albite, calcite, and sphene, minerals typical of the greenschist facies of regional metamorphism. The limestones contain chlorite, and the quartzites contain sericite. The banded ferruginous rocks are cherty and contain limonite or hematite. The magnesium-rich schists contain combinations of chlorite, tremolite, talc, and serpentine. The mafic dikes contain chlorite or hornblende. The calcium zeolites in the vesicles of Lingadhalli mafic flows have been converted into clinozoisite and epidote, and the sodium zeolites into albite. Muscovite–chloritoid–chlorite–quartz schists occur in the Tumkur district. Kyanite, even though not a common mineral in this setting, occurs in the Chitaldrug district.

The next higher degree of metamorphism is represented by another broad zone in southern India, where hornblende, biotite, almandine, plagioclase, staurolite, kyanite, sillimanite, and muscovite are the common minerals. This mineral assemblage corresponds to the almandine–amphibolite facies of TURNER and VERHOOGEN (1962, p. 544). The Holenarsipur schist belt in the Hassan district affords a good illustration of the subfacies in which staurolite, kyanite, sillimanite, and almandine are characteristic constituents. In the Bababudan belt cummingtonite occurs in the dark hornblende-bearing rocks.

In the corresponding metamorphic zone in the southern parts of the Chitaldrug schist belt the limestones contain rhodonite, cummingtonite, phlogopite, and grossularite. Dark amphibolites and hornblende granulites become more common. The quartzites and banded ferruginous quartzites are garnet-bearing. Some impure limestones have been changed into "tarurites" which contain diopside, epidote, and other calcium silicate minerals. In certain locations minerals characteristic of the granulite facies, such as hypersthene, diopside, almandine, and cordierite formed, and the rocks are granulitic.

Near the east coast the Nellore schist belt has a Dharwarian trend, but is situated in the proximity of the Eastern Ghats belt. The metamorphic grade exhibited by these schists corresponds to the almandine–amphibolite facies. The biotite schists and hornblende schists of this area are generally garnet-bearing and frequently contain staurolite and kyanite.

Figure 18 shows that the isograd marking the granulite facies is very sinuous. From the Hassan district the isograd proceeds southwest toward

Gundlupet and turns north along the edges of the Biligirirangan charnock-ites. It then passes south of the Closepet granites and cuts the Kolar schist belt near Sakarsanhalli. It runs north of the massive charnockites in the Salem and North Arcot districts and reaches the coast near Madras. It probably connects up with the granulite isograd which runs west of the zone of khondalites and charnockites of Vizianagaram and reaches the coast south of Bezwada.

The members of the charnockite and the khondalite series are characteris-tic rocks of the granulite facies. They are products of high-grade deep-seated regional metamorphism under anhydrous conditions. The typical mineral assemblages in charnockitic rocks are combinations of hypersthene, diop-side, brown hornblende, garnet (almandine–pyrope), biotite, microperthite, potassium feldspars, antiperthitic plagioclase, and quartz. The khondalites are metamorphosed aluminium-rich sediments consisting mainly of silli-manite, almandine, perthite, and quartz. Scapolite is sometimes present in rocks of this facies, and sapphirine also occurs in certain assemblages. As the charnockite region is approached, the different rocks undergo certain changes. The hornblende schists become granulitic and finally change into pyroxene granulites. The Peninsular gneisses become more like charnockites; their feldspars become dark-colored, and perthitic or antiperthitic textures develop, even though hypersthene may not form and sphene is still present.

The high-grade metamorphism represented by the granulite facies pre-vails in the southern and eastern parts of the Peninsula, the region where khondalites and charnockites occur. Travancore (southern Kerala State) and the Eastern Ghats, which are characterized by an extraordinary abun-dance of garnet (almandine–pyrope), constitute the most strongly metamor-phosed parts of the Precambrian of India.

The charnockite region is on the whole more elevated than the nonchar-nockite region and contains some of the highest peaks in the Peninsula. No field evidence has so far been found to support FERMOR's (1936, p. 48) suggestion that the whole of the charnockite region has been vertically up-lifted along a belt of weakness, or fault lines or zones, at the junction between the charnockite and noncharnockite areas. There is evidence, however, to show that segments of Peninsular India mainly composed of charnockites, such as the Nilgiris, the Palnis, the Shevaroys, and the Cardamom Hills in Madras State, and the Biligirirangan Hills in Mysore State, have been up-lifted several thousand meters along fault zones now represented by ultra-mylonites and pseudotachylytes (see Fig. 19), which were called "trap-shotten" rocks by KING and FOOTE (1864, p. 271) because of their resem-blance to dark-colored fine-grained mafic traps.

There are two types of charnockite, viz. one which is granulitic, often foliated, and sometimes mylonitized, and another type which is granitic, coarse-grained, and sometimes porphyritic. The granulitic rock is generally conformable to the regional strike of the gneisses, whereas instances of transgression are observed in the granitic type. The granulitic, or gneissic, type is the older of the two and was formed by high-grade regional metamorphism of preexisting rocks, and this metamorphism was followed much later by palingenetic fusion and widespread metasomatism when the granitic, frequently intrusive, type of charnockite was generated. Epidiorite, dolerite, quartz-dolerite, and olivine-dolerite dikes are common in southern India. There is no pattern in their distribution or particular preference for dikes of any petrographic type to be concentrated in certain areas. It is significant that in virtually all the different varieties of dikes which are situated in the charnockite region and in a zone adjoining it, the plagioclase feldspars are clouded. The general correspondence between the zones of clouded dikes and charnockites indicates a causal relationship. It is known that temperatures high enough and prevailing for a sufficient period of time produce

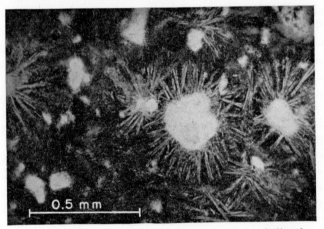

Fig. 19 Star-like aggregates of skeleton crystals of oligoclase radiating from plagioclase porphyroclasts in pseudotachylyte. Biligirirangan Hills, Mysore State. Photo, C. S. Pichamuthu.

clouding in plagioclase feldspars. The clouding in the dikes in southern India is a regional phenomenon and must be related to the metamorphism connected with the production of the granitic charnockites. The two periods of metamorphism which were responsible for the formation of the different charnockite types were thus separated by the period during which mafic dikes were intruded. The clouded feldspars in the mafic dikes are therefore highly significant for the proper understanding of certain episodes in the metamorphic history of the Precambrian of southern India (PICHAMUTHU, 1959).

6.3. *The Satpura region*

The Sausar–Balaghat region, which is in Madhya Pradesh and in Maharashtra States, was affected by varying metamorphic conditions. This region forms a part of the Satpura belt. In the Balaghat or eastern end the phyllites contain sericite, talc, and ottrelite, and as one proceeds westward toward the Chhindwara–Nagpur area, the degree of metamorphism increases. The Sausar series includes calcium granulites, chondrodite marbles, scapolite granulites, garnet–sillimanite gneisses, and pyroxene granulites. Retrogressive metamorphism has produced a variety of amphibolites and amphibole schists. Later stress at lower temperatures is responsible for the conversion of anthophyllite schist to chlorite schist and for the serpentinization of forsterite in dolomitic marbles. S. N. SARKAR (1957, 1958) found that the tectonics of this region is complicated because it was affected by three different orogenic cycles separated by long time intervals.

In the Singhbhum–Dhalbhum area, which is an eastward continuation of the Satpura belt, medium-grade metamorphic conditions prevail, and even though chlorite and sericite occur, the schists contain hornblende, biotite, staurolite, kyanite, and garnet. West of this area, in the Kolhan, the conditions of the greenschist facies prevail, as witnessed by the presence of shales, slates, and phyllites containing talc, serpentine, hematite, and sericite. In general the intensity of metamorphism in the Satpura belt is not as high as in the Eastern Ghats region.

6.4. *The Aravalli region*

The Aravalli belt in Rajasthan exhibits a gradual increase in the degree of metamorphism from the northeast to the southwest. Comparatively little altered sediments occur in Gwalior, but the metamorphic grade increases progressively in the Ajmer–Merwara and Udaipur areas, and finally calcium granulites containing diopside (coccolite), microcline, and sometimes scapolite and wollastonite, are met near Idar in Gujarat State.

7. Mineralization and mineral deposits

7.1. *General*

The rocks of the Dharwar group are very important economically because they contain valuable deposits of iron, manganese, chromium, copper, gold, lead, zinc, tungsten, and uranium. The intrusive gneisses and granites themselves do not commonly carry valuable ore deposits, even though they have contributed their metal contents to the adjoining Dharwars. The granite pegmatites, however, often contain valuable muscovite deposits and sometimes ores of the rarer metals, such as uranium (pitchblende and samarskite) and tantalum (columbite).

The Precambrian ore deposits of India can be broadly grouped into metallogenetic provinces and epochs. Each epoch covers a long time interval and cannot be sharply defined. Reliable age determinations are few, and great distances separate mineral deposits. It is therefore possible only to make certain broad generalizations.

7.2. *Gold*

Almost every known gold ore in India was worked by the ancients more than 2,000 years ago. Considering the hardness of the rocks and the crude methods of mining and hoisting which must then have been in vogue, it is noteworthy that at the Kolar mines the ancients had gone down to a depth of more than 200 m.

Gold mineralization is characteristic of the Dharwar schist region, which is an old Precambrian terrane where erosion has exposed rocks at a deep level in the crust. The Peninsular gneiss covers extensive areas which are interrupted by elongated belts of older schistose rocks with a consistent trend. Such belts, interpreted by EMMONS (1937, p. 20) as elongated roof pendants, are closely connected with the gold deposits. The gold veins, which are typical of a deep environment, range from hypothermal to mesothermal.

The Kolar goldfield in Mysore State is well known because it is the chief gold-producing center in India and contains the deepest mines in the world, some of the shafts being more than 3,300 m deep. Rock temperatures at these depths are of the order of 60° C. The Dharwar schist belt, in which the Kolar goldfield occurs, has a N.–S. trend; it is 65 km long and 5 km–6 km broad, and is composed of metamorphosed and folded hornblende-bearing rocks and sills of mafic intrusives. Some gneisses and ferruginous quartaites occur along the margins. The Champion gneiss is present on the eastern side of the field. Some geologists believe that the gold-bearing veins and the hornblende schists are genetically connected, and others regard the veins as the hydrothermal end stage of the Champion gneiss. There are in all about 30 gold-bearing lodes averaging about 1 m in width. Only five of them have been worked, but almost all the gold came from the Champion reef. The lodes are generally lenticular, swelling and contracting at irregular intervals in both strike and dip. With few exceptions they lie parallel to the foliation of the schists. Gold mineralization is confined to the vicinity of the contacts of the schistose and massive varieties of amphibolites. Tourmaline is a common accessory mineral. Galena, arsenopyrite, pyrrhotite, pyrite, chalcopyrite, ilmenite, magnetite, and scheelite are some of the minerals associated with gold. Sphalerite and telluride minerals are also present.

The Hutti mine is the other gold-producing center in Mysore State. Hundreds of old gold workings occur scattered in the Dharwar rocks, but with the exception of Bellara, which was worked for a few years, none of the others has been reopened.

In the Wainad region (Nilgiri district) of Madras State there are numerous gold-bearing quartz lodes which have a N.–N.W. strike, almost at right angles to the foliation of the country rocks, which are mainly hornblende gneisses and biotite gneisses. The gold is associated with pyrite.

7.3. *Copper, lead, and zinc*

Singhbhum is an important metallogenetic province with deposits of wolframite, apatite and magnetite, copper, uranium, argentian galena, and gold. All the mineral deposits occur in impregnated zones, lenticular veins, and lenses parallel to the lamination of the enclosing phyllites and schists. The general order of formation is as follows:

Wolframite–quartz veins	
Magnetite–apatite rocks	Pneumatolytic zone
Uranium minerals	
Chalcopyrite	
Argentian galena	Hydrothermal zone
Gold	

The mineralization of the Copper Belt in the Singhbhum district of Bihar is related to the intrusion of a sodium granite along a thrust zone. The belt is about 130 km long and is dotted by many ancient workings. The ore channels are sheeted zones which contain one or more veins of solid sulfides together with mineralized sheared country rock on both walls. The solid ore varies from a few centimeters to some meters in thickness. The main sulfides are chalcopyrite and pyrrhotite; the subordinate ore minerals are pyrite, pentlandite, violarite, and millerite. At the surface the sulfides have been oxidized. There are no zones of enrichment, and the products of supergene alteration give place gradually to normal primary sulfides.

In the Hazaribagh district of Bihar State chalcopyrite occurs in lenticular stringers and disseminations in schists and quartzites. In Madhya Pradesh copper mineralization is present in dolomitic limestone. The common minerals are chalcopyrite, tetrahedrite, galena, pyrite, and magnetite, which contain a little gold and silver. In the Nellore district of Andhra there are extensive old workings. In Mysore State copper is associated with a felsite which cuts the Jogimardi trap at Ingladhal; recent drilling operations near Arsikere have revealed the existence of a promising chalcopyrite mineralization.

Rajasthan has long been known for its copper mines. In Jaipur chalcopyrite occurs in the upper part of a zone of Ajabgarh slates and schists.

There are many copper-ore deposits in the Himalayas at intervals from Kashmir to Sikkim. In the Darjeeling district of West Bengal disseminations of copper minerals occur in slates and schists of the Daling series.

Galena occurs at many places in India, but the deposits are small and of no economic importance except at Zawar in Rajasthan, where mixed ores of lead and zinc have been mined for several years. The principal ore minerals are galena and sphalerite associated with pyrite and some other sulfide minerals, which occur as disseminations and replacement bodies in dolomitic limestones which are interbedded with phyllites and quartzites of Aravalli age. The ore bodies are likely to persist to considerable depths without much change, because the mineralization took place through a series of cleavage planes which were formed during the course of widespread regional metamorphism.

7.4. *Iron and manganese*

There are at least two metallogenetic epochs during which iron and manganese ores of sedimentary origin were deposited. The metallogenetic provinces are large, and the basins of deposition are outlined by the occurrence of banded iron- and manganese-bearing limestones and quartzites, whereas the workable ore deposits are confined to limited areas within such provinces.

The syngenetic iron and manganese ores occur in the sedimentary formations of the Dharwars. Banded ferruginous quartzites are characteristic deposits in the Precambrian of India and are composed of alternating layers of magnetite or hematite and silica (quartz, jasper, or chert). By subsequent chemical changes, the iron as oxide minerals became segregated into workable deposits.

The iron ores of Singhbhum and Mayurbhanj extending into Keonjhar and Bonai, Bhilai in Madhya Pradesh, Rourkela in Orissa, and Bellary and Bababudan Hills in Mysore, are some of the important deposits in India. The banded ferruginous quartzites which are the source of the ore are considered to have been formed by precipitation of iron and silica carried into the sea in solutions derived by leaching from the adjacent land masses. Hydrous ferric oxide has often replaced the silica of the iron-bearing quartzites, converting them into massive bodies of hematite ore. The replacement by iron oxide and the removal of silica are thought to have been caused by descending meteoric waters.

According to DUNN (1941), the banded iron-bearing quartzites are not sedimentary but formed by the secondary silicification of material now represented by ferruginous, chloritic, or carbonaceous shales or phyllites, many of which were originally tuffs. The iron was supposed to be derived from the oxidation of the tuffs and flows *in situ*. Later, solutions were believed to have moved and redeposited the iron, with the subsequent formation of the iron-ore bodies.

The vanadian–magnetite deposits of Mayurbhanj, Dhalbhum, and Keonjhar, which form a belt nearly 80 km long, occur as magmatic segregations in association with gabbro, anorthosite, picrite, and peridotite (DUNN and DEY, 1937).

In India manganese deposits generally occur interbedded with Precambrian rocks, including the gondites. In parts of the Eastern Ghats area manganese mineralization is associated with kodurites, but such deposits are of comparatively small importance. There are also residual enrichments of a lateritic character (FERMOR, 1909). Braunite and psilomelane are the common minerals, but hollandite, jacobsite, sitaparite, and pyrolusite are often present.

The bedded manganese ores of India, like those of Brazil, the Gold Coast, and South Africa, which are also of Precambrian age, were originally sediments which contained varying proportions of manganese. Regional movements and profound metamorphism, intensified in some instances by the contact effects of later intrusions, changed the sands and clays into quartzites, phyllites, and mica schists; the pure manganese-bearing sediments into crystalline manganese ores; and the mixtures of sandy clays and manganiferous sediments into gondites.

The stratigraphical control in the distribution of manganese ores is clearly seen in Mysore State. There is a prominent ferruginous quartzite zone which is also manganese-bearing and is associated with limestones. As a distinctive marker bed, this zone serves to throw light on the structure of the Mysore Dharwars, because the zone has been folded into a huge plunging anticlinorium, the long limbs of which can be traced through the two biggest schist belts in Mysore. Almost all the important manganese mines are situated in this stratigraphical horizon.

7.5. *Chromium, titanium, and vanadium*

Mysore State is an important producer of chromite. Segregations of chromite are present in a belt of serpentinized ultramafic rocks in the southern part of the state. The ultramafic intrusion is of the Alpine type and is situated in the axis of the anticlinorium into which the Dharwars in southern Mysore were folded. The belt, which extends for about 160 km, contains many ore bodies which occur as lenses and veins in the ultramafic complex. Near Kadakola in the Mysore district chromite occurs in serpentinized dunite which is traversed by magnesite veins suggesting the action of CO_2-bearing waters, and in the Nuggihalli belt both magnesite and chalcedony are present, and the process of serpentinization is not quite clear.

The Singhbhum deposits occur in a series of ultramafic intrusions. Although younger than the associated metasediments, the intrusives participated in the last set of crustal movements and suffered complex folding. The original rocks were chiefly saxonite (enstatite peridotite), with subsidiary pyroxenite, lherzolite, and dunite. The ore bodies are usually in the form of bands which are primary segregations. Flow breccias consisting of angular pieces of chromite in a matrix of serpentine are also present. West of Chaibasa in Singhbhum chromite deposits occur in partly serpentinized saxonites, dunites, and pyroxenites.

Several large deposits of chromite are known to exist in the Orissa district. In Keonjhar the ore bodies are considered to be primary differentiates of an ultramafic magma, the echelon lenses of ore having been intruded in successive stages so that several generations of chromite are recognizable.

In the so-called "Chalk Hills" in Madras State the altered chromite-bearing peridotites are traversed by networks of magnesite veins and dikes, indicating the action of CO_2-bearing waters. There are also massive deposits of magnesite which are being extensively worked. An occurrence of great geological interest exists in the Salem district, where anorthosites carry conformable layers of chromitite extending several kilometers along the strike and ranging in thickness from a few centimeters to more than 3 m.

The chromite deposits of Kondapalle in Andhra State are lenses and pockets in partly serpentinized pyroxenites associated with charnockites.

Ilmenite derived from garnet-bearing gneisses and charnockites occurs in beach sands in parts of the Kerala, Madras, Andhra, and Orissa coasts. The richest deposits are those of Kerala, where ilmenite is associated with monazite, zircon, garnet, rutile, and sillimanite.

Small veins and aggregates of ilmenite are present in the mica pegmatites of Bihar. Massive deposits of titanian and vanadian magnetite occur in parts of Singhbhum and Mayurbhanj associated with gabbros, anorthosites, and ultramafic rocks, and in the Nuggihalli schist belt of Mysore along with mafic and ultramafic rocks.

7.6. *Uranium and thorium*

One of the important uranium-ore fields of India is the extensively mineralized "Copper Belt" of Singhbhum. The uranium mineralization is closely associated with conglomerates, apatite–magnetite bands, and schists rich in tourmaline, chlorite, and biotite. Uranium occurs along zones of shearing and crushing mainly in the form of disseminated uraninite, which in the zone of weathering yields autunite, torbernite, and metatorbernite. The uranium mineralization followed the apatite–magnetite mineralization but preceded the deposition of sulfides (BHOLA and others, 1958).

Near Udaipur in Rajasthan uranium mineralization covers an area of about 250 km² of phyllite and shale, partly chloritic and partly carbonaceous, dolomitic limestone, and siliceous fault breccias. Uraninite, with its alteration product, gummite, and other secondary minerals, occurs in the shear zones and anastomoses through the country rock which was rendered dense, and colored pinkish, greenish, or buff, by the mineralizing solutions.

Workable deposits of uranium ore also occur in some of the zoned granite pegmatites intrusive into the schists and phyllites in the Bhilwara district on the eastern margin of the Aravalli synclinorium in Rajasthan. The pegmatites are commercial sources of ruby mica (muscovite) and beryl. The ore is chiefly uraninite with subordinate cyrtolite, and the secondary minerals are autunite and metatorbernite.

The charnockites, leptynites, and some of the granite gneisses and associated pegmatites of Peninsular India contain monazite which has been concentrated in beach deposits along with other heavy minerals such as ilmenite, zircon, rutile, sillimanite, and, sometimes, garnet, magnetite, and columbite. The chief areas where these beach placers occur are some parts of the coasts of Kerala, Madras, and Andhra States. Inland, placer deposits of a somewhat similar composition occur in the alluvium capping the peneplaned surfaces of the Archean in the Ranchi, Purulia, and adjoining districts in the States of Bihar and West Bengal.

7.7. *Nonmetallic minerals*

Beryl is widely distributed in pegmatites associated with Precambrian granites and gneisses. The more productive beryl deposits occur in the Hazaribagh, Kodarma, and Gaya areas of Bihar, in many parts of southern and eastern Rajasthan, and in the Nellore and Coimbatore districts in southern India. Columnar beryl crystals 5 m–7 m long, and more than 1 m across, and weighing from 10 metric tons to 20 metric tons, have been mined at several localities in Rajasthan.

Corundum occurs as a constituent of syenites, ultramafic rocks, and strongly metamorphosed aluminium-rich sediments. It occurs in the anorthite gneisses and corundum syenites of the Salem district in Madras. In Mysore State corundum occurs commonly in amphibolites and in the pegmatites which intrude them, and also in metamorphic rocks associated with sillimanite, cordierite, and kyanite.

Graphite occurs in workable quantities in the khondalites and associated gneisses in Orissa and Andhra States. Graphite schists exist in several parts of India, but they are rather poor in graphite and are intimately mixed with clays.

Kyanite deposits of great economic value are those of Lapsa Buru in Bihar and of a few other places where kyanite occurs in mica schists and hornblende schists close to the shear zone of Singhbhum. Other deposits occur in Madhya Pradesh, Rajasthan, Andhra, and Mysore.

Magnesite formed by the alteration of ultramafic rocks occurs in the Salem district and in the Hassan and Mysore districts. Economically valuable deposits are those of the "Chalk Hills" near Salem and of Kadakola in Mysore State.

Mica occurs in three prominent belts in Peninsular India. The most important is the mica belt of Bihar, which extends from the Gaya district in the west for about 150 km through Hazaribagh and Monghyr to the Bhagalpur district in the east, and has a width of about 20 km–25 km. It is the source of the greater part of the world supply of high-grade muscovite. Intrusive veins, tongues, and masses of muscovite-bearing pegmatite penetrate the country rocks, which are chiefly mica schists grading into mica gneisses and hornblende schists. Usually, the veins strike and dip parallel to the enclosing schists and vary in thickness from a few centimeters to 30 m or more. Some of the mica-bearing veins are pipe-shaped and extend downward for several hundreds of meters. The veins are formed of coarse-grained aggregates of quartz and albite, with a little microcline in places, and of such accessory minerals as tourmaline, apatite, some columbite–tantalite, and beryl. The next well-known mica belt is in the Nellore district of Andhra State. It stretches for about 100 km with a width of 13 km–16 km. The country rocks are mica schists and hornblende schists in which sheets, lenses, and large masses of pegmatite are common. The pegmatites conform in strike with the schists and dip steeply or vertically. They consist of very coarse-grained intergrowths of quartz, orthoclase, microcline, and plagioclase, with tourmaline, garnet, apatite, beryl, and some rare-earth minerals. Large crystals of muscovite sometimes occur which measure 5 m along the folia and up to 3 m across the basal plane. Rajasthan also is now an important mica-producing area. The pegmatites are distributed over a belt of country about 100 km wide, stretching from Jaipur to Udaipur, a distance of more than 300 km. The northwestern border of the main mining area follows the axis of the Aravalli Range. The muscovite occurs in coarse-grained granite pegmatites which are intrusive into the rocks of the gneissic complex and into the Aravalli schists. They form steeply dipping sheets following the general schistosity, but bosses, pipes, and apophyses also occur.

Sillimanite is widely distributed as a constituent of certain Archean schists and gneisses, but workable deposits occur only in the Khasi Hills of Assam, in the Rewa district of Madhya Pradesh, and in the Bhandara district of Maharashtra State. The Khasi Hills deposits are in the form of massive sillimanite bodies associated with gneisses of the Shillong series.

8. Geological evolution

8.1. *The Dharwar time*

There is great uncertainty as to the nature of the rock formations belonging to the beginning of Precambrian time, and so far there is no definite proof for the existence in India of the basement on which the Dharwar volcanic rocks and sediments were originally deposited. Repeated folding and metamorphism have obscured the contacts and rendered the identification of basement rocks extremely difficult. The pebbles of gneiss in the oldest Dharwar conglomerates are probably the only fragmentary evidence there is of the basement.

The oldest Dharwar is composed mainly of volcanic rocks with sedimentary intercalations. The basaltic flows were often subaqueous, as witnessed by pillow lavas discovered in all the Dharwar schist bands. Much of the material associated with these old rocks is probably tuffaceous in origin but was deposited in bodies of water. At the culmination of the Lower Dharwar time there was an intrusion of granite, which in its present-day metamorphosed form is known as the Champion gneiss. This intrusion is considered to be an important source of gold mineralization in the Dharwars.

After the igneous activity in the Lower Dharwars a cycle of sedimentation commenced by the accumulation of gravel and pebbles, followed by the deposition of sand, clay, carbonate sediments, and ferruginous cherts. When a great thickness of sediments had accumulated, an intense diastrophism took place at the end of the Middle Dharwar time. Folding and granite intrusions accompanied the mountain building, and there is evidence of injections of granite, now occurring as ovoid or irregular masses generally enclosed by the schists. They are strongly reminiscent of the mantled gneiss domes described by ESKOLA (1949, pp. 462–475). The Middle Dharwars were probably at this time elevated into a region of lofty mountains. There then followed a long interval of time during which the mountains were gradually razed down to the sea level and finally sunk under the sea.

Upon this old planation surface commenced a new cycle of sedimentation comprising the Upper Dharwar time. Geological history is known to repeat itself, and when this drowned surface was covered by an enormous load of sediments high mountains rose once again. Immense bodies of granite, now recognized as the Peninsular gneiss, originated at the close of the Dharwar time and were emplaced in older rocks, which were granitized. Sometimes valuable ore deposits were formed. These metasomatic processes further helped to modify the original lithological properties of the older rocks. Then both the metasediments and the granite were subjected to severe crustal disturbance which compressed the Dharwars into tight folds. The Peninsular gneiss generally conforms to the trends of the Dharwar schists.

The Dharwars were folded into a huge anticlinorium plunging in a north-northwest direction (see pp. 38, 83). The two main limbs of this anticlinorium are present in the Shimoga and Chitaldrug schist belts. An elongated ultramafic belt with valuable chromite deposits marks the axis of this anticlinorium. Because this fold plunges north, deeper parts of the crust become exposed as one proceeds southward, and metamorphism increases progressively from the lowest to the highest grade.

The younger granites represented by the porphyritic Closepet granite probably were formed next. The Closepet granite has not been dated, but because there is comparatively little evidence of deformation, it must have originated after the Dharwar region had undergone progressive metamorphism.

The ages and the structural dispositions of the Precambrian formations indicate that the oldest rocks in Peninsular India occur in Mysore State, which is the type area for Dharwars (approximate age, 2,400 Myr). This region possesses several properties of a continental nucleus. There are narrow belts of folded sedimentary rocks and volcanic rocks suggestive of frequent orogenic activity, with a high ratio of volcanic rocks to sedimentary rocks, and basalt flows often in the form of pillow lavas. Also, gold–quartz veins and iron formations are relatively common. The western limit of what is now visible of this continental nucleus is covered by the Arabian Sea, and parts of the northern boundary lie under the Deccan trap flows. It may, however, be presumed that this continental nucleus is a roughly triangular area bounded in the east by the Eastern Ghats province (age about 1,600 Myr) and in the north by the Satpura province (age about 1,000 Myr). These two provinces may be considered to be later Precambrian accretions composed of younger sediments which underwent their own orogenic cycles and which were folded by pressures directed toward the Archean nucleus. But the Dharwars may originally have formed the basement of the Eastern Ghats and the Satpura orogenic belts.

8.2. *The Eastern Ghats time*

The next major episode in the Precambrian history of India is the Eastern Ghats cycle, which comprises the usual sequence of sedimentation, igneous activity, and metamorphism. Because of the higher grades of metamorphism to which the rocks of this region were subjected, charnockites and khondalites now prevail. In the main the structural trend in this province is almost perpendicular to the prevalent strike in the Archean nucleus. It is significant that the junction of the two provinces is often characterized by copper mineralization, and that the mafic dikes which are so common in the Dharwar terrane appear to terminate at the border, for they are rarely found in the Eastern Ghats region. In the southern extremity of Mysore State the effect of the impact of the Eastern Ghats strike on the Dharwar strike is seen not only in the bending and final truncation of the N.–S. Dharwar trend, but in the development of mylonitized and faulted zones at the junction of the two strikes (PICHAMUTHU, 1961).

8.3. *The Satpura time*

On the northern continental slopes of the Archean nucleus the Satpura sediments were deposited. Some of them were rich in manganese and now occur in a metamorphic state as gondites, which form a part of the Sausar series. Others were rich in hematite and gave rise to banded iron-bearing quartzites, now classified as members of the Iron-ore series. Tectonic disturbances threw the beds into repeated isoclinal and even recumbent folding. Orogeny and granitization caused the formation of migmatites and granites. Swarms of muscovite-bearing pegmatites were intruded in some parts of the belt. A major thrust, which can be traced for nearly 160 km in Bihar, is associated with copper and uranium mineralization and is probably the fault zone which separates the Satpura from the Eastern Ghats province.

8.4. *The Aravalli–Delhi time*

The Aravalli region in Rajasthan has been the scene of three major orogenic cycles, each with its own metasediments, granites, migmatites, and pegmatites. The Gneiss complex probably served as the basement for the Aravalli geosyncline. The sediments of the Aravallis proper are largely argillaceous in composition and indicate deep-water conditions of deposition. The Aravalli cycle was followed by the Delhi cycle of sedimentation, with which the intrusion of the Erinpura granite is associated. The Delhi orogenic belt is superimposed on the Aravalli belt, and both have the same regional trend except in the extreme southwest in Gujarat, where there is splaying of the strike.

Rajasthan is probably the locus of another continental nucleus, because some of the oldest Precambrian rocks of India are supposed to exist there.

The younger Precambrian formations occur in narrow belts of folded sedimentary and volcanic rocks. Some uranium mineralization is also present.

8.5. *The Cuddapah time*

After a prolonged period of denudation parts of the Archean nucleus formed of steeply tilted, strongly metamorphosed, and greatly eroded rocks sank below a shallow sea and were covered by the Cuddapah deposits, now composed mainly of quartzites, slates, and limestones. Mafic igneous intrusions are plentiful in some of the Cuddapah formations. The sedimentary beds are virtually devoid of fossils, even though they comprise rocks suitable for the preservation of fossils. They are generally very feebly metamorphosed and also dip at low angles. There is thus a sharp contrast between the Archean rocks and the Cuddapah rocks, and, hence, the Cuddapahs are considered to belong to the Purana time, separated from the Archean by a profound discordance called the Eparchean unconformity.

The type area of the Cuddapah rocks is the crescent-shaped outcrop lying on the Dharwar foreland of the Eastern Ghats belt. The rocks have not been violently disturbed, but on the eastern concave side they have been folded along axes roughly parallel to the Eastern Ghats trend lines. According to HOLMES (1955, p. 98), this folding on the eastern margin of the basin could be interpreted as meaning that the Cuddapahs belong to the end of the Eastern Ghats cycle and of the period immediately following. If so, the Cuddapahs would also be older than the rocks of the Satpura and the Delhi belts.

Along the southern boundary of the present-day limits of the main expanse of the Deccan traps, there is an irregularly shaped basin of rocks known as the Kaladgis, which are somewhat similar to the Cuddapahs. There is no positive proof that the two basins were once connected.

North of the Satpuras there are rock sequences which are lithologically similar to the Cuddapahs. On the assumption that the Aravallis and the Dharwars are both Archean, and that the unconformity separating the Delhis from the Aravallis is the same as the Eparchean unconformity between the Cuddapahs and the Dharwars, the Delhis and the Cuddapahs have been considered by some geologists to be contemporaneous. The two basins of deposition which are so far apart were probably separated by an Archean land barrier, and, consequently, it is impossible by stratigraphical techniques to correlate, with any certainty, the Cuddapahs of the type area with their probable equivalents in northern India. There are, as yet, not sufficient geochronological data for solving some of the important problems relating to the geological evolution of the Precambrian of India.

Acknowledgment

The writer is very grateful to Professor ARTHUR HOLMES for critically reading the manuscript and for making many valuable suggestions.

D

Bibliography

AIRY, G. B. (1855). On the computation of the effect of the attraction of mountain masses. *Phil. Trans. Roy. Soc. London, Ser. B.* **145**, 101.

ASWATHANARAYANA, U. (1956). Absolute ages of the Archaean orogenic cycles of India. *Am. J. Sci.* **254**, 19.

ASWATHANARAYANA, U. (1959). Age of the samarskite of Kishangarh, Rajasthan, India. *Bull. Geol. Soc. Am.* **70**, 111.

ASWATHANARAYANA, U. (1962). Age of the Cuddapahs, India. *Nature* **193**, 70; **194**, 566.

AUDEN, J. B. (1933). Vindhyan sedimentation in the Son Valley, Mirzapur district. *Mem. Geol. Surv. India* **62**, 141.

AUDEN, J. B. (1935). Traverses in the Himalaya. *Records Geol. Surv. India* **69**, 123.

AUDEN, J. B. (1936). The structure of the Himalaya in Garhwal. *Records Geol. Surv. India* **71**, 432.

AUDEN, J. B. (1949). Dykes in Western India, a discussion of their relationships with the Deccan Traps. *Trans. Natl. Inst. Sci. India* **3**, 123.

BHOLA, K. L., CHATTERJI, B. D., DAR, K. K., MAHADEVAN, C., MAHADEVAN, V., MEHTA, N. R., NAGARAJA RAO, N., NANDI, H., NARAYANDAS, G. R., SAHASRABUDHE, G. H., SHIRKE, V. G., and UDAS, G. R. (1958). A survey of uranium and thorium occurrences in India. *Proc. Second U.N. Intern. Conf. Peaceful Uses At. Energy* **2**, 462.

BURRARD, S. G. (1912). On the origin of the Himalaya mountains. *Surv. India Prof. Paper* No. 12.

CAHEN, L. (1961). Review of geochronological knowledge in middle and northern Africa. *Ann. N.Y. Acad. Sci.* **91**, 535.

CHATTERJEE, S. C. (1936). *The anorthosites of Bengal.* Calcutta University Press.

CHATTERJEE, S. C. (1945). The gabbro rocks found near Gorumahisani Pahar, Mayurbhanj State, Orissa. *Proc. Natl. Inst. Sci. India* **11**, 255.

CHATTERJEE, S. C. (1959a). Epochs of igneous activity in India. *Bull. Mysore Geologists' Assoc.* **17**, 1.

CHATTERJEE, S. C. (1959b). The problem of the anorthosites with special reference to the anorthosites of Bengal. Presidential Address, Section of Geology and Geography. *Proc. Indian Sci. Congr., 46th* **2**, 75.

COULSON, A. L. (1933). The geology of Sirohi State, Rajputana. *Mem. Geol. Surv. India* **63**, 1.

CROOKSHANK, H. (1938). The western margin of the Eastern Ghats in Southern Jeypore. *Records Geol. Surv. India* **73**, 398.

CROOKSHANK, H. (1948). Minerals of the Rajputana pegmatites. *Trans. Mining Geol. Met. Inst. India* **42**, 105.

CROOKSHANK, H. (1963). Geology of southern Bastar and Jeypore from the Bailadila Range to the Eastern Ghats. *Mem. Geol. Surv. India* **87**, 1.

CROSS, W. (1914). The position of the kodurites in the quantitative classification. *J. Geol.* **21**, 791.

DUBEY, V. S. (1930). Helium ratios of the basic rocks of the Gwalior Series. *Nature* **126**, 807.

DUBEY, V. S. (1960). Igneous activities and periods of orogenesis in Gondwana land. Presidential Address, Section of Geology and Geography. *Proc. Indian Sci. Congr., 47th* **2**, 72.

DUNN, J. A. (1929). The geology of North Singhbhum including parts of Ranchi and Manbhum districts. *Mem. Geol. Surv. India* **54**, 1.

DUNN, J. A. (1937). The mineral deposits of Eastern Singhbhum and surrounding areas. *Mem. Geol. Surv. India* **69**, 122.

DUNN, J. A. (1940). The stratigraphy of South Singhbhum. *Mem. Geol. Surv. India* **63**, 303.

DUNN, J. A. (1941). The origin of banded hematite ores in India. *Econ. Geol.* **36**, 355.

DUNN, J. A. (1942). Granite and magmation and metamorphism. *Econ. Geol.* **37**, 231.

DUNN, J. A. and DEY, A. K. (1937). Vanadium-bearing titaniferous iron-ores of Singhbhum and Mayurbhanj, India. *Trans. Mining Geol. Inst. India* **31**, 117.

DUNN, J. A. and DEY, A. K. (1942). The geology and petrology of Eastern Singhbhum and surrounding areas. *Mem. Geol. Surv. India* **69**, 281.

EMMONS, W. H. (1937). *Gold deposits of the World.* McGraw-Hill.

ESKOLA, P. E. (1949). The problem of mantled gneiss domes. *Quart. J. Geol. Soc.* **104**, 461.

FERMOR, L. L. (1909). The manganese-ore deposits of India. *Mem. Geol. Surv. India* **37**, 1.

FERMOR, L. L. (1914). On the geology and coal resources of Korea State, Central Provinces. *Mem. Geol. Surv. India* **41**, 148.

FERMOR, L. L. (1919). Some problems of ore genesis in the Archaean of India. Presidential address, Section of Geology. *Indian Sci. Congr., 6th. Proc. Asiatic Soc. Bengal* **15**, 188.

FERMOR, L. L. (1930). On the age of the Aravalli Range. *Records Geol. Surv. India* **62**, 391.

FERMOR, L. L. (1931). General Report of the Geological Survey of India for 1930. *Records Geol. Surv. India* **65**, 1.

FERMOR, L. L. (1936). An attempt at the correlation of the ancient schistose formations of Peninsular India. *Mem. Geol. Surv. India* **70**, 1.

FERMOR, L. L. (1950). Pre-Cambrian formations of India. Discussion. *Geol. Mag.* **87**, 140.

FOOTE, R. B. (1876). The geological features of the south Mahratta country and adjacent districts. *Mem. Geol. Surv. India* **12**, 1.

FOOTE, R. B. (1882). Notes on a traverse across some gold-fields of Mysore. *Records Geol. Surv. India* **15**, 191.

FOOTE, R. B. (1886). Notes on the geology of parts of Bellary and Anantapur districts. *Records Geol. Surv. India* **19**, 97.

FOOTE, R. B. (1888). The Dharwar system, the chief auriferous rock series in south India. *Records Geol. Surv. India* **21**, 40.

FOOTE, R. B. (1895). The geology of the Bellary district, Madras Presidency. *Mem. Geol. Surv. India* **25**, 1.

GHOSH, P. K. (1941). The charnockite series of Bastar State and Western Jeypore. *Records Geol. Surv. India* **75**, Prof. Paper No. 15.

GLENNIE, E. A. (1932). Gravity anomalies and the structure of the earth's crust. *Surv. India Prof. Paper* No. 27.

GLENNIE, E. A. (1951). Density or geological corrections to gravity anomalies for the Deccan Trap areas in India. *Roy. Asiatic Soc. Geophys. Suppl.* **6**, 179.

GOLDSCHMIDT, V. M. (1954). *Geochemistry.* Oxford.

GRIESBACH, C. L. (1891). Geology of the Central Himalayas. *Mem. Geol. Surv. India* **23**, 1.

GULATEE, B. L. (1952). The Aravalli Range and its extensions. *Surv. India Tech. Paper* No. 6.

GULATEE, B. L. (1955). Gravity in India. *Surv. India Tech. Paper* No. 10.

GULATEE, B. L. (1956). Gravity anomalies over Precambrian formations in Peninsular India. *Surv. India Tech. Paper* No. 11.

GUPTA, B. C. (1934). The geology of Central Mewar. *Mem. Geol. Surv. India* **65**, 107.

GUPTA, B. C. and MUKHERJEE, P. N. (1933). The geology of Gujarat and Southern Rajputana. *Records Geol. Surv. India* **73**, 163.

HAYDEN, H. H. (1913). Relationship of the Himalaya to the Indo-Gangetic plain and the Indian Peninsula. *Records Geol. Surv. India* **43**, 138.

HEDBERG, H. D. (1961). The stratigraphic panorama. *Bull. Geol. Soc. Am.* **72**, 499.

HERON, A. M. (1917). The geology of north-eastern Rajputana and adjacent districts. *Mem. Geol. Surv. India* **45**, 1.

HERON, A. M. (1923). The geology of Western Jaipur. *Records Geol. Surv. India* **54**, 345.

HERON, A. M. (1924). The soda-bearing rocks of Rajputana. *Records Geol. Surv. India* **56**, 179.

HERON, A. M. (1935). Synopsis of the pre-Vindhyan geology of Rajputana. *Trans. Natl. Inst. Sci. India* **1**, 17.

HERON, A. M. (1936). The geology of south-eastern Mewar, Rajputana. *Mem. Geol. Surv. India* **68**, 1.

HERON, A. M. (1949). Synopsis of the Purana formations of Hyderabad. *J. Hyderabad Geol. Surv.* **5**, Part 2, 1.

HERON, A. M. (1953). The geology of Central Rajputana. *Mem. Geol. Surv. India* **79**, 1.

HOLLAND, T. H. (1900). The charnockite series, a group of Archaean hypersthenic rocks in Peninsular India. *Mem. Geol. Surv. India* **28**, 119.

HOLLAND, T. H. (1901a). Geology of the neighbourhood of Salem, Madras Presidency. *Mem. Geol. Surv. India* **30**, 103.

HOLLAND, T. H. (1901b). The Sivamalai Series of elaeolite-syenites and corundum syenites in the Coimbatore district, Madras Presidency. *Mem. Geol. Surv. India* **30**, 169.

HOLLAND, T. H. (1902). Notes on rock specimens collected by Dr. F. H. HATCH on the Kolar gold field. *Mem. Geol. Surv. India* **33**, 74.

HOLLAND, T. H. (1909). *The Imperial Gazetteer of India* **1**, 50.

HOLMES, A. (1949). The age of uraninite and monazite from the post-Delhi pegmatites of Rajputana. *Geol. Mag.* **86**, 288.

HOLMES, A. (1950). Age of uraninite from a pegmatite near Singar, Gaya district, India. *Am. Mineralogist* **35**, 19.

HOLMES, A. (1955). Dating the Precambrian of Peninsular India and Ceylon. *Proc. Geol. Assoc. Can.* **7**, 81.

HOWIE, R. A. (1955). The geochemistry of the charnockite series of Madras, India. *Trans. Roy. Soc. Edinburgh* **62**, 725.

HOWIE, R. A. and SUBRAMANIAM, A. P. (1957). The paragenesis of garnet in charnockite, enderbite, and related granulites. *Mineral. Mag.* **31**, 565.

IYER, L. A. N. (1932). A study of the granitic intrusions in Ranchi and Singhbhum districts. *Records Geol. Surv. India* **65**, 490.

JAYARAM, B. (1925). Progress report of work done during the field season of the year 1921–22. *Records Mysore Geol. Dept.* **22**, 32.

JHINGRAN, A. G. (1958). The problem of Bundelkhand granites and gneisses. Presidential address, Section of Geology and Geography. *Proc. Indian Sci. Congr., 55th* **2**, 98.

JONES, H. C. (1922). The iron-ores of Singhbhum and Orissa. *Records Geol. Surv. India* **54**, 203.

JONES, H. C. (1934). The iron ore deposits of Bihar and Orissa. *Mem. Geol. Surv. India* **63**, 167.

KAILASAM, L. N. (1958). Geophysical exploration in the coastal sedimentary belt of Madras State. *Current Sci. India* **27**, 477.

KING, W. (1872). On the Kadapah and Karnul formations in the Madras Presidency. *Mem. Geol. Surv. India* **8**, 1.

KING, W. and FOOTE, R. B. (1864). On the geological structure of parts of the districts of Salem, Trichinopoly, Tanjore, and south Arcot in the Madras Presidency. *Mem. Geol. Surv. India* **4**, 1.

KRISHNAN, M. S. (1935). The Dharwars of Chota Nagpur—their bearing on some problems of correlation and sedimentation. Presidential address, Section of Geology. *Proc. Indian Sci. Congr., 22nd*, 175.

KRISHNAN, M. S. (1937). The geology of Gangpur State, Eastern States. *Mem. Geol. Surv. India* **71**, 1.

KRISHNAN, M. S. (1953). The structural and tectonic history of India. *Mem. Geol. Surv. India* **81**, 1.

KRISHNAN, M. S. (1960a). Precambrian stratigraphy of India. *Intern. Geol. Congr., 21st, Copenhagen, 1960, Rept. Session Norden*, Part 9, 95.

KRISHNAN, M. S. (1960b). *Geology of India and Burma*. Fourth edition. Madras.

KRUMMENACHER, D. (1961). Déterminations d'âge isotopique faites sur quelques roches de l'Himalaya du Nepal par la méthode potassium-argon. *Schweiz. Mineral. Petrogr. Mitt.* **41**, 273.

LARSEN, E. S., JR. (1938). Some new variation diagrams for groups of igneous rocks. *J. Geol.* **46**, 505.

MACLAREN, J. M. (1906). Notes on some auriferous tracts in southern India. *Records Geol. Surv. India* **34**, 96.

McDOUGALL, I. (1963). Potassium–argon age measurements on dolerites from Antarctica and South Africa. *J. Geophys. Res.* **68**, 1535.

MAHADEVAN, C. (1949). A re-examination of some aspects of Puranas and Archaeans of south India. Presidential address, Section of Geology and Geography. *Proc. Indian Sci. Congr., 36th* **2**, 63.

MALLET, F. R. (1874). On the geology and mineral resources of Darjiling district and western Duars. *Mem. Geol. Surv. India* **11**, 1.

MIDDLEMISS, C. S. (1915). The origin of the kodurite series. General report of the Geological Survey of India for the year 1914. *Records Geol. Surv. India* **45**, 102.

MIDDLEMISS, C. S. (1917). Complexities of Archaean geology in India. Presidential address, Section of Geology, 4th Indian Sci. Congress. *J. Proc. Asiatic Soc. Bengal* **13**, 195.

MURTHY, P. B. (1950). Genesis of asbestos and barite, Cuddapah district, Rayalaseema, South India. *Econ. Geol.* **45**, 681.

NAHA, K. (1955). A preliminary note on the geometry of folds around Galudih and Ghatsila, Singhbhum, Bihar. *Sci. Cult. (Calcutta)* **20**, 614.

NAHA, K. (1956). Structural set up and movement plan in parts of Dhalbhum, Bihar. *Sci. Cult. (Calcutta)* **22**, 43.

NAHA, K. (1965). Metamorphism in relation to stratigraphy, structure, and movements in part of east Singhbhum. *Quart. J. Geol. Mining Met. Soc. India* **37**, 41.

NAHA, K. and GHOSH, S. K. (1960). Archaean palaeogeography of eastern and northern Singhbhum, Eastern India. *Geol. Mag.* **97**, 436.

NARAYANASWAMI, S. (1959). Cross-folding and en echelon folding in Precambrian rocks of India and their relation to metallogenesis. *J. Geol. Soc. India* **1**, 80.

NEWBOLD, T. J. (1846). Summary of the geology of southern India. *J. Roy. Asiatic Soc.* **8**, 138, 213.

NEWBOLD, T. J. (1848). Summary of the geology of southern India. *J. Roy. Asiatic Soc.* **9**, 1, 20.

NEWBOLD, T. J. (1850). Summary of the geology of southern India. *J. Roy. Asiatic Soc.* **12**, 78.

NICOLAYSEN, L. O. (1957). Solid diffusion in radioactive minerals and the measurement of absolute age. *Geochim. Cosmochim. Acta* **11**, 41.

NICOLAYSEN, L. O., BURGER, A. J., TATSUMI, T., and AHRENS, L. H. (1961). Age measurements on pegmatites and a basic charnockite lens occurring near Lützow–Holm Bay, Antarctica. *Geochim. Cosmochim. Acta* **22**, 94.

NIYOGI, D. (1960). Structural pattern of the Kishangarh alkaline rocks. *Quart. J. Geol. Mining Met. Soc. India* **32**, 27.

OLDHAM, R. D. (1893). *A manual of the geology of India and Burma*. Second Ed. Calcutta.

OLDHAM, R. D. (1917). The structure of the Himalayas and of the Gangetic plains as elucidated by geodetic observations in India. *Mem. Geol. Surv. India* **42**, Part 2, 1.

O'ROURKE, J. E. (1961). Paleozoic banded iron formations. *Econ. Geol.* **56**, 331.

O'ROURKE, J. E. (1962). The stratigraphy of Himalayan iron ores. *Am. J. Sci.* **260**, 294.

PASCOE, E. H. (1950). *A manual of the geology of India and Burma.* Third Ed. Calcutta.

PAULOSE, C. V. (1956). Charnockites and associated rocks of the Cape Comorin Area, South India. *Bull. Mysore Geologists' Assoc.* **9**.

PICHAMUTHU, C. S. (1930). On the trap rocks of the Chitaldrug schist belt. *Records Mysore Geol. Dept.* **28**, 20.

PICHAMUTHU, C. S. (1935a). The conglomerates and grits of Kaldurga, Kadur district, Mysore. *Proc. Indian Acad. Sci.* **2**, 254.

PICHAMUTHU, C. S. (1935b). The iron formations and associated rocks of the eastern Bababudans, Kadur district, Mysore. *J. Mysore Univ.* **8**, 1.

PICHAMUTHU, C. S. (1938). Spilitic rocks from Chitaldrug, Mysore State. *Current Sci. (India)* **7**, 55.

PICHAMUTHU, C. S. (1947). Some aspects of Dharwar geology with special reference to Mysore State. Presidential Address, Section of Geology and Geography. *Proc. Indian Sci. Congr., 34th* **2**, 1.

PICHAMUTHU, C. S. (1950a). Soda metasomatism in the ferruginous quartzites of the Bababudan Hills, Mysore State. *Proc. Indian Acad. Sci.* **31**, 191.

PICHAMUTHU, C. S. (1950b). Pillow structures in the lavas of Dharwar age in the Chitaldrug district, Mysore State. *Current Sci. (India)* **19**, 110.

PICHAMUTHU, C. S. (1951). Some observations on the structure and classification of the Dharwars of Mysore State. *Current Sci. (India)* **20**, 117.

PICHAMUTHU, C. S. (1953). *The charnockite problem.* Mysore Geologists' Assoc., Bangalore, India.

PICHAMUTHU, C. S. (1956). The problem of the ultrabasic rocks. *Proc. Mysore Geologists' Assoc.* 1955, 1.

PICHAMUTHU, C. S. (1957). Pillow lavas from Mysore State, India. *Bull. Mysore Geol. Assoc.* **15**.

PICHAMUTHU, C. S. (1959). The significance of clouded plagioclase in the basic dykes of Mysore State, India. *J. Geol. Soc. India* **1**, 68.

PICHAMUTHU, C. S. (1961). Tectonics of Mysore State. *Proc. Indian Acad. Sci.* **53B**, 135.

PICHAMUTHU, C. S. (1962). Some observations on the structure, metamorphism, and geological evolution of Peninsular India. *J. Geol. Soc. India* **3**, 106.

PICHAMUTHU, C. S. (1963). The "Dharwar system" and its position in the Indian Precambrian. *J. Geol. Soc. India* **4**, 79.

PILGRIM, G. E. and WEST, W. D. (1928). The structure and correlation of the Simla rocks. *Mem. Geol. Surv. India* **53**, 1.

PRATT, J. H. (1855). On the attraction of the Himalayan Mountains and the regions beyond upon the plumb line in India. *Phil. Trans. Roy. Soc. London, Ser. B* **145**, 53.

RADHAKRISHNA, B. P. (1956). *The Closepet granites of Mysore State, India.* Mysore Geologists' Assoc., Bangalore.

RAJAGOPALAN, C. (1946). Studies in charnockites from St. Thomas Mount, Madras—Part I. *Proc. Indian Acad. Sci.* **24**, 315.

RAJAGOPALAN, C. (1947). Studies in charnockites from St. Thomas Mount, Madras—Part II. *Proc. Indian Acad. Sci.* **26**, 237.

RAMA RAO, B. (1927). The Kodamites or the cordierite micaceous gneisses of Channapatna area. *Records Mysore Geol. Dept.* **24**, 134.

RAMA RAO, B. (1935a). Correlation of Indian Precambrians with Lake Superior formations. *Records Mysore Geol. Dept.* **33**, 70.

RAMA RAO, B. (1935b). The distinguishing characteristics of the Champion gneiss and the Peninsular gneiss of Mysore State and their probable mode of origin. *Records Mysore Geol. Dept.* **33**, 80.

RAMA RAO, B. (1936). Recent studies on the Archaean complex of Mysore. Presidential address, Section of Geology. *Proc. Indian Sci. Congr., 23rd* 215.

RAMA RAO, B. (1940). The Archaean complex of Mysore. *Mysore Geol. Dept. Bull.* **17**.

RAMA RAO, B. (1945). The charnockite rocks of Mysore (southern India). *Mysore Geol. Dept. Bull.* **18**.

RAMACHANDRA RAO, M. B. (1937). The petrology of the hornblendic rocks of the Kolar schist belt. *Mysore Geol. Dept. Bull.* **16**.

RUSSELL, R. D., FARQUHAR, R. M., CUMMING, G. L., and WILSON, J. T. (1954). Dating galenas by means of their isotopic constitution. *Am. Geophys. Union* **35**, 301.

SAMBASIVA IYER, V. S. (1918). On the distinct sedimentary origin of some quartzites of Mysore. *Proc. Indian Sci. Congr., 5th.* Abstract.

SAMPAT IYENGAR, P. (1917). Report on the autoclastic conglomerate, Kaldurga. *Records Mysore Geol. Dept.* **15**, 106.

SAMPAT IYENGAR, P. (1920). The acid rocks of Mysore. *Mysore Geol. Dept. Bull.* **9**.

SARKAR, S. N. (1957, 1958). Stratigraphy and tectonics of the Dongargarh system: a new system in the Precambrians of Bhandara–Drug–Balaghat area, Bombay and Madhya Pradesh. *J. Sci. Eng. Res., Kharagpur Indian Inst. Technol.* **1**, 237; **2**, 145.

SARKAR, S. N. and SAHA, A. K. (1959). A revised correlation of the "Iron Ore Series", north and south of the Copper belt thrust in Singhbhum and adjacent areas. *Quart. J. Geol. Mining Met. Soc. India* **31**, 129.

SARKAR, S. N. and SAHA, A. K. (1962). A revision of the Precambrian stratigraphy and tectonics of Singhbhum and adjacent regions. *Quart. J. Geol. Mining Met. Soc. India* **34**, 97.

SARKAR, T. C. (1941). The lead ratio of a crystal of monazite from the Gaya district, Bihar. *Proc. Indian Acad. Sci.* **13A**, 245.

SATHAPATHI, N. (1953). Petrology and petrogenesis of nepheline syenites and associated rocks of Koraput, Orissa. Unpublished D.Sc. thesis, Andhra University.

SEN, S. (1952). The genesis of alkaline rocks of Kishangarh, Rajasthan. *Current Sci. (India)* **21**, 242.

SHARMA, N. L. (1953). Problems in the correlation of the pre-Vindhyan rocks of Rajasthan. Presidential address, Section of Geology and Geography. *Proc. Indian Sci. Congr., 40th* **2**, 1.

SMEETH, W. F. (1899). Report of the Chief Inspector of Mines, Mysore State. Appendix.

SMEETH, W. F. (1901). General report on the work of the Department for the years 1900 and 1901. *Records Mysore Geol. Dept.* **3**, 1.

SMEETH, W. F. (1910). General report of the work of the Department for the year 1909–10. *Records Mysore Geol. Dept.* **11**, 1.

SMEETH, W. F. (1912). General report of the work of the Department. *Records Mysore Geol. Dept.* **12**, 1.

SMEETH, W. F. (1915). Annual report for the year 1914. *Records Mysore Geol. Dept.* **14**, 1.

SMEETH, W. F. (1916). Outline of the geological history of Mysore. *Dept. Mines Geol., Mysore State, Bull.* **6**.

SMEETH, W. F. (1926). Some views about the Archaeans of southern India. Presidential address, Section of Geology. *Records Mysore Geol. Dept.* **23**, 37.

SMEETH, W. F. and WATSON, H. E. (1918). Radioactivity of Archaean rocks from the Mysore State, South India. *Phil. Mag.* **35**, 206.

SNELLING, N. J. (1963). Age of the Roraima formation, British Guiana. *Nature* **198**, 1079.

SRIRAMARAO, M. (1947). Geology and petrography of the Bezwada and Kondapalle Hill ranges. Part II. Charnockites and associated rocks and chromite. *Proc. Indian Acad. Sci.* **26**, 133.

STARIK, I. Y., KRYLOV, A. Y., RAVICH, M. G., and SILIN, Y. I. (1961). The absolute ages of East Antarctic rocks. *Ann. N.Y. Acad. Sci.* **91**, 576.

Straczek, J. A., Subramanyam, M. R., Narayanaswami, S., Shukla, K. D., Vemban, N. A., Chakravarty, S. C., and Venkatesh, V. (1956). Manganese ore deposits of Madhya Pradesh, India. *Intern. Geol. Congr., 20th: Symposium on manganese* **4**, 63.

Subramaniam, A. P. (1950). A petrographic study of the alkaline rocks of Sivamalai. *Proc. Indian Acad. Sci.* **30B**, 69.

Subramaniam, A. P. (1956). Mineralogy and petrology of the Sittampundi complex, Salem district, Madras State, India. *Bull. Geol. Soc. Am.* **67**, 317.

Subramaniam, A. P. (1959). Charnockites of the type area near Madras—a reinterpretation. *Am. J. Sci.* **257**, 321.

Turner, F. J. and Verhoogen, J. (1962). *Igneous and metamorphic petrology*. Indian edition. Bombay.

Vemban, N. A. (1946). A chemical and petrological study of some dyke rocks in the Precambrian (Cuddapah traps). *Proc. Indian Acad. Sci.* **23**, 347.

Vemban, N. A. (1961). Structure and tectonics of the manganese-ore belt of Madhya Pradesh and adjoining parts of Bombay. *Proc. Indian Acad. Sci.* **53**, 125.

Venkatasubramanian, V. S. (1953). Application of Rb–Sr method to the age determination of phlogopite. *Proc. Indian Acad. Sci.* **38A**, 376.

Venkatasubramanian, V. S. and Krishnan, R. S. (1960). Radioactivity and geochronology of igneous and metamorphic rocks of the Precambrian Era of the Indian Peninsula. *Proc. Natl. Inst. Sci. India* **26A**, Suppl. II, 89.

Vitanage, P. W. (1959). Geology of the country around Polonnaruwa. *Mem. Geol. Surv. Ceylon* **1**, 11.

Wadia, D. N. (1931). The syntaxis of the north-west Himalaya: its rocks, tectonics, and orogeny. *Records Geol. Surv. India* **65**, 189.

Wadia, D. N. (1942). The making of India. General Presidential address. *Proc. Indian Sci. Congr., 29th* **2**, 3.

Wadia, D. N. (1957). *Geology of India*. Third edition. London.

Walker, T. L. (1902). The geology of Kalahandi State, Central Provinces. *Mem. Geol. Surv. India* **33**, 1.

Walker, T. L. (1907). Nepheline syenites from the Hill Tracts of Vizagapatam district, Madras Presidency. *Records Geol. Surv. India* **36**, 19.

West, W. D. (1936). Nappe structure in the Archaean rocks of the Nagpur district. *Trans. Natl. Inst. Sci. India* **1**, 93.

West, W. D. (1939). The structure of the Shali "window" near Simla. *Records Geol. Surv. India* **74**, 133.

THE PRECAMBRIAN OF CEYLON[1]

C. S. Pichamuthu

Department of Geology, Bangalore University, India

Contents

[1] Manuscript received April 25, 1962. Revised manuscript received April 28, 1964.

1. Introduction

The most characteristic feature of the topography of Ceylon is the existence of three well-defined surfaces of erosion whose general elevations are 30 m, 500 m, and 1,800 m above the sea level. Steep scarp faces sometimes demarcate these terraces. ADAMS (1929) thought that they represented three stages of denudation brought about by successive uplifts of the island as a whole. WADIA (1941b, 1943c), however, believed that the terraces are the result of successive Recent block uplifts along curvilinear faults which took place on an already peneplaned Archean terrane. On purely physiographical grounds, ADAMS made the suggestive observation that the Deccan plateau of India represents a continuation of the second peneplain of Ceylon, and that the third highest-lying peneplain corresponds to the uplands of the Nilgiris in India, whose highest peaks have about the same elevation as those of Ceylon.

Precambrian rocks occupy about nine-tenths of the island, the rest consisting of narrow belts of Jurassic, Miocene, Pleistocene, and Recent sedimentary rocks and sediments along the coasts. There is a great similarity between Ceylon and Peninsular India not only in lithology and structure but also in the unusual abundance of thorium-bearing minerals, a peculiarity that the two areas share with Madagascar.

2. History of geological exploration

Apart from some publications by various casual observers, much information on the geology and mineral resources of Ceylon was furnished by A. K. COOMARASWAMY between 1900 and 1908 in a series of short papers. The earliest comprehensive account, however, of the geology of Ceylon was given by ADAMS (1929) in a report which included the first geological map of Ceylon. The next important publication was the monograph on the geology of Ceylon by COATES (1935). The geological map which accompanied his paper was different in several particulars from the previous map of ADAMS. After 1938 D. N. WADIA was the chief contributor, especially on the physiography and economic minerals of Ceylon. A brief account of the geology and mineral deposits of Ceylon was presented by FERNANDO (1948) together with a provisional geological map (see Fig. 1). Studies along modern lines of the problems presented by the Precambrian in certain parts of Ceylon were made by VITANAGE (1959) and COORAY (1954, 1959, 1960, 1961a, 1962).

3. Areal divisions

The main areal divisions of the Precambrian of Ceylon are shown in Fig. 2. These divisions are based partly on the geological map of Ceylon published by FERNANDO (1948) and partly on a previous map of COATES (1935). The Highland series (metasediments and charnockites) extends as a belt of

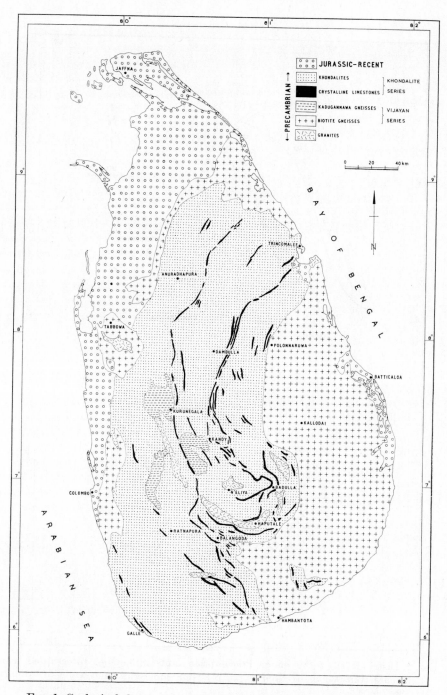

FIG. 1. Geological sketch map of Ceylon. According to FERNANDO (1948).
Published with the permission of the Government Mineralogist, Ceylon.

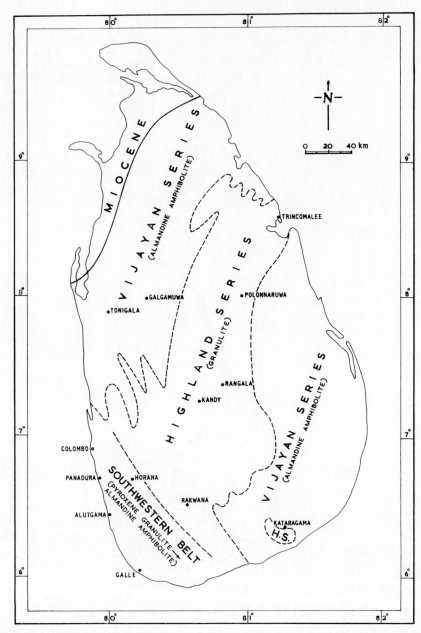

Fig. 2. Distribution of the major Precambrian units in Ceylon. Interrupted lines
    indicate transitional boundaries. H. S.: Highland series. According to COORAY
    (1962).

varying width running across the center of the island from Trincomalee on the northeast coast to about 50 km from the southwest coast. The Central Highlands of Ceylon lie wholly within this belt.

The Highland series is bounded on the east and the west by the Vijayan series (migmatitic gneisses and granites). The boundaries are transitional zones having lithological, metamorphic, and structural features characteristic of both the series.

An enclave of rocks identical with those in the Highland series and known as the Kataragama complex is present in southeastern Ceylon (see Fig. 2), where it is completely surrounded by Vijayan rocks.

The Highland series belt passes southwestward into a coastal belt about 40 km wide and 150 km long which is structurally and lithologically different from the rest of the Highland series. It is probably a part of a separate geosynclinal belt that continues into southern India. It has many of the characteristics of the transitional zones and interdigitates northward into the western Vijayan series.

4. Stratigraphy

4.1. *General*

COATES (1935) classified the Archean rocks of Ceylon (see Table 1) and

TABLE 1

Lithological classification of the Precambrian of
Ceylon. According to COATES (1935)

Young pegmatites
Dolerite dikes
Wanni gneisses (pink granitic gneisses)
Charnockite series
Kadugannawa gneiss (calcium silicate gneiss)
Khondalite series
Bintenne gneiss (old biotite gneiss)

gave individual names to some of the gneisses. He distinguished two main groups of gneisses, an old biotite gneiss sometimes with augen structure which he called the Bintenne gneiss, and a young rock which he named the Wanni gneiss, which is often pink and exhibits intrusive relations to the charnockites. He also recognized several lithological subgroups within the two broad divisions.

WADIA (1940, p. 17) considered that the classification of the Ceylon gneisses made by COATES was only regional because the rocks are all biotite gneisses with minor local lithological variants which cannot be distinguished from the fundamental gneisses. He proposed the name "Vijaya gneiss" for the well-developed series of biotite gneisses of the Colombo district which, he believed, formed a part of the fundamental or basement complex into which the charnockites and the other granites were intruded. Among the intrusives he included the charnockite series of granites and norites, the zircon granite of Balangoda, and the doleritic and ultramafic dikes and sills. His classification of the Precambrian rocks of Ceylon is given in Table 2. Later he (WADIA, 1941a) recognized the fact that there

TABLE 2

Precambrian stratigraphy of Ceylon.
According to WADIA (1940, 1941a)

	Trincomalee series	Quartz-bearing metamorphic rocks, quartzites, leptynites, granulites
Khondalite group	Ratnapura series	Argillaceous, calcareous, and ferruginous metamorphosed sediments
	Galle gneiss	Scapolite–wollastonite gneisses
Vijaya series	Wanni gneiss Bintenne gneiss Vijaya gneiss	Fundamental biotite gneiss complex

are other types of biotite gneisses, particularly in the eastern and northern parts of Ceylon (the Wanni and the Bintenne gneisses of COATES), which are local modifications of the fundamental biotite gneiss complex. He introduced the name "Vijaya series" for the Fundamental gneiss of Ceylon, which he considered the counterpart of the Peninsular gneiss of India.

According to FERNANDO (1948), there is only an apparent uniformity among the several lithological types of gneisses, which, furthermore, did not all originate in the same way. Consequently, the name "Vijaya gneiss" has no particular significance. He proposed instead the name "Vijayan series" for the heterogeneous group comprising orthogneisses, paragneisses, migmatites, granitized gneisses and schists, and the granitized remains of old crystalline rocks which together are supposed to constitute the Basement Complex of Ceylon. He divided the Precambrian of Ceylon into two groups, viz. the Vijayan series, comprising granites, gneisses, and schists, and the Khondalite series, composed of metamorphosed sediments which bear a general resemblance to the corresponding rocks of the Eastern Ghats belt of India (see Table 3).

TABLE 3

Precambrian stratigraphy of Ceylon. According to FERNANDO (1948)

Khondalite series	Paragneisses and paraschists, including quartzites, quartz schists, granulites, leptynites, calcium silicate gneisses, calcium silicate granulites, crystalline calcitic and dolomitic limestones, with intrusive granites
Vijayan series	Orthogneisses, paragneisses, and schists with intrusive granites

4.2. *The Vijayan series*

The Vijayan series is a sequence of rocks of several ages and modes of origin that have been intricately mixed and intimately folded together (see Fig. 3). Except for the broad subdivision of the complex into the Wanni

FIG. 3. Disrupted and deformed amphibolite bands in granodiorite (Vijayan series). Galkadawala, near Tonigala, northwestern Ceylon. Photo, P. G. Cooray.

gneisses and the Kadugannawa gneisses in the northwest, and the Bintenne gneisses in the southeast, each of which consists of several types, little is known about their mutual relationships and boundaries.

4.3. *The Khondalite series*

The Khondalite series is generally considered to overlie the Vijayan series in a highly folded synclinal basin. It is a group of bedded metasediments and comprises quartzites, quartz schists, fine-grained silicic gneisses, granulites, calcium silicate gneisses, crystalline limestones and dolomites, and typical khondalites. The metasediments vary from highly aluminous in the southwest (the Ratnapura facies) to highly siliceous in the northeast (the Trincomalee facies). Well-defined bands of crystalline calcitic limestones are associated with the quartzites, and like them can be traced for many kilometers along the strike.

The members of the Khondalite series grade into one another, so that it has not been possible even broadly to subdivide the series. The crystalline calcitic limestones serve as useful marker beds from the distribution of which the synclinorial nature of the basin is inferred.

4.4. *The Highland series*

Cooray (1961a) divided the Precambrian of Ceylon into two parts, viz. the Highland series, which occurs as a N.E.–S.W.-running belt in the center of the island, and the Vijayan series on either side of it. The Highland series consists mainly of metasediments and abundant charnockites, and the Vijayan series is made up of granitic and migmatitic gneisses (see Fig. 4).

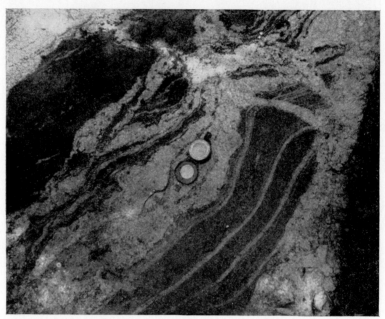

FIG. 4. Migmatite formed by pegmatite invading amphibolite and hornblende–biotite gneiss (Vijayan series). Mayilewa, near Galga-muwa, northwestern Ceylon. Photo, P. G. Cooray.

The Highland series comprises, therefore, the metasediments of the Khonda-lite series together with the charnockites and the rocks intrusive into them. The relationship between the Highland series and the Vijayan series is difficult to evaluate, because there exist no recognizable basal conglomerates, unconformities, transgressive boundaries, or thrust planes. In many places a transitional zone is present between the two series which contains char-nockites, charnockitic gneisses, granitic gneisses, and some metasediments. The zone varies in width between 10 km and 60 km.

4.5. *The Charnockite series*

The rocks of the Charnockite series are widely distributed in Ceylon and are most abundant in the southwest and in the central highland country. There are only isolated exposures in the east and in the northern half of the island. The pyroxene-bearing gneisses and granulites are interbedded and intimately associated with the several members of the Khondalite series, such as quartzites (see Fig. 5), silicic gneisses, calcium silicate gneisses, and granulites. Very often there is a gradual transition from the pyroxene-bearing rocks to the metasediments.

5. Petrography and petrology

5.1. *The khondalites*

5.1.1. Khondalites

The khondalites are essentially garnet–sillimanite–graphite–quartz–orthoclase rocks with ilmenite and magnetite as the main accessories; rutile may be present (WALKER, 1902). Quartz is variable in amount. The usual feldspar is orthoclase which is generally microperthitic but sometimes coarsely perthitic. A pale pink garnet (almandine–pyrope) occurs as poikiloblastic–porphyroblastic crystals with inclusions of quartz, feldspar, and sillimanite. Sillimanite occurs as prismatic crystals which enclose the garnet like a sheath or continue through it. Graphite in ragged bladed crystals is always present, and zircon is well rounded.

A variant of khondalite is a garnet granulite in which a pinkish-mauve garnet (almandine–pyrope) occurs in a banded or gneissose rock which is

FIG. 5. Interbedded quartzites and mafic charnockites (Highland series). Cottaganga Estate, Rangala, central Ceylon. Photo, P. G. Cooray.

composed of quartz, orthoclase, plagioclase (oligoclase–andesine), biotite, and rutile. Graphite and sillimanite may be present. Zircon, magnetite, and ilmenite are common accessories. Monazite and apatite are rare.

The khondalites and garnet granulites are metamorphic derivatives of aluminium-rich sediments, possibly shales.

Narrow bands of dark gray fine-grained schistose rocks rich in graphite and sulfide minerals are often interbedded with garnet–sillimanite gneisses. They are composed of quartz, orthoclase, plagioclase, biotite, and graphite, with zircon, rutile, and pyrite as accessories. Sillimanite may be present. According to COORAY (1961a, p. 57), the high carbon content and the presence of pyrite suggest that these rocks were originally sapropelic sediments formed in an oxygen-deficient environment. Such rocks are to be expected in a metasedimentary succession containing garnet–sillimanite–graphite gneiss, quartzite, and crystalline limestone.

5.1.2. Crystalline limestones

Crystalline limestones are often interbedded with narrow bands of garnet–sillimanite–graphite schist, quartzite, or charnockite. The limestones vary from fine-grained to coarse-grained rocks, and from calcitic or dolomitic varieties to more or less impure limestones containing forsterite, diopside, phlogopite, and scapolite. Apatite, spinel, graphite, pyrite, and rare sphene are the usual accessories.

Microscopic investigation shows that the crystalline limestones are made up of a mosaic of calcite and dolomite in which the silicate minerals occur as scattered individual crystals or in clusters. The carbonate minerals are intimately intergrown. Lamellar twinning is common to both calcite and dolomite, and the lamellae are sometimes bent.

The crystalline limestones were formed by the regional metamorphism of dominantly calcareous sediments containing varying amounts of clayey and ferruginous matter.

5.1.3. Calcium silicate granulites and gneisses

Calcium silicate granulites and gneisses comprise a wide range of rocks in which calcite is relatively unimportant and diopside and scapolite are almost always present. Other minerals include orthoclase, plagioclase, hornblende, phlogopite, sphene, apatite, graphite, and pyrrhotite. The field relations of these rocks indicate that they form an integral part of the original sedimentary succession, and that the mineral assemblages in these rocks do not result from the metasomatic introduction of material from extraneous sources.

The calcium silicate rocks are coarse-grained or medium-grained granulites which are often porphyroblastic. They are interbedded with garnet–graphite schists, quartzites, and charnockites.

The Kadugannawa gneiss is a dense black hornblende rock with varying quantities of biotite and feldspars, in which calcite is always present

(COATES, 1935, pp. 133–135). It bears some resemblance to the calcium silicate gneisses which are associated with khondalites near Visakhapatnam in the Eastern Ghats region of India (FERMOR, 1909, p. 243).

5.1.4. Quartzites and quartz schists

The quartzites and quartz schists include the more or less pure quartzites, feldspar-bearing quartzites, sillimanite quartzites, garnet-bearing quartzites, quartz schists, quartz–magnetite–sillimanite schists, and garnet–quartz rocks. The pure quartzites are coarsely granular massive whitish rocks in which generally no foliation or bedding is visible. They are, however, highly jointed and fractured. The garnet-bearing quartzites either are spotted rocks or contain garnets concentrated along certain planes. The sillimanite quartzites are generally flaggy and have a bedded appearance.

The quartzite strata vary from about 30 cm to several hundred kilometers in thickness and are interbedded with other metasedimentary rocks and with charnockites (see Fig. 5). They are frequently folded. All signs of previous sedimentary structures have been destroyed by complete recrystallization and metamorphism.

Microscopic investigation shows that the rocks of this group are composed of a mosaic of coarsely granoblastic grains of quartz with varying amounts of biotite, muscovite, microcline (or orthoclase), sodic plagioclase, almandine, and sillimanite. The chief accessory heavy minerals are well-rounded and stumpy zircons, ilmenite, magnetite, rutile, and monazite.

5.2. *The charnockites*

The charnockites of Ceylon are almost invariably composed of hypersthene, clinopyroxene (diopside), and plagioclase, with quartz and alkali feldspar as additional minerals in the silicic and intermediate rocks. Microcline, which is a normal constituent of charnockites elsewhere, is generally absent. Hornblende and biotite are frequently present in the mafic charnockites, and garnet (almandine–pyrope) may occur in all charnockites. Apatite, zircon, magnetite, and ilmenite are the main accessories. Diopside appears to be the primary mineral, with hypersthene forming from it, and hornblende from both. Garnet was the last mineral to form because it contains all the other minerals as inclusions; it is derived from the pyroxenes.

There are several rock types, which though not typical members of the charnockite series, yet have a definite affinity with it, because they are hybridized or migmatized products formed by the admixture of silicic material with mafic charnockite. Some of the charnockitic biotite gneisses contain scapolite and rounded grains of zircon.

COATES (1935) believed that the intermediate varieties of charnockites are direct consolidation products of a magma from which the rocks of the series are derived, and that the extreme varieties are the result of more perfect differentiation induced by local conditions. Some of the charnockites display intrusive relationships to the biotite gneisses and to the metasediments, but the considerable lithologic variation in the charnockitic rocks observed even in a comparatively small area is contrary to what one would expect from a plutonic mass.

VITANAGE (1957) examined the zircons present in some rocks of Ceylon and showed that the charnockites of the Polonnaruwa area are of sedimentary origin because they contain a mixed assemblage of stumpy, equidimensional, and rounded zircon grains similar to those found in the quartzites and in the biotite gneisses with which they are interbedded, and strikingly different from the euhedral elongate zircons occurring in the Tonigala granite of the west coast and in the microcline-granitic gneisses of the east coast.

The work of COORAY (1961a, p. 78) in the Rangala area showed that the charnockites are not a differentiated magmatic sequence, and are not intrusive into the surrounding rocks. Their field relations and their structural and textural features indicate that they form a fundamental part of the metamorphic complex, and that they bear the same stamp of plutonic metamorphism as do the metasedimentary granulites, gneisses, and schists with which they are associated. The chemical composition of the mafic charnockites suggests that they were originally either marly sediments rich in iron, magnesium, and calcium, or lava flows or tuffs laid down contemporaneously with sandstones, shales, and limestones. The silicic and intermediate charnockites are probably of more than one mode of origin, the most obvious being their formation by migmatization of mafic charnockites. The rare pegmatitic charnockites which exhibit intrusive relationships have resulted by palingenesis and mobilization from the silicic charnockites.

5.3. *Gneisses and granites*

The Bintenne gneiss. The name "Bintenne gneiss" was given by COATES (1935, p. 115) to an extensive gneiss formation in southeastern Ceylon. The Bintenne gneiss is a homogeneous light-colored granitic gneiss composed of quartz, microcline, plagioclase (albite–oligoclase), and biotite. The accessory minerals are sphene, magnetite, zircon, apatite, and muscovite. Garnet and sillimanite are absent.

The Balangoda group. COOMARASWAMY (1904c) gave the name "Balangoda group" to zircon-bearing granites and pegmatites which are most abundant in the Balangoda district. Similar rocks occur also in the southwestern and central parts of Ceylon. Apart from zircon, the rocks contain monazite, thorianite, and beryl. The associated pegmatites are particularly rich in minerals containing uranium, thorium, and lanthanides.

The Tonigala group. A hornblende granite which contains pink orthoclase and microcline and shows an intrusive relationship to the charnockites is called the Tonigala granite. It is widely distributed in the northern half of Ceylon and in the Eastern Province, but only isolated exposures exist in the central highlands and in the southwestern part of the island.

Silicic garnet gneiss (leptynite). Certain silicic quartz–feldspar–garnet gneisses, ranging from fine-grained to medium-grained and with or without hornblende, which are associated with charnockites have been named leptynites both in India (HOLLAND, 1900) and in Ceylon (COATES, 1935). In Ceylon such gneisses are frequently interbanded with quartzites, charnockites, and mafic rocks. The contact of leptynite and mafic charnockite is generally a transitional zone formed of intermediate charnockite. Orthoclase, plagioclase, biotite, and garnet are commonly present. Quartz occurs in the shape of long thin ribbons. Apatite, zircon, magnetite, ilmenite, and pyrite are the usual accessories.

5.4. *Mafic dikes*

Mafic dikes are comparatively rare in Ceylon. COORAY (1961a, pp. 96–100) has described an unusual suite of narrow dikes from central Ceylon which are intrusive into the charnockites and gneisses and which vary in composition from mafic to ultramafic. They are dark rocks which contain pyroxene or pyroxene and scapolite as essential constituents, and hornblende, tremolite, acmite, plagioclase, and biotite as subordinate minerals. Sphene, pyrite, and apatite are the chief accessories. Such dikes were noticed by COOMARASWAMY (1905b, pp. 363–369) and COATES (1935, pp. 169–172) in other parts of Ceylon. The dikes do not resemble any known igneous rocks and were probably formed metasomatically by the alteration of wall-rock material on joint planes (COORAY, 1961a, p. 100).

A few dolerite dikes occur in the eastern and southeastern parts of Ceylon. They are composed of augite and labradorite with magnetite as an abundant accessory.

5.5. *Petrochemistry*

The chemistry of the rocks occurring in Ceylon has not been investigated in any detail. Representative chemical analyses of the important types of rocks are given in Tables 4 and 5. WASHINGTON (1916) was probably the first to analyse Ceylon charnockites, and his conclusions followed the views of HOLLAND (1900) that the charnockites constitute an igneous series.

ADAMS (1929) made a systematic study of the petrology of Ceylon rocks and published chemical analyses of the charnockites, leptynites, khondalites, and limestones. The Ceylon charnockites, according to ADAMS (1929, p. 478), are hypersthene granites which are somewhat more mafic than the original charnockite of India, since they contain less SiO_2 and more MgO, CaO, and FeO. He (ADAMS, 1929, p. 480) concluded that the relatively small development of charnockite in Ceylon is probably a comagmatic part of the much larger Indian area. The khondalites (sillimanite–garnet rocks) correspond closely in chemical composition to shales and phyllites (ADAMS, 1929, p. 489, Table V).

VITANAGE (1959) published a series of chemical analyses of charnockites and associated gneisses from the Polonnaruwa area. They vary from highly

TABLE 4

Chemical composition of rocks belonging to the Khondalite series in Ceylon

Weight %

Constituent	Khondalites		Leptynites		Calcium silicate gneiss	Calcium silicate granulite	Quartz-plagioclase-garnet granulite	Crystalline limestone
	1	2	3	4	5	6	7	8
	15 km on Passara–Ella road	Passara	193 km on Koslanda–Pottuvil road	Ella–Haputale road	51 km on Rattotta–Laggala road	Kaikawala	Hattota Amuna, Pallegama	Narampanawa
SiO_2	57.96	64.79	76.25	68.54	46.42	49.53	58.84	0.51
Al_2O_3	24.01	18.14	11.16	13.69	10.30	2.34	18.23	0.31
TiO_2	1.38	0.89	0.15	0.93	0.22	0.42	1.01	0.02
Fe_2O_3	3.51	1.50	0.34	0.07	6.61	6.84	2.52	0.03
FeO	6.16	5.90	1.38	4.66	3.84	5.08	7.14	0.17
MnO	0.24	0.36	0.45	0.53	0.29	0.99	0.28	0.02
MgO	1.05	1.33	0.11	0.81	7.02	9.96	4.03	21.03
CaO	0.68	1.07	1.16	2.89	22.26	22.55	4.07	31.37
Na_2O	0.35	2.33	3.75	1.62	1.75	0.38	2.50	tr.
K_2O	2.13	2.92	4.89	5.41	0.37	0.42	2.04	tr.
P_2O_5	0.11	0.12	0.14	0.26	0.05	0.13	tr.	tr.
H_2O+	2.17	0.65	0.25	0.47	0.59	0.45	} 0.07	n.d.
H_2O-	0.40	0.02	0.04	0.03	0.05	0.02		n.d.
CO_2	0.02	0.01	–	–	0.43	0.81	n.d.	46.04
Total	100.17	100.03	100.07	99.91	100.20	99.92	100.73	99.50

1, 2. ADAMS (1929, p. 489). Analyst, E. G. RADLEY.
3, 4. ADAMS (1929, p. 486). Analyst, E. G. RADLEY.
5, 6. COORAY (1961a, p. 44). Analyst, J. P. R. FONSEKA.
7. COORAY (1961a, p. 52). Analyst, J. P. R. FONSEKA.
8. COORAY (1961a, p. 37). Analyst, J. P. R. FONSEKA.
tr., trace.
n.d., not determined.

TABLE 5

Chemical composition of charnockites and associated rocks in Ceylon

Weight %

Constituent	Charnockites				Charnockitic biotite gneiss	Bintenne gneiss	Amphibolite	Ultramafic dike
	1	2	3	4	5	6	7	8
	Culvert 34/2, Kandy–Weragantota road	1.6 km from Haputale	Galboda Estate, Rangala	Lebanon Estate, Madulkele	Dambutulu-gala	Gal-Oya	Culvert 36/8, Kandy–Weragantota road	Bambrella division, Knuckles group
SiO_2	73.11	69.10	61.56	48.43	69.41	71.00	45.83	46.78
Al_2O_3	14.19	11.69	13.30	18.30	12.70	14.51	16.00	4.96
TiO_2	0.97	1.23	1.65	0.84	0.05	0.07	0.78	0.16
Fe_2O_3	0.82	2.63	0.56	0.23	0.26	0.91	5.02	7.83
FeO	1.30	3.38	9.25	9.88	4.27	1.75	9.32	4.29
MnO	0.05	0.04	0.60	0.75	0.05	0.17	1.03	0.52
MgO	0.50	1.26	1.71	7.58	1.40	0.95	5.61	12.89
CaO	2.26	2.62	6.93	10.97	3.52	1.70	10.93	19.63
Na_2O	3.12	3.59	1.80	2.39	2.51	3.58	2.85	0.92
K_2O	3.32	4.55	1.40	0.49	3.69	5.46	1.47	0.70
P_2O_5	tr.	0.05	0.38	0.02	1.13	–	0.02	0.03
H_2O+	0.31	0.28	0.54	0.35	0.44	0.59	0.54	0.17
H_2O-	0.13	0.16	0.11	0.10	0.06	0.04	0.12	0.13
CO_2	–	–	–	–	–	–	0.56	0.47
Total	100.08	100.58	99.79	100.33	99.49	100.73	100.08	99.48

1. COORAY (1961a, p. 76). Analyst, J. P. R. FONSEKA.
2. ADAMS (1929, p. 481). Analyst, R. J. C. FABRY.
3. 4. COORAY (1961a, p. 76). Analyst, J. P. R. FONSEKA.
5. VITANAGE (1959, p. 39). Analyst, O. C. WICKREMASINGHE.
6. VITANAGE (1959, p. 43). Analyst, O. C. WICKREMASINGHE.
7. COORAY (1961a, p. 84). Analyst, J. P. R. FONSEKA.
8. COORAY (1961a, p. 99). Analyst, J. P. R. FONSEKA.

tr., trace.

silicic rocks to mafic rocks and are characterized by relatively low total alkali-metal contents and by a low $K_2O:Na_2O$ ratio.

The memoir by COORAY (1961a) on the geology of the country around Rangala contains chemical analyses of calcium silicate granulites and gneisses, garnet granulites and khondalites, charnockites, and amphibolites (see Tables 4 and 5). The chemical composition of the garnet granulites and khondalites shows that these rocks are metamorphic derivatives of very aluminum-rich sediments. Some of the graphite schists interbedded with garnet–sillimanite gneisses and charnockites contain as much as 10% graphite and appreciable quantities of pyrite. The high carbon content and the presence of pyrite suggest that the graphite schists were originally sapropelic sediments formed in an oxygen-deficient environment.

According to COORAY (1961a, p. 78), the mafic charnockites appear to be an integral part of the metasedimentary succession, and their chemical composition indicates that they have a common origin either as sediments rich in iron, magnesium, and calcium, such as marls, or as contemporaneous lava flows or tuffs. The intermediate and silicic charnockites have probably been derived by the migmatization of mafic charnockites, a process which has involved the addition of Si, Al, and K and the removal of Ca, Mg, and Fe from the mafic charnockites. The $Fe_2O_3:FeO$ ratio is low (<0.3) in most charnockites, a fact which, according to GOLDSCHMIDT (1954), is indicative of high-temperature metamorphism.

6. Structural geology

By using certain bands of crystalline limestones as marker beds, ADAMS (1929) interpreted the geological structure of Ceylon as a great syncline whose axis runs throughout the length of the island in a general N.–S. direction. The syncline closes in the south by the great sweep of inward-dipping strata around the southern part of Ceylon. The fold is open toward the north, where the strike of the gneiss diverges. The syncline thus plunges toward the north and disappears beneath Miocene strata at the northern end of Ceylon. Flanking the central axis of this great syncline, there are several minor parallel anticlines and synclines.

The geological map published by COATES (1935) shows that the strike of the charnockites in the southwestern part of Ceylon follows that of the schists and gradually changes from west-northwest in the extreme south to north-northwest near Colombo. North of Colombo the strike continues in the Wanni gneiss area as a sinuous curve which veers as far as north-northeast, but returns to N.–S. in the most northerly exposures.

In the provisional geological map (see Fig. 1) of FERNANDO (1948) the limestone bands are conspicuously picked out, and the map shows that the axis of the main syncline is itself folded in a crescent shape. In the northern parts of Ceylon the trend of the Precambrian strata corresponds to the strike direction in the Eastern Ghats of Peninsular India.

According to OLIVER (1957), in the eastern and western parts of Ceylon, which are occupied by members of the Vijayan series, E.–W. trends prevail and several incipient dome or arcuate structures are present; the granitization of the rocks of the Vijayan series took place during the operation of N.–S.-directed pressures which affected the rocks of the Khondalite group only to the extent of causing undulation of the fold axes. It appears that domes or arcuate structures could be produced by the differential upward movements of granitized material in a manner somewhat analogous to the ascent of salt plugs and domes. The main trends and fold axes of the Precambrian rocks of Ceylon are shown in Fig. 6.

In the Rangala area described by COORAY (1961a) there are major differences in the tectonic style of the rocks of the Highland series in the west and of the Vijayan series in the east. The former rocks are thrown into a series of regular folds which belong to the N.N.W.–S.S.E.-trending fold system which COOMARASWAMY (1906) called the Taprobanian. In the Vijayan series, however, no regular fold system is discernible, even though the dominant trend of the rocks is similar to that of the Highland series. The foliation planes are vertical or very steep, and the axes of the minor folds plunge in several directions. Where the rocks are strongly granitized, the foliation planes and banding of the gneisses are highly contorted. These structural differences are considered as probable results of the varying degree of metamorphism of the two groups.

7. Geochronology

Until about 1955 it was thought that the Khondalite series in Ceylon is younger than the Vijayan series and overlies the latter in a much folded synclinorial basin. Recent investigations, however, appear to cast doubt on this assumption. The potassium–argon dating of mica from a microcline gneiss from the Polonnaruwa area belonging to the Vijayan gneiss yielded an age of (620 ± 25) Myr, which indicates that the Vijayan series suffered metamorphism (and granitization and migmatization) about 600 Myr ago. There is also the possibility that the Vijayan gneisses are not basement rocks but constitute a younger series of granitized and migmatized rocks, even though such a generalization is not justified without more data. As usual in such instances, care has to be taken to distinguish between the age of the original rock and the age, or ages, of subsequent metamorphism.

The potassium–argon dating of the mica from the zircon granites and pegmatites associated with the Khondalite series also yielded similar ages, viz. from (618 ± 25) Myr to (632 ± 25) Myr. This Late Precambrian age probably dates the youngest cycle of granitization (potassium metasomatism) of the khondalite metasediments of the eastern part of Ceylon (VITANAGE, 1959, p. 58).

The mica in the conformable pink granite pegmatites associated with the

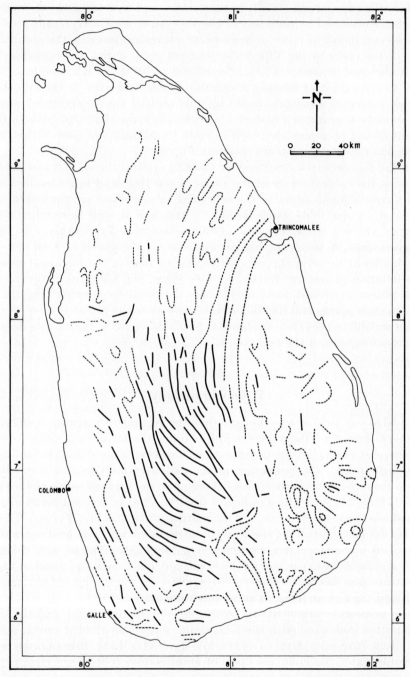

FIG. 6. Tectonic map of Ceylon showing the main trends (interrupted lines) and fold axes (thick lines) of the Precambrian rocks. According to OLIVER (1957).

Dambulla–Habarana migmatitic garnet–sillimanite–biotite gneisses yielded a lower age, viz (563 ± 25) Myr, than the age of the mica in the microcline gneisses. This low age may indicate the date of the plastic folding and migmatization of this belt of khondalites (VITANAGE, 1959, p. 58). It is significant that potassium feldspar from an augen gneiss in the N.–S.-running shear zone in the khondalite–charnockite metasedimentary belt also yielded an age in the same range, viz (520±50) Myr.

The potassium feldspar from an allanite–biotite–feldspar pegmatite in the charnockitic biotite gneiss area in Polonnaruwa gave an age of (510±50) Myr, which is consistent with the uranium–lead ages of the zircons and thorianites from the southwestern part of Ceylon. The marked similarity in the ages of the minerals from the granite pegmatites is strongly suggestive of a Cambrian pegmatite cycle common to Ceylon and, probably, southern India, and possibly extending into, or being renewed in, the Early Ordovician.

Thorianites, mainly from the Balangoda and Galle districts, yielded an average uncorrected age of 490 Myr, the range being from 355 Myr to 580 Myr (HOLMES, 1955, pp. 100–101). Their most probable age, according to HOLMES, is 485 Myr.

WETHERILL (1954, p. 683) determined the uncorrected age of a sample of monazite from Ceylon as 535 Myr and its isotopic lead age as (495±50) Myr. Because the age of some monazites of Travancore is about 500 Myr or less, it is probable that the Balangoda group of granite pegmatites of Early Ordovician age is represented in southern India also (see p. 46).

The average age of 21 gem-quality crystals of zircon from Ceylon, determined by the LARSEN method, is about 561 Myr, and the age of 12 of them, corrected for the estimated thorium content, is 574 Myr (GOTTFRIED, SENFTLE, and WARING, 1956, p. 160). The ages of a specimen of the Ceylon zircon were determined by TILTON and ALDRICH (1955, p. 531) as 540 Myr, 544 Myr, 555 Myr, and 538 Myr, from the $^{206}Pb/^{238}U$, $^{207}Pb/^{235}U$, $^{207}Pb/^{206}Pb$, and $^{208}Pb/^{232}Th$ ratios, respectively. The probable true age was given as 550 Myr (TILTON and others, 1957, p. 369).

A new gemstone from Ceylon named ekanite was described by ANDERSON and his co-workers (1961) and GÜBELIN (1962). The mineral is remarkable in that it contains 28% ThO_2, 3% UO_3, and 0.65% PbO. Its ages, as calculated from the $^{207}Pb/^{206}Pb$, $^{206}Pb/^{238}U$, $^{207}Pb/^{235}U$, and $^{208}U/^{232}Th$ ratios, are (560±50) Myr, 560 Myr, 565 Myr, and 531 Myr, respectively. These ages are in fair agreement with the ages obtained by GOTTFRIED, SENFTLE, and WARING (1956) and TILTON and ALDRICH (1955) for the Ceylon zircons.

A fairly consistent age of (530±30) Myr has been obtained for some of the Ceylon micas, potassium feldspars, thorianites, monazites, zircons, and ekanites. The granite pegmatites containing these minerals probably represent a period of widespread plutonic activity which has been recognized in India (HOLMES, 1955, pp. 102–103), Madagascar (HOLMES and CAHEN, 1955), East Africa (CAHEN, 1961, p. 543), Western Australia (GRACE, 1940),

Antarctica (NICOLAYSEN and others, 1961, pp. 96–97; STARIK and others, 1961, pp. 578–581), and Brazil (MARBLE, 1954).

The main Khondalite series has not yet been dated. A zircon concentrate from black sand on the southwestern coast of Ceylon was analysed by A. HOLMES and R. W. LAWSON in 1914, and its uncorrected age was calculated as 1,050 Myr (HOLMES, 1955, p. 101). The zircon concentrate was of mixed origin, some of the zircon being derived from the younger zircon-bearing granites and pegmatites, and some from the khondalites, charnockites, and associated gneisses, granites, and pegmatites. The most probable age of the thorianites from the Balangoda and Galle districts is 485 Myr (see p. 115). The Khondalite series of Ceylon must, therefore, be very much older than 1,050 Myr, an age which is consistent with the age of similar rocks of the Eastern Ghats belt of India.

8. Metamorphism

The metamorphic status of the Precambrian rocks of Ceylon is comparable with that of the rocks of the Eastern Ghats belt of Peninsular India. There is a close correspondence in the rock types and in the structural trends of the two regions. The work of COORAY (1962) in Ceylon has indicated that it is probable that at one time charnockites occurred throughout the area covered at present by Precambrian rocks.

In the Highland series the charnockites are characteristic products of granulite-facies metamorphism. The majority of the rocks of the Highland series belong to the pyroxene-granulite subfacies of FYFE, TURNER, and VERHOOGEN (1958). There are certain rocks of lower facies such as amphibolites and granitic gneisses which have formed retrogressively.

The rocks of the Vijayan series (granites, granitic gneisses, and migmatites) have been derived from preexisting rocks of the granulite facies by widespread migmatization and granitization under almandine-amphibolite facies conditions and in the presence of water. In this process pyroxene granulites were transformed to amphibolites, and charnockites were first modified to charnockitic biotite gneisses and finally to leucocratic gneisses.

The transitional zone between the Highland series and the Vijayan series is predominantly composed of charnockitic biotite gneisses which were produced by the retrogressive metamorphism of charnockites, probably in the presence of water. The ultimate result of such diaphthoretic changes was the disappearance of charnockites and charnockitic rocks by their conversion to leucocratic biotite gneisses and biotite–hornblende gneisses.

In the southwestern belt the metasediments and charnockites resemble those of the Highland series, but the widespread development of hornblende and biotite suggests conditions of the hornblende–granulite subfacies. The migmatites bear evidence of having reached a metamorphic grade as low as almandine–amphibolite facies.

9. Mineralization and mineral deposits

9.1. *General*

Graphite and precious stones are the principal minerals produced in Ceylon. Large deposits of ilmenite, rutile, monazite, and zircon occur in the beach sands. The lanthanide minerals are characteristic of Ceylon.

9.2. *Gems and semiprecious stones*

Ceylon is famous for the abundance of a variety of precious and semi-precious stones. Probably there is no other place in the world where so many minerals of gem quality are concentrated in such a comparatively small area. Almost the entire elliptical gem-bearing region of Ceylon falls within the Ratnapura district. The gemstones are believed to have formed in rocks belonging to the Khondalite series, either as primary constituents or in the zone of igneous contacts, or in the associated granite pegmatites. The precious stones, however, occur rarely in the parent matrix, but are obtained from old alluvial deposits of rivers draining a basin of gem-bearing crystalline rocks.

The gemstones found in Ceylon include sapphire, ruby, chrysoberyl, alexandrite, cat's-eye, beryl, emerald, aquamarine, topaz, tourmaline, garnet, zircon, amethyst, moonstone, and ekanite. Traditional methods of mining and cutting are still employed. No production figures are available, but exports of precious and semiprecious stones during 1962 amounted to 227,803 carats.

9.3. *Graphite*

Graphite mining is the largest and most important mineral industry in Ceylon. The deposits are the biggest and most productive in the world, and Ceylon has been the world's principal source of graphite for several decades. The entire production of graphite is exported. The quantity of graphite exported in 1962 was 8,630 tons.

Usually the graphite veins are remarkably persistent for several kilometers along the strike of the country rocks, and this directional trend is noticeable even when the deposits are isolated pockets and lenses, and not continuous veins. The graphite was introduced into the natural divisional planes of the rocks and is epigenetic in origin. It may have been derived from the original carbonaceous sediments of the Khondalite series, as suggested by the fact that graphite scales and flakes are disseminated in crystalline limestones, calcium silicate granulites, schists, and sillimanite gneisses which are members of the Khondalite series. Graphite occurs also in pegmatites and in quartz veins, but such deposits are not of economic importance.

9.4. *Ilmenite, rutile, and zircon*

Along the coasts of Ceylon the beach sands at several places contain much ilmenite, rutile, and zircon derived from disintegrated crystalline rocks in which they occurred as primary constituents. Some of these black sand deposits comprise 75%–80% ilmenite, 6%–10% rutile, and 6%–7% zircon.

Ilmenite is widely distributed as fine grains and crystals in the rocks of the Charnockite series, and in the gneisses, granulites, and crystalline limestones. It is present in many pegmatites and quartz veins, sometimes as masses weighing more than 50 kg. Picroilmenite, arizonite ($Fe_2Ti_3O_9$), and titanian magnetite which is vanadium-bearing also occur in Ceylon.

Zircon is a common accessory mineral in many granites and gneisses and in the aplitic and pegmatitic derivatives of the granites. It is also present in the charnockites.

9.5. *Lanthanide minerals*

Ceylon is specially rich in lanthanide minerals. Among them mention may be made of monazite, xenotime, allanite, aeschynite, gadolinite, thorianite, thorite, fergusonite, and uraninite.

Monazite occurs as an accessory mineral in some granites and gneisses, and as well-formed crystals in the pegmatites which intrude the khondalite rocks in some localities in southwestern Ceylon. It is also a constituent of the granulites. It contains on an average about 10% ThO_2, and in its thorium content resembles the monazite from the Travancore coast of India. Monazite-bearing sands occur along the southwest coast of Ceylon. They are seasonal concentrates and are collected during the southwest monsoon months, namely from May to July. Thorianite was first discovered in Ceylon. Its U_3O_8 content varies from 11% to 35%, and the rest is ThO_2. Ekanite, a new gem mineral discovered in Ceylon is rich in thorium (see p. 115).

Bibliography

ADAMS, F. D. (1926). Note on the origin of the graphite veins of Ceylon. *Bull. Can. Inst. Mining Met.* **168**, 496.

ADAMS, F. D. (1929). The geology of Ceylon. *Can. J. Res.* **1**, 425.

ANDERSON, B. W., CLARINGBULL, G. F., DAVIS, R. J., and HILL, D. K. (1961). Ekanite, a new metamict mineral from Ceylon. *Nature* **190**, 997.

BASTIN, E. S. (1912). The graphite deposits of Ceylon. *Econ. Geol.* **7**, 419.

BOURNON, COMTE DE (1823). *Observations sur quelques-uns des minéraux, soit de l'île de Ceylan, soit de la côte de Coromandel, rapportés par M. Leschenault de la Tour.* Paris.

CAHEN, L. (1961). Review of geochronological knowledge in middle and northern Africa. *Ann. N.Y. Acad. Sci.* **91**, 535.

COATES, J. S. (1926). *Sessional Paper VI—Monazite, ilmenite and zircon in Ceylon.* Colombo.

COATES, J. S. (1935). The geology of Ceylon. *Ceylon J. Sci.* **19**, 101.

COOMARASWAMY, A. K. (1900). Ceylon rocks and graphite. *Quart. J. Geol. Soc.* **56**, 590.

COOMARASWAMY, A. K. (1902a). The crystalline limestones of Ceylon. *Quart. J. Geol. Soc.* **58**, 399.

COOMARASWAMY, A. K. (1902b). Origin of the crystalline limestones of Ceylon. *Geol. Mag.* **9**, 375.

COOMARASWAMY, A. K. (1902c). The Point de Galle Group (Ceylon); wollastonite–scapolite gneisses. *Quart. J. Geol. Soc.* **58**, 680.

COOMARASWAMY, A. K. (1903). Occurrence of corundum *in situ* near Kandy. *Geol. Mag.* **10**, 348.

COOMARASWAMY, A. K. (1904a). The crystalline rocks of Ceylon. *Spolia Zeylanica* **1**, 105.

COOMARASWAMY, A. K. (1904b). Uraninite (thorianite). *Spolia Zeylanica* **1**, 112.

COOMARASWAMY, A. K. (1904c). The Balangoda Group. *Geol. Mag.* **1**, 418.

COOMARASWAMY, A. K. (1905a). The rocks and minerals of Ceylon. *Spolia Zeylanica* **3**, 50.

COOMARASWAMY, A. K. (1905b). Intrusive pyroxenites, mica pyroxenites, and mica rocks in the Charnockite Series or granulites of Ceylon. *Geol. Mag.* **2**, 363.

COOMARASWAMY, A. K. (1906). *Administration Report, Mineralogical Survey, Ceylon.*

COORAY, P. G. (1954). The nature and occurrence of some charnockite rocks from Ceylon. *Proc. Pan-Indian Sci. Congr.* Section C, 52.

COORAY, P. G. (1959). Charnockite–quartzite association in the Rangala–Madulkele area, Ceylon. *J. Geol. Soc. India* **1**, 126.

COORAY, P. G. (1960). Khondalites and charnockites of the Laggala–Pallegama area, Ceylon. *Bull. Mysore Geologists' Assoc.* **18**.

COORAY, P. G. (1961a). Geology of the country around Rangala. *Mem. Geol. Surv. Ceylon* **2**.

COORAY, P. G. (1961b). The mode of emplacement of some dykes and veins in the Precambrian rocks of Ceylon. *Proc. Geologists' Assoc. (Engl.)* **72**, 73.

COORAY, P. G. (1962). Charnockites and their associated gneisses in the Precambrian of Ceylon. *Quart. J. Geol. Soc.* **118**, 239.

DAVY, J. (1818). Description of certain rocks in the south of Ceylon. *Quart. J. Sci.* **5**, 233.

DAVY, J. (1821). On the geology and mineralogy of Ceylon. *Geol. Trans.* **5**, 311.

DICK, A. (1892). On Geikielite, a new mineral from Ceylon. *Mineral. Mag.* **10**, 148.

DIERCHE, M. (1898). Beitrag zur Kenntniss der Gesteine und Graphitvorkomnisse Ceylons. *Jahrb. Reichanstalt* **48**, 231.

DIXON, A. C. (1880). The rocks and minerals of Ceylon. *J. Roy. Asiatic Soc., Ceylon* **6**.

DUNSTAN, W. R. and BLAKE, G. S. (1905). Thorianite, a new mineral from Ceylon. *Proc. Roy. Soc.* **76**, 253.

DUNSTAN, W. R. and JONES, B. M. (1906). A variety of thorianite from Galle, Ceylon. *Proc. Roy. Soc.* **77**, 546.

FERMOR, L. L. (1909). The manganese ore deposits of India. *Mem. Geol. Surv. India* **37**.

FERMOR, L. L. (1936). An attempt at the correlation of the ancient schistose formations of Peninsular India. *Mem. Geol. Surv. India* **70**.

FERNANDO, L. J. D. (1948). The geology and mineral deposits of Ceylon. *Bull. Imp. Inst. London* **46**, 303.

FLETCHER, L. (1892). On baddeleyite, a new mineral from Rakwana, Ceylon. *Mineral. Mag.* **10**, 148.

FYFE, W. S., TURNER, F. J., and VERHOOGEN, J. (1958). Metamorphic reactions and metamorphic facies. *Mem. Geol. Soc. Am.* **73**.

GOLDSCHMIDT, V. M. (1954). *Geochemistry.* Oxford.

GOTTFRIED, D., SENFTLE, F. E., and WARING, C. L. (1956). Age determination of zircon crystals from Ceylon. *Am. Mineralogist* **41**, 157.

GRACE, J. N. A. (1940). Occurrence of xenotime in Western Australia. *J. Roy. Soc. W. Australia* **26**, 95.

GRÜNLING, F. (1900). Uber die Mineralvorkommen von Ceylon. *Z. Krist.* **33**, 209.

GÜBELIN, E. J. (1962). Ekanite. *The Gemmologist* **31**, 142.

GYGAX, R. (1847). On the mineralogy of Ceylon. *J. Roy. Asiatic Soc., Ceylon* **1**, 1.

HENDERSON, L. (1848). On ceylonite found near Trincomalee. *J. Roy. Asiatic Soc., Ceylon* **2**, 97.

HOLLAND, T. H. (1900). The charnockite series, a group of Archaean hypersthenic rocks in Peninsular India. *Mem. Geol. Surv. India* **28**, 119.

HOLMES, A. (1955). Dating the Precambrian of Peninsular India and Ceylon. *Proc. Geol. Assoc. Can.* **7**, 81.

HOLMES, A. and CAHEN, L. (1955). African geochronology. *Colonial Geol. Mineral Resources* **5**, 3.

HOLMES, A. and LAWSON, R. W. (1914). Lead and the end product of thorium. *Phil. Mag.* **28**, 823.

IMPERIAL INSTITUTE, LONDON (1904). Occurrence of thorium in Ceylon. *Bull.* **2**, 13.

IMPERIAL INSTITUTE, LONDON (1905). Occurrence and uses of minerals containing thorium. *Bull.* **3**, 151.

IMPERIAL INSTITUTE, LONDON (1906). Varieties of Ceylon graphite and their uses. *Bull.* **4**, 355.

IMPERIAL INSTITUTE, LONDON (1907). Ceylon graphite and its uses. *Bull.* **5**, 17.

IMPERIAL INSTITUTE, LONDON (1916). Monazite and other minerals in Ceylon. *Bull.* **14**, 321.

LACROIX, A. (1891). Gneissose rocks of Salem and Ceylon. *Records Geol. Surv. India* **24**, 157.

MACVICAR, J. G. (1904). *On Ceylon, its geology, scenery and soil.* Colombo.

MARBLE, J. P. (1954). Recent analyses of Brazilian radioactive minerals. Report Comm. Measurement Geol. Time, 1952–53. *Natl. Res. Council, Natl. Acad. Sci. (U.S.) Publ.* No. 319, 143.

MIDDLEMISS, C. S. (1903). *The rocks on the Kadugannawa incline.* Colombo.

MODDER, F. H. (1897). A geological and mineralogical sketch of the Northwestern Province, Ceylon. *J. Roy. Asiatic Soc., Ceylon* **15**, 39.

NEVILL, H. (1871). Notes on the geological origin of Southwest Ceylon, together with its relation to the rest of the island. *J. Roy. Asiatic Soc., Ceylon* **5**, 11.

NICOLAYSEN, L. O., BURGER, A. U., TATSUMI, T., and AHRENS, L. H. (1961). Age measurements on pegmatites and a basic charnockite lens occurring near Lutzow–Holm Bay, Antarctica. *Geochim. Cosmochim. Acta* **22**, 94.

OLIVER, R. L. (1957). The geological structure of Ceylon. *Ceylon Geogr.* **11**, 9.

PARKINSON, J. (1901). Notes on the geology of south-central Ceylon. *Quart. J. Geol. Soc.* **57**, 204.

PRIOR, G. T. (1903). Fergusonite from Ceylon. *Mineral. Mag.* **10**, 234.

PRIOR, G. T. and COOMARASWAMY, A. K. (1903). Serendibite, a new borosilicate from Ceylon. *Mineral. Mag.* **13**, 224.

SPENCER, E. (1930). A contribution to the study of moonstone from Ceylon. *Mineral. Mag.* **22**, 291.

SPENCER, L. J. (1904). Irregularly developed crystals of zircon from Ceylon. *Mineral. Mag.* **14**, 43.

STARIK, I. Y., KRYLOV, A. Y., RAVICH, M. G., and SILIN, Y. I. (1961). The absolute ages of East Antarctic rocks. *Ann. N.Y. Acad. Sci.* **91**, 576.

TILTON, G. R. and ALDRICH. L. T. (1955). The reliability of zircons as age indicators. *Trans. Am. Geophys. Union* **36**, 531.

TILTON, G. R., DAVIS, G. L., WETHERILL, G. W., and ALDRICH, L. T. (1957). Isotopic ages of zircon from granites and pegmatites. *Trans. Am. Geophys. Union* **38**, 360.

VITANAGE, P. W. (1957). Studies of zircon types in the Ceylon Precambrian complex. *J. Geol.* **65**, 117.

VITANAGE, P. W. (1959). Geology of the country around Polonnaruwa. *Mem. Geol. Surv. Ceylon* **1**.

VREDENBURG, E. (1904). Gem sands from Ceylon. *Records Geol. Surv. India* **31**, 44.

WADIA, D. N. (1940). *Administration Report of the Government Mineralogist [Ceylon] for 1939.* p. 16.

WADIA, D. N. (1941a). *Administration Report of the Government Mineralogist [Ceylon] for 1940.* p. 16.

WADIA, D. N. (1941b). The making of Ceylon. *Spolia Zeylanica* **23**, 1.

WADIA, D. N. (1942). The making of India. General Presidential address. *Proc. Indian Sci. Congr., 29th* **2**, 3.

WADIA, D. N. (1943a). Rare earth minerals of Ceylon. *Records Dept. Mineral., Ceylon, Profess. Paper* **1**, 3.

WADIA, D. N. (1943b). A brief account of the mineralogy of graphite deposits of Ceylon—a note on the origin of the graphite. *Records Dept. Mineral., Ceylon, Profess. Paper* **1**, 15.

WADIA, D. N. (1943c). The three superposed peneplains of Ceylon—their physiography and geological structure. *Records Dept. Mineral., Ceylon, Profess. Paper* **1**, 25.

WADIA, D. N. and FERNANDO, L. J. D. (1944a). Ilmenite, monazite and zircon. *Records Dept. Mineral., Ceylon, Profess. Paper* **2**, 3.

WADIA, D. N. and FERNANDO, L. J. D. (1944b). Gems and semi-precious stones of Ceylon. *Records Dept. Mineral., Ceylon, Profess. Paper* **2**, 13.

WALKER, T. L. (1902). The geology of Kalahandi State, Central Provinces. *Mem. Geol. Surv. India* **33**, 1.

WASHINGTON, H. S. (1916). The charnockite series of igneous rocks. *Am. J. Sci.* **41**, 323.

WETHERILL, G. W. (1954). Variations in the isotopic abundances of neon and argon extracted from radioactive minerals. *Phys. Rev.* **96**, 679.

E

THE PRECAMBRIAN OF
THE SEYCHELLES ARCHIPELAGO[1]

B. H. Baker

Mines and Geological Department, Nairobi, Kenya

Contents

1. Introduction

1.1. *General information*

The Seychelles Archipelago is situated in the western Indian Ocean between latitudes 4° S. and 11° S. and longitudes 46° E. and 58° E., and consists of well over 100 islands within a belt nearly 700 mi. in length (see Fig. 1). The archipelago is composed of four main island groups, namely the Mahé–Praslin group containing the larger granitic islands in the northeast, and the Amirantes, Farquhar–Providence, and Astove–Aldabra groups to the west and the south-west. The Mahé–Praslin group is the largest and most important island group, and consists of 24 inhabited islands composed mainly of Precambrian granite, Mahé being the largest of these with an area of 56 mi.² out of the total area of the archipelago of some 156 mi.² The other islands are relatively recently formed sand cays built on atolls or patch-reefs, or are elevated reefs.

[1] Manuscript received May 4, 1962. Revised manuscript received July 23, 1962. Published by permission of the Officer Administering the Government of the Seychelles.

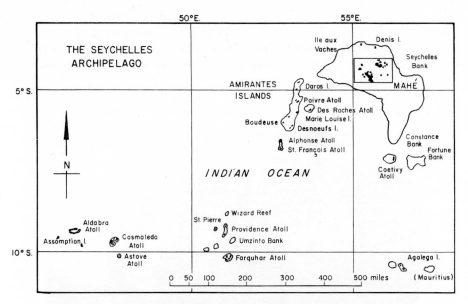

FIG. 1. Map of the Seychelles Archipelago.

Topographically the islands are rugged and rise steeply from the sea to altitudes approaching 3,000 ft. The land forms are typical of homogeneous rock massifs subjected to tropical weathering, and steep rocky slopes descend unbroken to the coast. Valleys follow a rectilinear pattern controlled by joints and dykes. The zone of weathering is thick, and the slopes are commonly littered with granite boulders derived by the eluviation of the subsoil from the weathered mantle. In the interior of the islands, however, there are many cliffs and bare rock pavements (see Fig. 2) between which the steep slopes are clothed with dense tropical rain forest. The subsoil is lateritic in appearance, being composed of iron-bearing bauxitic and kaolinic clays which commonly retain the textures of the parent rocks. Behind the fringing reefs there are discontinuous coastal flats composed of coral sand, on which most of the agriculture takes place.

1.2. *Previous work*

CHARLES DARWIN (1889, pp. 235–237) summarized the knowledge about the reefs of the Seychelles, basing his account on the reports of other observers, for he did not visit the archipelago himself. VELAIN (1879) was the first geologist to publish petrographic accounts of the Mahé granite. He was followed by BAUER (1898), who examined the rock collection made by the German zoologist A. BRAUER. MILLER and MUDIE (1961) carried out potassium–argon datings on Mahé and Praslin granites and on the Silhouette syenite, finding that the Mahé granite is Late Precambrian in age.

BAKER and MILLER (1963) summarized the geology of the main islands, presented new age data, and discussed the origin of the Seychelles Bank.

A summary of the work carried out by geophysicists working with the International Indian Ocean Expedition on the Seychelles Bank and between the East African coast and the Seychelles was given by DAVIES (1964).

A comprehensive survey of the geology of the whole Archipelago was made by BAKER (1963).

FIG. 2. The northern part of Mahé Island, Seychelles Archipelago, seen from Copolia trigonometrical beacon. Port Victoria, the capital town of the Seychelles, is in the centre of the photograph. In the foreground, large exfoliation surfaces of Mahé granite.

2. Geology

2.1. *General remarks*

The oldest rocks of the archipelago are the granites that form the Mahé–Praslin island group (see Fig. 3). For these granites radiometric dating yielded an age exceeding 510 Myr (MILLER and MUDIE, 1961). Three types of granite are recognized, viz. the grey Mahé granite, the faintly gneissose St. Anne–Ile aux Cerf granite, and the reddish Praslin–La Digue granite. The three types are closely related mineralogically and are regarded as congeneric and, in the absence of evidence of any contacts between them, as facies of the same intrusion. The granites are penetrated by numbers of dolerite dykes and metadolerite dykes, but dolerites are absent in the syenite and microgranite which form the Silhouette and Ile du Nord islands in the western part of the group, because the syenite and microgranite are younger than the dolerites and have been dated as Early Tertiary (BAKER and MILLER, 1963).

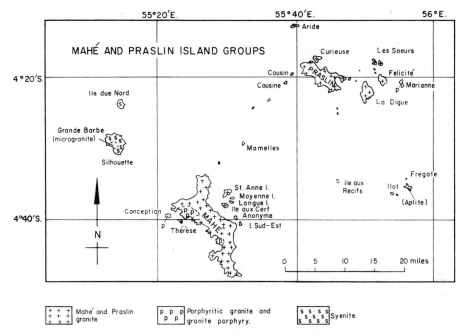

FIG. 3. Geological sketch map of the Mahé–Praslin Island group, Seychelles Archipelago.

2.2. *The Mahé granite*

The island of Mahé is composed of an homogeneous hornblende granite which grades into a porphyritic rock in two small areas. The typical granite is a pale grey rock, locally slightly darker grey in colour. The grain size varies between 4 mm and 7 mm, and the texture is hypidiomorphic-granular, with a tendency to develop subhedral feldspar insets locally. The quartz grains tend to occur in sub-rounded aggregates.

In outcrops the granite forms cliffs and rock pavements showing sub-horizontal sheet structure in some areas. Normally, however, the granite is traversed only by widely spaced joints, but well-developed vertical fluting of rock surfaces by rain-water erosion is often seen.

Certain zones in the granite contain numerous flow-aligned xenoliths, particularly in northern Mahé, along parts of the north-western coast near Bel Ombre, and in isolated localities elsewhere. The xenoliths are mostly dioritic, but some zones contain large numbers of small medium-grained epidiorite xenoliths, and the majority of xenoliths appear to have been derived from mafic igneous rocks and to have been modified to hornblendic hybrids of intermediate or silicic composition. The granite in the immediate vicinity of the larger xenoliths is frequently desilicified, the commonest type observed being a hornblende diorite with flow-aligned hornblende prisms.

In the area of Port Glaud, Port Launay, and Mare Cochons, and forming the off-shore islands of Therese and Conception, the granite is porphyritic, with subhedral microperthite insets up to 10 mm in diameter set in a fine granular matrix of quartz, oligoclase, and hornblende. A similar but smaller area of porphyritic granite occurs at Anse Louis, and in both areas the granite grades imperceptibly into the normal variety.

Mineralogically the granite shows little variation, the main minerals being microperthite, quartz, and oligoclase, with minor amounts of hastingsite, biotite, and ilmenite, and with epidote, zircon, and sphene as accessory minerals. The microperthite is often poorly twinned on the Carlsbad law and displays sometimes patch perthite and inversion to microcline. It is rarely euhedral, but has sutured margins with drop-like inclusions of quartz or rarely a partial marginal overgrowth of albite. Quartz occurs as rounded aggregates of grains which show slight optical strain, and sometimes it forms myrmekitic intergrowths with plagioclase in intergranular spaces.

Plagioclase occurs mainly in the patch perthite, but where it is found as discrete grains it is in the form of small tabular oligoclase crystals, or more rarely as large tabular insets in the adamellites and granodiorites of xeno-lithic areas. The green ferroan hastingsite occurs as small intergranular aggregates, often with fibrous outgrowths. It is characteristically associated with ilmenite and sphene and is intergrown with biotite in some rock specimens.

The granite of the islands of St. Anne, L'Ile Moyenne, Round, L'Ile Longue, and Ile aux Cerf, off the north-eastern coast of Mahé, is distinguish-able from the Mahé granite only by its slightly gneissose appearance in some exposures, caused by patches and streaks of slightly darker rock. The occur-rence of mortar structure at grain margins suggests that the gneissosity was caused by movements at a late stage in consolidation.

Non-plane aplite veins and dykes occur in all parts of the granite, but are particularly numerous in the north. Quartz veins are rare and are narrow plane veins which crystallized in tension cracks.

The chemical composition of rocks from Mahé and Ile aux Cerf is pre-sented in Table 1.

The chemical composition of the granites is comparable to that of horn-blende granites in general, but the norms indicate plagioclase in excess of orthoclase, showing that the granites tend towards granodiorite in com-position.

2.3. *The Praslin–La Digue granite*

The Praslin–La Digue group of islands to the northeast of Mahé is com-posed of ten inhabited islands, of which Praslin (14.3 mi.²) is the largest. All but Marianne Island are composed of a granite closely related to the Mahé granite but distinguished from it by a reddish colour and the presence of biotite rather than hornblende. In contrast to the Mahé granite, the micro-perthite is usually turbid and there is less oligoclase. Biotite occurs in small

TABLE 1

Chemical composition of Precambrian granitic
rocks from the Seychelles Archipelago

Weight %

Constituent	1	2	3	4	5
SiO_2	72.83	74.12	71.17	71.78	52.60
Al_2O_3	13.20	12.78	13.34	14.63	17.12
Fe_2O_3	1.09	1.40	2.03	0.91	4.19
FeO	1.50	1.28	2.20	1.32	5.52
MgO	0.05	0.08	0.28	0.09	4.30
CaO	0.95	0.51	0.92	0.97	6.99
Na_2O	4.34	4.08	4.48	4.55	3.76
K_2O	4.85	5.05	4.30	3.42	1.90
TiO_2	0.38	0.25	0.64	0.52	1.48
P_2O_5	0.04	0.04	0.09	0.05	0.68
MnO	0.12	0.08	0.15	0.10	0.23
H_2O (110° C)	0.09	0.10	0.20	0.12	0.10
Loss on ignition	0.46	0.60	0.58	0.99	0.72
Total	99.90	100.37	100.38	99.45	99.59

1. Granite. North-western end of Grand 'Anse, Mahé.
2. Granite. Near trigonometrical beacon, Ile aux Cerf.
3. Granite. Northern end of Anse aux Pins, central Mahé.
4. Granite aplite. Anse Etoile, north-eastern Mahé.
5. Quartz diorite. Baie Nord-Ouest, north-east of Bel Ombre,
    north-western Mahé.
Analyst (all rocks), G. LUENA, Geological Survey of Tanzania.

quantities as scattered flakes, and in some rocks a little hornblende is present. Granite porphyry dykes occur in northwestern Praslin, eastern Curieuse, and central Félicité as broad tabular dyke-like bodies, and aplite veins are common.

Quartz veins are numerous on Praslin and are of two types, viz. stockworks of anastomosing veins of fine-grained granular quartz trending northeast and associated with narrow shear belts, and narrow coarser-grained plane veins with vugs and well-terminated quartz crystals trending northwest and occupying tension joints.

The granite weathers into large blocks which frequently exhibit well-developed fluting caused by the action of rain-water (see Figs. 4 and 5).

Marianne Island at the eastern end of the group is composed of granite porphyry containing pink tabular orthoclase and oligoclase phenocrysts in equal amounts, and in some exposures sparse quartz phenocrysts are also visible. These minerals are set in an aplitic matrix of granular quartz and feldspar which contains granules of hornblende and wisps of biotite.

Frégate Island, at the southeastern extremity of the granitic island group, differs from the other islands in being composed of granite aplite and quartz porphyry. Aplite forms most of the island and grades locally to microgranite

FIG. 4. Part of a field of very large granite boulders at the northeastern point of La Digue, Seychelles Archipelago. The boulders
are up to 40 ft high and are the result of prolonged eluviation of the
weathered mantle. They show surface fluting caused by rain-water
erosion.

or to a patchy porphyritic rock having feldspar phenocrysts up to 4 mm in
diameter. Patches and vein stockworks of porphyritic granite occur locally
in the aplite. The quartz porphyry consists of rounded quartz phenocrysts in
a pale felsitic base and forms elongated zones with diffuse margins in the
aplite. Several dolerite dykes traverse the whole of the granitic complex.
The Frégate rocks are closely related to the Praslin–La Digue granite,
although they differ texturally and do not have the characteristic red colour.

2.4. Dolerites and metadolerites

Dolerite dykes are plentiful on nearly all of the granitic islands and occur
as dykes between 1 in and 30 ft in width injected into a N.W.-trending
joint system. Most dykes display varying degrees of alteration, the commonest change being the formation of felted prismatic uralite and more
rarely the saussuritization of feldspar with the production of much epidote
and some quartz. Several dykes on Mahé are unaltered, however, and contain olivine and a mesostasis of analcite, and are olivine alkali dolerites,
probably belonging to a separate and younger intrusive phase.

The chemical composition of dolerites is given in Table 2. The calculated
norms of the three dolerites indicate the presence of a little free quartz in
the basalt dyke and of a little olivine in the other two rocks. In composition
the dolerites closely resemble the oceanic basalts, because their SiO_2 and
K_2O contents are too low for them to be tholeiitic.

TABLE 2

Chemical composition of dyke rocks
from the Seychelles Archipelago
Weight %

Constituent	1	2	3
SiO_2	45.74	47.61	47.68
Al_2O_3	17.22	18.58	17.19
Fe_2O_3	6.28	3.36	3.13
FeO	7.84	6.90	7.95
MgO	5.13	4.28	7.52
CaO	7.67	10.23	11.21
Na_2O	3.33	3.80	2.61
K_2O	0.60	0.60	0.21
TiO_2	2.53	1.48	1.25
P_2O_5	0.73	0.72	0.02
MnO	0.22	0.16	0.19
H_2O ($+110°$ C)	0.10	0.11	0.08
Loss on ignition	2.39	2.23	1.19
Total	99.78	100.06	100.23

1. Basalt dyke. Coast south of Glacis, Mahé.
2. Porphyritic dolerite dyke. West end of L'Ile
   Longue.
3. Dolerite dyke. North end of Anse Nord-Est,
   Mahé.
Analyst (all rocks), G. LUENA, Geological Survey of Tanzania.

2.5. Structure

The only megascopically observed structures in the intrusive rocks are jointing and narrow shear zones. The gneissosity of the St. Anne–Ile aux Cerf granite is considered to be an ill-defined and irregular flow foliation.

The joint system in the Mahé and Praslin–La Digue granites consists of a W.N.W.- and N.N.W.-trending symmetrical arrangement of major and minor joints with widely spaced N.W.-trending joints. The great majority of quartz veins are narrow and planar, and occupy N.W.-trending joints. In a few places, however, quartz veins occur in N.E.-trending shear fractures. The displacement of dykes and the orientation of shear foliation of these shear fractures consistently indicate dextral movement. It is probable that the joints and shears are the result of a stress plan involving N.E.–S.W.-directed compression followed by relaxation, with an element of dextral shearing along the same lines.

FIG. 5. Massive granite boulder on the south shore of La Digue, Seychelles
Archipelago. The boulder displays pronounced vertical fluting caused
by rain-water erosion. The cliff is 25 ft high.

3. Geological synthesis

The Precambrian of the Seychelles Archipelago consists of one or more
batholiths of postorogenic type. The age of the intrusives was determined by
radiometric dating by MILLER and MUDIE (1961), who made eight datings
by the potassium–argon method on whole-rock samples and obtained
good concordant ages ranging from 495 Myr to 536 Myr and averaging 515
Myr. Datings on separated biotite that they made and three datings on
separated hornblendes (BAKER and MILLER, 1963) gave higher ages: for
biotite from the Mahé granite, 654 Myr; and for hornblende from the Mahé
granite, 509 Myr, 549 Myr, and 580 Myr. In addition a hornblende separated
from the Praslin granite yielded an age of 647 Myr. It is probable that the
higher ages around 650 Myr are close to the real age of the granites and that
the lower whole-rock ages are caused by partial loss of radiogenic argon.

Three whole-rock datings of basalt and epidiorite dykes from north-western Mahé gave ages of 647 Myr, 645 Myr, and 550 Myr, and pyroxenes from three samples of Silhouette Island syenite yielded ages of 34 Myr, 62 Myr, and 43 Myr. Two whole-rock datings on an olivine dolerite dyke on Praslin Island yielded ages of 52 Myr and 48 Myr.

The occurrence of Precambrian granites in an oceanic environment is of special geological interest. Unfortunately the reported occurrence of horn-felsic metasediments on Silhouette and Ile aux Cerf (BAUER, 1898) was not verified (BAKER, 1963). Nevertheless it must be inferred that the Seychelles granites were emplaced in a crust at least 1.5 km thick and that a substantial amount of subaerial erosion must have taken place to expose the granites at the present time, indicating that the Seychelles Archipelago was a much larger land mass in former times.

The granitic islands stand on a submarine bank called the Seychelles Bank, which lies at depths of 200 ft or less and covers an area of approximately 16,000 mi.^{2}. It is likely that this bank represents the former Seychelles land mass and that its present-day form is a result of marine and subaerial erosion, subsidence, and the growth of coral reefs. The central part of the bank is likely to be composed of granite with a metasedimentary envelope, and the outer parts of younger shelf-type sediments with coral reefs above. This conclusion has recently been verified by marine seismic refraction shots on the Seychelles Bank, which indicate a granite body at least 13 km thick, and by geomagnetic traversing, which indicates rocks of low magnetization such as granite extending over a wide area of the Bank (DAVIES, 1964).

The ages of the Silhouette syenite and of the Praslin basalt dyke indicate that the syenite–microgranite ring complex is Early Tertiary and was accompanied by alkali basalt dyke injection.

The Seychelles Archipelago is interpreted as the remnants of a former isthmus connecting India and Africa (GARDINER, 1906), or as a continental fragment left during the breakup of Gondwanaland by continental drift (MILLER and MUDIE, 1961; KING, 1962), the African affinity of the granites being suggested by their Late Precambrian age, which coincides with ages obtained from the East Africa–Mozambique orogenic belt. The structure and geological history of the East African coastal regions and of the two sides of the Mozambique Channel suggest the presence of a Mozambique "geosyncline" extending from the Mozambique Channel to the western part of the Somali basin (DIXEY, 1960). This view is based on the coastal geology of these areas, which indicates that large-scale periodic subsidences of off-shore areas have taken place, with the deposition of greatly expanded successions of Late Carboniferous–Triassic (Karroo), Jurassic, Cretaceous, and Tertiary sediments. The Seychelles Archipelago may therefore represent the partially submerged eastern rim or foreland of a broad basin of subsidence, viz. the Somali basin, comparable to Madagascar in its relation to the Mozambique Channel.

Bibliography

BAKER, B. H. (1963). Geology and Mineral Resources of the Seychelles Archipelago. *Mem. Geol. Surv. Kenya*, No. 3.

BAKER, B. H. and MILLER, J. A. (1963). Geology and Geochronology of the Seychelles Islands and the structure of the floor of the Arabian Sea. *Nature* **199**, 346.

BAUER, M. (1898). Beiträge zur Geologie der Seychellen, insbesondere zur Kenntniss des Laterits. *Neues Jahrb. Mineral. Geol.* **2**, 163.

DARWIN, C. (1889). *Coral reefs*. Third edition. London.

DAVIES, D. (1964). Geophysical discoveries in the N.W. Indian Ocean. *New Scientist* **24**, 510.

DIXEY, F. (1960). The geology and geomorphology of Madagascar, and a comparison with Eastern Africa. *Quart. J. Geol. Soc.* **116**, 255.

GARDINER, J. S. (1905). Reports of the Percy Sladen Expedition to the Indian Ocean. *Nature* **71**, 562.

GARDINER, J. S. (1906). Reports of the Percy Sladen Expedition to the Indian Ocean. *Geograph. J.* **28**, 313.

GARDINER, J. S. (1907). The Seychelles Archipelago. *Geograph. J.* **29**, 148.

GASKELL, T. F. and SWALLOW, J. C. (1953). Seismic refraction experiments in the Indian Ocean and in the Mediterranean Sea. *Nature* **172**, 535.

KING, L. C. (1962). *The morphology of the Earth*. London.

MILLER, J. A. and MUDIE, J. D. (1961). Potassium–argon age determinations on granite from the Island of Mahé in the Seychelles Archipelago. *Nature* **192**, 1174.

VELAIN, C. (1879). Notes sur la constitution géologique des Iles Seychelles. *Bull. Soc. Geol. France* **7**, 278.

WISEMAN, J. D. H. and SEWELL, R. B. S. (1937). The floor of the Arabian Sea. *Geol. Mag.* **74**, 219.

THE PRECAMBRIAN OF MADAGASCAR [1]

HENRI BESAIRIE

Service Géologique Tananarive, Malagasy Republic

Contents

1. Introduction

The Precambrian occupies two-thirds of Madagascar. It has been the object of an extensive survey accompanied by a complete mapping in the scale 1 : 200,000. The geologically most interesting areas were mapped in the scale 1 : 100,000, and that mapping is already well advanced. The Precambrian of Madagascar includes the following cycles and formations (see Fig. 1).

(1) Major orogeny with intraformational granitization, that generally produced allanite and affected a large part of the old massif. It took place 550 Myr ago.

(2) Granitization and charnockitization, that affected the extreme south and part of the eastern coast, and took place 875 Myr ago.

(3) Ambatofinandrahana and Vavavato intrusive complexes in the central part of Madagascar, with an age of 1,125 Myr.

(4) Quartzite series.

[1] Manuscript received July 22, 1960. Revised manuscript received February 27, 1961.

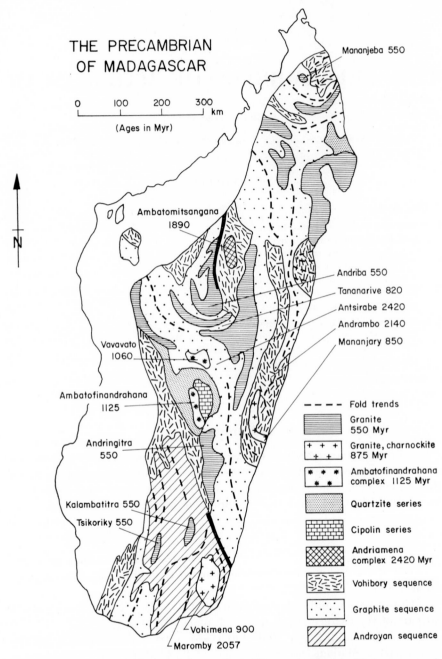

THE PRECAMBRIAN OF MADAGASCAR

(Ages in Myr)

Mananjeba 550

Ambatomitsangana 1890

Andriba 550
Tananarive 820
Antsirabe 2420
Andrambo 2140
Mananjary 850

Vavavato 1060

Ambatofinandrahana 1125

Andringitra 550

Kalambatitra 550
Tsikoriky 550

Vohimena 900
Maromby 2057

- - - Fold trends

Granite 550 Myr

Granite, charnockite 875 Myr

Ambatofinandrahana complex 1125 Myr

Quartzite series

Cipolin series

Andriamena complex 2420 Myr

Vohibory sequence

Graphite sequence

Androyan sequence

FIG. 1. Distribution of Precambrian rocks (with ages in Myr) in Madagascar and a scheme showing the principal chronostratigraphic units of the Precambrian.

(5) Crystalline limestone series.

(6) Andriamena mafic intrusive complex, with an age of 1,890 Myr.

(7) Major orogeny 2,420 Myr ago.

(8) Vohibory sequence.

(9) Graphite sequence.

(10) Androyan sequence.

Brief descriptions of the subdivisions are given in the following paragraphs, starting with the oldest formations.

2. Subdivisions of the Precambrian

2.1. *The Androyan sequence*

The Androyan sequence ("System"), in the extreme south of Madagascar, consists of a granulite–migmatite unit produced from siliceous aluminous and calcareous sediments. It is highly metamorphic, predominantly in the granulite facies, and occurs as intensely folded, steeply dipping, often almost vertical, isoclinal folds, generally trending in a N.–S. direction. In details, its tectonic geology is complicated. Three stratigraphic groups may be distinguished, as follows:

(1) The Fort-Dauphin group, the basal group, consists essentially of orthoclase granulites containing garnet and cordierite, and of charnockites.

(2) The Tranomaro group, very rich in calcareous and magnesian paragneisses, consists of diopside pyroxenites, werneritites, wollastonitites, plagioclasites, sakenites (aluminous plagioclasites) containing spinel or sapphirine, crystalline limestones, quartzites, cordierite granulites and garnet granulites, and charnockites.

(3) The Ampandrandava group, consisting of gneiss, migmatites, quartzites, crystalline limestones with multiple beds of diopside- and spinel-bearing pyroxenites, plagioclasites, sakenites containing spinel, sapphirine and corundum, garnet granulites, and charnockites.

2.2. *The Graphite sequence*

The Graphite sequence ("System") occupies the major part of the old basement. It was affected by metamorphism of varying degree, with products ranging from granulites to mica schists. The main petrographic feature is the abundance of graphite. Tectonically, an isoclinal generally almost N.–S. trends predominates, but local E.–W. virgations occur. The dating on an alluvial monazite from Antsirabe by the isotopic-lead method yielded an age of $(2,420 \pm 30)$ Myr. Several zonal groups, related to three main facies, may be distinguished in the Graphite sequence, as follows.

(1) The Ampanihy facies, mainly consisting of granulites and graphite gneiss, with manganese-bearing gondites, charnockites, quartzites, crystalline limestones, and anorthosites.

(2) The Manampotsy facies, consisting of gneiss, graphite-bearing mica schists, khondalites, and quartzites.

(3) The Ambatolampy facies, consisting of gneiss, graphite-bearing mica schists, and quartzites.

In the Ampanihy district, a large intrusive anorthosite body occurs in granulite (see Fig. 2).

The Graphite sequence contains a gold mineralization in interbedded quartz veins. A monazite with an age of 2,420 Myr is associated with the mineralization. The Androyan sequence and the Graphite sequence are clearly related to the Mozambiquian of East Africa and to the Dharwar of India.

2.3. *The Vohibory sequence*

The Vohibory sequence ("System") lies conformably on the Graphite sequence in southern Madagascar, but in some other places the two seem to be separated by an unconformity. Petrographically, a characteristic feature is the abundance of rocks belonging to the amphibolite facies, many of which are produced by the metamorphism of mafic eruptive rocks. Tectonically, the sequence is irregular, with frequent short and contorted folds. The conventional age of the Vohibory sequence is 2,140 Myr and is based on the age of a galena occurring in an interstratified gold–quartz vein at Andrambo. Several zonal groups may be distinguished, related to the main facies to follow.

(1) The typical Vohibory facies, with granulites, orthoamphibolites, para-amphibolites, serpentinites, crystalline limestones, and quartzites with copper mineralization (at Vohibory).

(2) The greenstone–schist facies, partially derived from mafic eruptive rocks, with hornblendites, tremolitites, anthophyllitites, talc schists, chlorite schists, and banded magnetite quartzites. This facies contains a general gold mineralization and, locally, a copper mineralization (e.g. at Vohemar).

(3) The mica-schist facies, with kyanite-, sillimanite-, and muscovite-bearing mica schists.

The Vohibory sequence has often been affected by strong retrograde metamorphism.

The Androyan, Graphite, and Vohibory sequences as a whole were affected by metamorphism 2,420 Myr ago, the major orogeny being dated on a monazite from Antsirabe.

2.4. *The Andriamena mafic intrusive complex*

The Andriamena complex is represented by old mafic intrusions which occur mainly in the Vohibory sequence and were metamorphosed afterwards. The dominant rocks are pyroxenolites more or less transformed into talc schists and soapstones, and various orthoamphibolites.

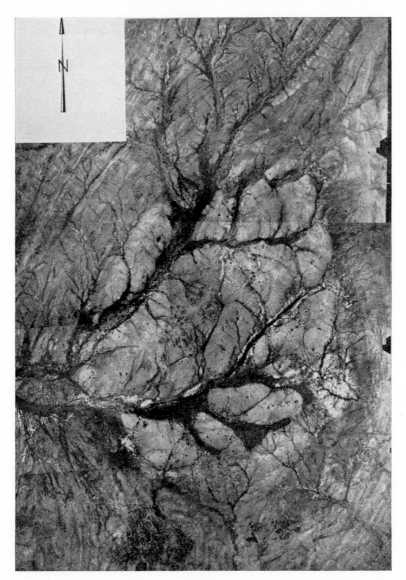

FIG. 2. The Saririaka anorthosite body (light-colored central part, area 9 km × 12 km), intrusive into the Graphite sequence granulites. Ampanihy district, southern Madagascar. Scale 1 : 100,000. Aerial photos, published by permission of *Service Géographique de Madagascar*.

An economically important chromium mineralization is associated with mafic rocks at Andriamena and north of Tamatave. The complex also contains a lead mineralization, from which three galenas yielded very similar conventional ages, the most reliable being 1,890 Myr for a galena from Ambatomitsangana.

2.5. *The limestone and quartzite sequences*

Unconformably on the old basement there lie, in the central region of the island, first, a crystalline limestone sequence associated with schists, and second, an interbedded quartzite sequence similarly associated with schists. Tectonically, they are more weakly folded than are the older formations. The intensity of metamorphism is variable and is displayed by the range from garnetiferous schists to slates. The quartzites are sometimes very weakly metamorphosed and display ripple marks and cross-bedding. These quartzites are distributed over a much wider area than are the crystalline limestones, and they may be found in several places on the island, especially in the north. They are cut by granites with an age of 1,125 Myr.

2.6. *The Ambatofinandrahana intrusive complex*

A series of crystalline limestones and quartzites is cut by granites, gabbros, syenites, and nepheline-syenite veins that form the Ambatofinandrahana intrusive complex. A lead–copper mineralization in crystalline limestones is genetically related with the granite. Two galena ages are concordant and yield a conventional age of 1,125 Myr. The Vavavato granites contain zircons dated at 1,060 Myr by the lead–alpha method. The complex contains rutile mineralizations, and bastnaesite and chevkinite pegmatites.

3. Metamorphic and igneous events

3.1. *Granitization and charnockitization 875 Myr ago*

Granitization and charnockitization are particularly well known in the extreme south, where they affect the Tranomaro and Fort-Dauphin groups. The granitization of the two groups has produced granites containing perthitic orthoclase, andesine, garnet, and biotite, closely associated with granodioritic charnockites (DE LA ROCHE, 1960). The granite of Vohimena contains a monazite dated at (900 ± 40) Myr by the lead-isotope method. Similar granites and charnockites on the eastern coast, at Mananjary, contain monazites dated at 850 Myr by the same method. In the Tananarive area the charnockite contains zircon with a lead–alpha age of 820 Myr.

3.2. *Orogeny and granitization 550 Myr ago*

In the basement all the old formations contain massifs of varying size, and many beds or sheets, of stratified granites with an age of 550 Myr obtained by various dating methods. Such granites are well developed in the central area north and south of Tananarive, in Andringitra in the west, and in the north. Most lead–alpha ages measured on zircons agree with the lead-isotope ages measured on monazites. Furthermore, intrusive granites and related pegmatites yield the same age on both zircons and on lepidolites dated by the rubidium–strontium method.

3.3. *Pegmatitization 485 Myr ago*

Finally, all basement rocks were cut locally by pegmatite veins, accurately dated at 485 Myr by the lead-isotope method on uraninite from industrial beryl pegmatites and on thorianite from phlogopite pyroxenites.

4. Mineral deposits

In the Precambrian of the Malagasy Republic the main mineral resources are graphite, chromite, monazite, ilmenite, quartz, nickel, iron, and abrasive materials. Brief descriptions of the deposits are presented in the paragraphs to follow.

Graphite is abundant and occurs as large flakes in mica schists, gneisses, and migmatites. A strong lateritization, transforming rocks into lateritic clays, facilitates mining, which is carried out in open pits. The graphite reserves are very large.

Chromite deposits were discovered in 1956. They occur as lenses of varying dimensions in pyroxenolites and talc schists in the Andriamena mafic complex. The average Cr/Fe ratio in the ore is greater than 2 and may be as high as 3. The Cr_2O_3 content always exceeds 48%. Deposits occur in the north-central part at Andriamena and in the Tamatave area. The certain reserves amount to about 6×10^6 metric tons.

Monazite and ilmenite occur in the Fort-Dauphin area beach sands, and they derive from the rocks of the Androyan sequence. Economically important reserves of good-quality ilmenite with 54%–58% TiO_2, monazite with more than 6% ThO_2, and zircon occur in old beach dunes. Their geological environment is similar to that in Travancore in India. Large deposits of ilmenite without monazite exist on the beaches and in the dunes of the north-eastern coast, north of Tamatave, but the ore is not of commercial quality and should be concentrated. The ilmenite derives from the schists of the Vohibory sequence. Ilmenite and ferrian ilmenite are known to occur in the anorthosites of the Ampanihy group.

Vein deposits of galena with quartz as a gangue mineral occur in the Andriamena mafic complex at Besakay and Tsaratanana, but the deposits are of little importance. Copper is common in the Ampanihy group of the Vohibory sequence. It occurs as chalcocite in massive veins and pneumatolytic veins in shear zones in amphibolites, but no economic deposit has been discovered. Bornite occurs also in massive veins in crystalline limestone; the veins are related to the Ambatofinandrahana intrusive complex.

Indications of nickel were discovered in 1960 in the intrusive post-tectonic peridotites and in their lateritic weathering products at Valozoro and Moramanga.

Large lenses of magnetite occur at Bekisopa in the Vohibory sequence. The nickeliferous deposits of Moramanga are capped by a thick limonite gossan.

The Graphite system gneiss, in the Ampanihy group, contains economically important deposits of garnet of industrial and gem quality.

Kyanite is abundant in mica schists of the Vohibory sequence at Mananjary and Malakialina. Corundum occurs in the mica schists of the Vohibory sequence and in syenitic rocks.

Other important industrial minerals, such as uranothorianite, phlogopite, and beryl, occur in the south in the Androyan sequence but are related to the pegmatitic and pneumatolytic activity that took place 485 Myr ago. Gem-quality beryl, tourmaline, and spodumene occur in pegmatites of the same age, around 500 Myr.

Bibliography

AHRENS, LOUIS H., BESAIRIE, HENRI, and BURGER, ALUYN J. (1959). Mesures d'âge de monazites de Madagascar. *Compt. Rend.* **248**, 3088.

AUROUZE, JEAN (1951). Sur la constitution géologique des régions de Mananara et de Marotandrano (Côte Nord-Est de Madagascar). *Compt. Rend.* **282**, 1861.

BEHIER, JEAN (1960). Contribution à la Minéralogie de Madagascar. *Ann. Géol. Madagascar* **29**, 1.

BESAIRIE, HENRI (1930). Recherches géologiques à Madagascar. Contribution à l'étude des ressources minérales. Thèse, Paris; *Bull. Soc. Hist. Nat. Toulouse* **60**, No. 2.

BESAIRIE, HENRI (1948a). Rcherches géologiques à Madagascar. Deuxième suite, l'extrême Sud et le Sud-Sud-Est. *Mém. Hors-sér., Serv. Géol. Madagascar*.

BESAIRIE, HENRI (1948b). Notices explicatives des cartes géologiques Ampanihy, Tsivory, Bekily, Esira, Behara, Fort-Dauphin. *Publ. Serv. Géol. Madagascar*.

BESAIRIE, HENRI (1952). Carte géologique de Madagascar au 1/1.000.000. *Publ. Serv. Géol. Madagascar*.

BESAIRIE, HENRI (1954). Le Précambrien de Madagascar. *Congr. Géol. Intern., Compt. Rend., 19e, Algiers*, 1952, **20**, 337.

BESAIRIE, HENRI (1956). Carte minière et des indices de Madagascar au 1/500.000 (treize feuilles). *Publ. Serv. Géol. Madagascar*.

BESAIRIE, HENRI (1957). La Carte tectonique de Madagascar 1957 et la géochronologie. *Compt. Rend., III Congr., Assoc. Sci. Pays de l'Ocean Indien, Tananarive, Sect. C, Géol.*, 7.

BESAIRIE, HENRI (1959). Géologie appliquée et prospection minière à Madagascar. *Intern. Geol. Cong., 20th, Mexico*, 1956, *Rept. Session, Assoc. serv. geol. Africanes*, 409.

BESAIRIE, HENRI (1960). Monographie géologique de Madagascar. In: *Lexique Stratigraphique International, IV, Afrique; Fasc. 11, Madagascar, Supplément.* Centre Natl. Rech. Sci., Paris.

BESAIRIE, HENRI (1964). Gîtes minéraux de Madagascar. *Doc. Bur. Géol. Madagascar* No. 167.

BESAIRIE, HENRI (1965). Carte géologique de Madagascar au 1/1,000,000. *Publ. Serv. Géol., Tananarive*.

BESAIRIE, HENRI et COLLIGNON, M. (1956). *Lexique stratigraphique international, IV, Afrique; Fasc. 11, Madagascar*. Centre Natl. Recherche Sci., Paris.

BESAIRIE, HENRI et HOLMES, ARTHUR (1954a). Premières mesures de géochronologie à Madagascar. *Mem. Inst. Sci. Madagascar*, Ser. D **6**, 191.

BESAIRIE, HENRI et HOLMES, ARTHUR (1954b). Sur quelques mesures de géochronologie à Madagascar. *Compt. Rend.* **238**, 758.

BESAIRIE, HENRI et COLLIGNON, M. (1960). *Complément au Lexique stratigraphique international, IV, Afrique ; Fasc.* 11, *Madagascar, Supplément,* 160. Centre Natl. Rech. Sci., Paris.

BESAIRIE, HENRI, EBERHARDT, PETER, HOUTERMANS, FRIEDRICH GEORG, et SIGNER, PETER (1956a). Mesure d'âge de quelques galènes de Madagascar. *Compt. Rend.* **242**, 317.

BESAIRIE, HENRI, EBERHARDT, PETER, HOUTERMANS, FRIEDRICH GEORG, et SIGNER, PETER (1956b). Deuxième série de mesures d'âge de galènes de Madagascar. *Compt. Rend.* **243**, 544.

BESAIRIE, HENRI et ROQUES, MAURICE (1959). Détermination de l'âge apparent de quelques zircons de Madagascar par la méthode plomb-alpha. *Intern. Geol. Congr., 20th, Mexico, 1956, Rept. Session, Assoc. serv. geol. Africanes,* 31.

BOULANGER, JEAN (1954). Etude géologique des schistes cristallins des feuilles Sakamena, Sakoa, Ianapera, Benenitra. *Trav. Bur. Géol. Madagascar* **56**.

BOULANGER, JEAN (1955). Etude des terrains de la série du Vohibory. Thèse Nancy ; *Mém. Hors-sér., Serv. Géol. Madagascar.*

BOULANGER, JEAN (1957). Les gîtes cuprifères du Vohibory. *Bull. Madagascar* **138**, 989.

BOULANGER, JEAN (1958). Géologie et prospection de la région côtière du Sud-Est de Madagascar. *Trav. Bur. Géol. Madagascar* **87**.

BOULANGER, JEAN (1960). Les anorthosites de Madagascar. *Ann. Géol. Madagascar* **26**.

BOULANGER, JEAN, NOIZET, G., et DE LA ROCHE, H. (1957). Géologie de l'extrême Sud de Madagascar. *East-Central and Southern Regional Comm. Geol., Second Meeting, Tananarive* 15. Comm. Tech. Co-operation, Africa South of Sahara (C.C.T.A./C.S.A.), London.

BRENON, PIERRE (1952). Contribution à l'étude pétrographique et géologique des terrains cristallins de Madagascar dans les régions Antsianaka-Anosimboangy et dans les bassins Bemarivo-Fanambana. Thèse, Nancy ; *Mém. Hors-sér., Serv. Géol. Madagascar.*

BRENON, PIERRE (1954). Les charnockites de Madagascar. *Proc. Pan-Indian Ocean Sci. Congr., Sect. C, Geology.* Perth, Western Australia.

BRENON, PIERRE (1958). Contribution à la géologie des gisements de thorianite de Madagascar. *Bull. Soc. Géol. France* **8**, 511.

DELBOS, LÉON (1957). Les granites des Ambatomiranty, de Behenjy et des Vavavato près de Tananarive. Thèse Clermont ; *Mém. Hors-sér. Serv. Géol. Madagascar.*

DELBOS, LÉON (1958). Les charnockites basiques du massif des Vavavato. *Compt. Rend. Soc. Géol. France* **13**, 300.

DELBOS, LÉON (1959). Essai de classification des granites malgaches. *Trav. Bur. Géol. Madagascar* **93**.

EMBERGER, ANDRÉ (1955). Synthèse géologique du pays Betsileo et de ses confins occidentaux. *Bull. Acad. Malgache (Tananarive, Madagascar)* **32**, 42.

EMBERGER, ANDRÉ (1958). Les granites stratoïdes du pays Betsileo (Madagascar). *Bull. Soc. Géol. France.* **8**, 537.

GIRAUD, PIERRE (1960). Les roches basiques de la région d'Andriamena et leur minéralisation chromifère. *Ann. Géol. Madagascar* **27**.

GIRAUDON, RENÉ (1959). Les roches ultrabasiques de la région de Tamatave. Mode de gisement, origine et minéralisations. *Compt. Rend. Soc. Géol. France* **7**, 172.

GIRAUDON, ROBERT (1960). La série basique de la Rianila et son cadre géologique dans la région de Tamatave (Madagascar). Thèse, Clermont ; *Mém. Hors-sér. Sérv. Géol. Madagascar.*

GUIGUES, JEAN (1951). Sur la constitution géologique de la région Mandoto-Ramartina. *Compt. Rend.* **223**, 184.

GUIGUES, JEAN (1952). Les terrains cristallins de la partie centrale de Madagascar entre Miandrivazo et Vatomandry. Thèse, Nancy; *Mém. Hors-sér. Serv. Géol. Madagascar.*

GUIGUES, JEAN (1954). Etude des gisements de pegmatites de Madagascar. *Trav. Bur. Géol. Madagascar.* **58**.

GUIGUES, JEAN (1955). Etude des gisements de pegmatites de Madagascar (suite). *Trav. Bur. Géol. Madagascar* **67**.

GUYONNAUD, GEORGES (1951). Etude géologique de la feuille Maevatanana. *Trav. Bur. Géol. Madagascar* **24**.

HOLMES, ARTHUR and CAHEN, LOUIS (1955). African geochronology. *Colonial Geol. Mineral Resources (Gt. Brit.)* **5**, No. 1, 3.

HOLMES, ARTHUR et CAHEN, LUCIEN (1957). Géochronologie africaine 1956. *Acad. Roy Sci. Coloniales (Brussels), Classe Sci. Nat. Méd., Mém.* **5**, No. 1.

LACROIX, ALFRED (1922). Minéralogie de Madagascar. Vol. 1–3. Paris.

LACROIX, ALFRED (1941). Les gisements de phlogopite de Madagascar et les pyroxénites qui les renferment. *Ann. Géol. Serv. Mines Madagascar* **10**.

LACROIX, ALFRED (1956). Notes posthumes: Minéralogie, pétrographie, Madagascar. *Trav. Bur. Géol. Madagascar* **78**, 1.

LAPLAINE, LOUIS (1951). Sur la constitution géologique des régions de Moramanga et Brickaville (Est de Madagascar). *Compt. Rend.* **233**, 703.

LAPLAINE, LOUIS (1957). Etude géologique du massif cristallin malgache à la latitude de Tananarive. Thèse, Nancy; *Ann. Géol. Madagascar* **24**.

LAUTEL, ROBERT (1953). Etude géologique du socle cristallin de Madagascar à la latitude de Tamatave. Thèse, Clermont; *Mém. Hors-sér. Serv. Géol. Madagascar.*

LENOBLE, ANDRÉ (1935). Constitution et structure du pays Betsileo. *Ann. Géol. Serv. Mines Madagascar* **5**, 45.

LENOBLE, ANDRÉ (1940). Les caractères stratigraphiques et lithologiques des séries pré-Karroo à Madagascar. *Mem. Acad. Malgache (Tananarive, Madagascar)* **32**, 1.

NOIZET, GEORGES (1953). Sur la constitution géologique des régions d'Ampanihy et de Tranoroa (Sud de Madagascar). *Compt. Rend.* **237**, 522.

NOIZET, GEORGES (1954). Etude géologique des schists cristallins des feuilles Imanombo, Ranomainty, Tranomaro, Marohotro. *Trav. Bur. Géol. Madagascar* **57**.

NOIZET, GEORGES (1959). Les formations de métamorphisme élevé de l'Androy mandraréen (Sud-Est de Madagascar). Thèse, Nancy; *Mém. Hors-sér. Serv. Géol. Madagascar.*

DE LA ROCHE, H. (1953). Etude géologique de la région de Mananjary. Thèse, Nancy.

DE LA ROCHE, H. (1957). Gisements nouveaux de monazite dans les sables littoraux de l'Extrême Sud-Est. *Bull. Madagascar* **134**, 585.

DE LA ROCHE, H. (1960). Métamorphisme des roches éruptives basiques et minéralisations cuprifères dans le Nord-Est de Madagascar. Etudes géologiques dans l'Extrême Sud-Est de Madagascar (Zone de métamorphisme élevée). Thèse, Nancy; *Ann. Géol. Madagascar* **28**.

ROUBAULT, MARCEL, LENOBLE, ANDRÉ, et GANGLOFF, M. (1953). Nouvelles observations sur les pegmatites de Madagascar. *Congr. Géol. Intern., Compt. Rend., 19e, Algiers, 1952* **4**, No. 6, 179.

DE SAINT OURS, JACQUES (1959). Etudes géologiques dans l'extrême Nord de Madagascar et l'Archipel des Comores. Thèse, Strasbourg; *Mém. Hors-sér., Serv. Géol. Madagascar.*

THE PRECAMBRIAN OF THE CONGO, RWANDA, AND BURUNDI [1]

L. CAHEN and J. LEPERSONNE

Musée royal de l'Afrique centrale, Tervuren, Belgique

Contents

[1] Manuscript received October 16, 1961. Revised manuscript received March 10, 1964.

Foreword

The present work provides the reader with a relatively succinct account of modern knowledge of the Precambrian of the Republic of the Congo (*République démocratique du Congo*, Congo-Léopoldville, former Belgian Congo), Rwanda and Burundi (formerly united under the name Ruanda-Urundi). (As from 1 July 1966, the names of certain places in Congo have been changed. It has not been possible to modify the proofs. The most important of these changes are: Léopoldville becomes Kinshasa; Elisabethville, Lubumbashi; Stanleyville, Kisangani. Similarly, names of places in Rwanda and Burundi have been changed. Astrida becomes Butare and Usumbura, Bujumbura.)

All the references to the geology of these three countries are to be found in the *Bibliographie géologique du Congo, du Rwanda et du Burundi* (formerly *Bibliographie géologique du Congo belge et du Ruanda-Urundi*), published by the *Musée royal de l'Afrique centrale* (formerly *Musée royal du Congo belge*), Tervuren, Belgium.

The authors' best thanks are due to Messrs. P. ANTUN, J. DELHAL, P. DUMONT, B. EGOROFF, P. RAUCQ, P. THONNART, J. THOREAU, N. VARLAMOFF, TH. VERBEEK, and A. WALEFFE for allowing us to draw from their, as yet unpublished, results.

1. Introduction

1.1. *General*

The geological formations of the Congo, Rwanda, and Burundi are usually divided into two groups (see Fig. 1). The young group, or the "cover", comprises beds younger than the Middle Carboniferous which are nonmetamorphic and nearly always horizontal. The other group, or the "basement", comprises the older formations, almost exclusively Precambrian, which are for the most part metamorphosed and folded but whose upper sequences are frequently flat-lying and nonmetamorphic. It is to a basement so defined that this chapter is devoted. Except for diamonds, coal, and bituminous shales, which belong to or are connected with the cover, the principal mineral resources occur in the basement, which, therefore, has been studied since the time Europeans first penetrated the interior of the country.

1.2. *Historical survey*

The principal stages in the advance of knowledge will be considered, as they pertain to each of the major stratigraphic units; only the main lines of geological exploration are discussed here.

In nearly all regions of the Congo geological knowledge has proceeded by means of successive approximations. In the first phase the aim was essentially to unravel those regions that might be of economic geological import-

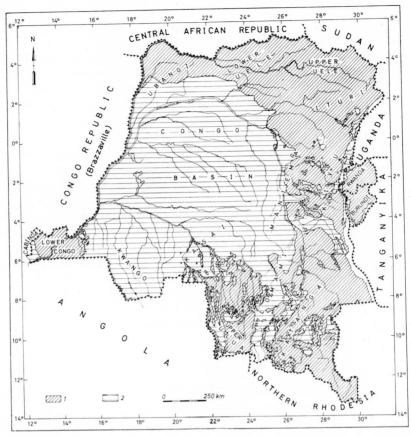

FIG. 1. Distribution of Precambrian and younger rocks, indicating the principal
      regions of Congo, Rwanda, and Burundi. 1, Precambrian (mainly) rocks. 2, Upper
      Palaeozoic, Mesozoic and Cenozoic rocks.

ance. This resulted in works that defined the major geological features of
the country traversed; works often characterized by generalizations based
on relatively few observations. Among the best studies of this period, which
lasted from 1878 to 1920 or 1925, one must mention those of J. CORNET in
1894 and 1897 on Katanga and the Lower Congo, which exercised a profound influence on the succeeding generation of Belgian geologists. Some
relatively detailed studies had already been made in Katanga before 1914,
notably by F. E. STUDT in 1908 and 1913 in the south of the country, and
by F. BEHREND in 1914 and E. GROSSE in 1918 in the north. The works of
these three authors contain the essentials of our present knowledge of this
key area. In the northeastern Congo it was the work of J. HENRY in 1924,
followed by that of F. F. MATHIEU and L. DE DORLODOT from 1929 to 1932,
that pointed the way. For Kasai the work of R. KOSTKA in 1913 is pertinent,
and for eastern Congo and Ruanda-Urundi of A. SALÉE in 1928 and 1932,
and of F. DELHAYE and A. SALÉE in 1928.

The second, more detailed, phase of study, usually in those regions that had been thought to hold a mineral or industrial interest, comprises the work of F. DELHAYE and M. SLUYS in 1924 and 1929 in western Congo; of geologists of the *Comité Spécial du Katanga*, under the direction of M. ROBERT, from 1920 to 1960; of E. POLINARD in 1925 and 1928 in Kasai; N. BOUTAKOFF in 1939 in Kivu; and M. SLUYS in 1945 in the Ituri. This phase was largely confined to the period between 1920 and 1945. However, even before the end of the second phase a third phase of detailed studies had begun in Katanga through the research of the *Union Minière du Haut Katanga*, continued, since 1945, in many areas of the Congo.

Except for Katanga, where a semiofficial Geological Survey has operated since 1920, geological research in the Congo has been, up to 1940, the by-product of mineral exploitation and research. For a long time the results were published only sporadically or remained buried in the files of the mining companies. It was not until the beginning of 1946 that the activity of the official Survey began to expand—the official Geological Survey was founded in 1939 and became active at the beginning of 1945, and at the same time the files of many large companies were progressively opened.

In attempting to define the state of geological knowledge in the Congo, compared with that of other African countries, one might suggest that the absence of co-ordination and of any official survey before 1939 gave rise to a certain incoherence, but that, by 1960, in terms of knowledge of its stratigraphy and mineral resources, the Congo bears comparison with most of its neighbours. However, outside Katanga only since 1958 have geological maps on a scale of 1 : 200,000 or larger been published. This indicates a certain backwardness that is now being corrected.

1.3. *Terminology*

The stratigraphical terminology of Precambrian rocks is far from accurate, and up to the present all attempts at gaining fairly general agreement have failed. It is true that even for fossiliferous strata agreement is far from being unanimous.

Two types of subdivision will be used in this paper.

The first type includes pure lithostratigraphical divisions, for which we have adopted the classic American nomenclature, that is from the largest to the smallest unit: group, formation, member.

Previously the terms "stage" and "bed" were used for what are here called a group and a formation (CAHEN, 1954, p. 5). The exclusively or predominantly chronostratigraphical, or even biostratigraphical, connotation of these two names excludes them from the terminology of Precambrian rocks.

The second type of subdivision is essentially based on the recognition of certain important geological features such as transgressions, hiatuses, un-conformities of greater or lesser importance which may or may not be accompanied by igneous activity, and extensive and abrupt changes in the lithological sequence.

These features are observed and indicate phenomena prevailing over relatively large areas. In a given geological province they provide reference points of a special type, not purely lithological, which permit the definition of major units with an essentially tectonostratigraphical nature. Their use is justified by the fact that there exist no more precise subdivisions for Precambrian rocks.

The terms previously used were, in ascending order, series, system, and group (CAHEN, 1954, p. 5). With respect to the improper meaning assigned to the word "system", which is, in fact, a chronostratigraphical term, and to the discussion about the meaning of the word "group" as the chronostratigraphical equivalent of an era—a chronological term that has not been applied to the Precambrian—it seems preferable to abandon these terms and only to use, where necessary, the word "sequence" for the formerly used "series".

For the formerly used "groups" the geographical name will be used which characterizes these units, eventually with elision of the last vowel and addition of an "-ian" or "-an" suffix. For the former "systems" the characteristic name will be used without a suffix. In this way, the names Katangan (formerly "Katanga Group"), Roan (formerly "Roan System"), and names such as "Upper Sequence" are obtained.

In principle, the major subdivision, formerly called the "group", is a series of fairly concordant beds separated from older and younger beds by well-marked unconformities. In other words, the sedimentary sequences belonging to such a subdivision are marked by the orogeny which caused the discordance taken as the upper limit.

The subdivisions immediately below these in rank, namely the former "system" and "series", are marked, both above and below, by minor unconformities, hiatuses, or clearly observable, significant changes in the sedimentation.

The distinction between boundaries of the subdivisions of the second and the third order is essentially one of degree, and admittedly might be somewhat subjective. Wherever the present-day knowledge is imperfect, the major subdivisions include only purely lithostratigraphical units.

The name "complex" will be used for a group of formations with common characteristics but with badly defined mutual relationships. The relationship of the complex itself with well-defined units with which it is in contact is often of a dubious nature.

The important orogenies that caused the unconformities marking the upper limits of the largest stratigraphical units generally bear the same name as the units; thus, the Kibaran and Kibaran Orogeny. Usually the less important tectonic episodes are not given special names, but are indicated by expressions such as "post-Mpioka" and "pre-Inkisi Phase".

2. Regional successions and geochronological setting

2.1. *Regional successions*

2.1.1. Introduction

The rocks of Precambrian age and those of dubious age, Precambrian or Lower Palaeozoic, crop out round the margins of the Congo Basin, which forms the central depression of the country. Historically, the study of the basement began on a regional basis by the determination and gradual extension of local rock sequences. The correlation of two adjacent regions has not always been accomplished, and thus difficulties in correlation from region to region still remain. In consequence, the correlation of rock sequences established in noncontiguous regions may give rise to discussion. The pur-

FIG. 2. Principal localities in Congo, Rwanda, and Burundi, mentioned in the text.

pose of this section is to outline the observed sequences and to note the geochronological data, the basis of all correlation.

There are five large regions that have relatively homogeneous geological characteristics and which stand out as having fairly well-known rock sequences, at least as regards their major features (see Figs. 1 and 2). They are Katanga, eastern Congo, including Rwanda and Burundi, northern Congo, Lower Congo, and Kasai, with which western Katanga is incorporated. From Kasai to northern Congo, by way of eastern Congo, the basement rocks crop nearly continuously out. By contrast, Lower Congo is separated from Kasai by the Kwango, a vast region where only cover rocks crop out, except very locally; while it is connected with northern Congo by way of the Congo (Brazzaville) and Central African Republics. The geology of these five large regions is briefly described in the following paragraphs.

2.1.2. Katanga

The important assemblage called the Katangan, which contains the copper, cobalt, uranium, zinc, and other resources of this region, rests with marked unconformity on underlying rocks, namely, the Kibaran from the west to the north of Katanga and the "Basement" of geologists in Zambia (the Muva and the Lufubu Systems) in the south (see Fig. 3). The discordance at the base of the Katangan can be followed for long distances. The relations of the Kibaran to the "Basement" are not at present known with certainty. It is probable that the Muva is more or less contemporaneous with the Kibaran, while the Lufubu is older (CAHEN, 1963a). In western Katanga the Kibaran rocks, relatively gently folded and slightly metamorphosed, are in contact with a foreland of a high metamorphic grade which is clearly different from the Kibaran. The direct superposition of the Kibaran on intensely metamorphosed rocks has been observed only in a small area. In other places geochronological data and the respective positions of the two assemblages show that the Kibaran is younger than the strongly metamorphosed rocks which form part of the ancient Kasai basement (see p. 205). In northern Katanga the Kibaran is in contact with another older assemblage, called the Ruzizian. Details of their relationship are given on p. 185.

2.1.3. Eastern Congo (northeastern Katanga, Maniema, and Kivu), Rwanda, and Burundi

In its major geological features, this region is a continuation of Katanga (see Fig. 3). The large Kibaran chain which runs diagonally across Katanga from the southwest to the northeast can be followed, as the Burundian, across Kivu, Burundi, and Rwanda and merges with the Karagwe–Ankolean of Uganda and Tanzania. A branch of this chain turns west level with the southern tip of Lake Kivu and covers a part of Kivu and Maniema.

In Burundi the type Burundian lies unconformably on the type Ruzizian. The same unconformity is known from the Itombwe Plateau, to south of

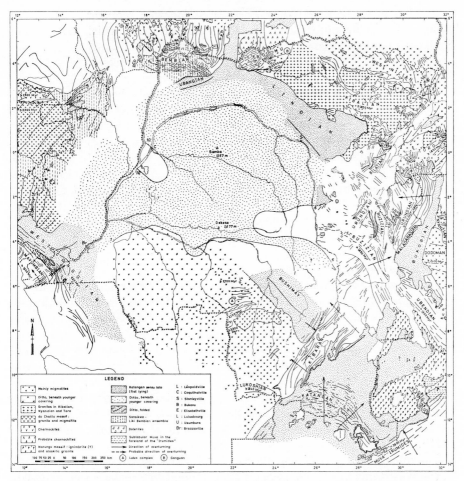

FIG. 3. Tectonic sketch map of Congo and neighbouring areas (modified from CAHEN, 1963a).

Lake Kivu, where beds forming a syncline resting with a marked uncon-formity on the Ruzizian very probably belong to the Burundian. In other regions, radial faults form the mutual boundary of these two assemblages. These faults are either recent or have been recently reactivated; this is notably the case in northeastern Katanga. In still other regions the contact has not yet been observed, and presumably consists of faults of uncertain age and type.

In southeastern Burundi, near the Tanzania frontier, the Malagarasian, equivalent to at least a part of the Katangan, lies unconformably on the Burundian.

In Maniema, the subtabular Lindian rests unconformably on older rocks, viz., the Burundian and the Ruzizian.

F

Finally, in northern Kivu, a possibly Palaeozoic sequence, called the Bilatian, rests unconformably on Precambrian rocks which have some similarity to the Ruzizian.

2.1.4. Northern Congo

There are, in this enormous geologically relatively homogeneous area, certain regional peculiarities which oblige one to distinguish three subregions, namely, the eastern, central, and western regions (see Fig. 3).

In the eastern region the Lindian rests unconformably on the Kibalian, which in turn lies unconformably on the West Nile Complex. In the central region, the Lindian rests unconformably on the Ganguan, which itself rests on the Bomu Complex, a probable equivalent of the West Nile Complex. Finally, in the western region, the Ubangian—an extension of at least a part of the Lindian—rests unconformably on the Liki–Bembian, which, again, lies unconformably on a little-known basement.

2.1.5. Lower Congo

In the western Congo the basement crops out in two regions, viz., in the Kwango (see Figs. 2 and 3), where some bosses of metamorphic and igneous rocks occur in the Kwango and Wamba Valleys, and in Lower Congo (see Figs. 2 and 3), which is one of the best studied parts of the Congo. Two major groups are recognized, namely, the West Congolian and the Mayumbian Complex, the first resting with an angular unconformity on the second. It is probable that the Mayumbian itself should be split into two major units (see p. 193). The West Congolian is divided into a number of units of which the lowermost, or the Sansikwa, is separated from the others by a slight unconformity that becomes more important towards the north.

The unconformity between the Sansikwa, considered locally as the base of the West Congolian (see p. 224), and the underlying rocks is well exposed, notably in two regions some distance apart, that is, in the Sansikwa Massif in the south and the Kimuaka Massif in the north.

2.1.6. Kasai and western Katanga (Lomami and Upper Lulua)

In the central part of the Kasai and western Katanga (see Fig. 3) relatively much information is available, a large part of the area having been mapped in 1:200,000. The Bushimay, equivalent to the lower part of the Katangan, rests unconformably on the Dibaya Granite–Migmatite Complex. South of this complex, also lying unconformably on the Dibaya Complex, is the Lulua Sedimentary–Volcanic Complex, whose age relationship with the Bushimay is unknown, but it is probably older. It is probably younger than the Luiza Metasedimentary Complex, against which it displays a faulted contact (see p. 178). The Dibaya migmatites may be younger than the Kasai–Lomami Norite–Gabbro and Charnockite Complex, which itself is younger than the oldest rocks, such as the Upper Luanyi gneiss.

2.2. Geochronological setting

2.2.1. Introduction

Many more or less accurate age data are available, based on minerals and rocks from either within Congo, Rwanda, and Burundi or surrounding regions.[1] However, as many more age determinations are still to come, the account to follow is still provisional for the various regions and horizons. The ages given in this paper are not necessarily identical to those quoted in the works from which they were drawn, where they might sometimes have been calculated using other decay constants. The difference is particularly noticeable in the conventional ages for common lead, which are 80 Myr–90 Myr older than the ages quoted in the papers of HOLMES and CAHEN (1957) and CAHEN (1961a), which are the sources for all the ages for which no other reference is given.

2.2.2. The Katangan Belt in Katanga

CAHEN and his associates (1961) recorded the ages obtained (see p. 246). Three of the Katanga uraninites (Shinklobwe, Luishya, and Kalongwe) yielded, by the uranium–lead method, fairly concordant apparent ages approximating (620 ± 20) Myr. A fourth uraninite (Swambo) and a part of the Shinkolobwe mineralization might be older (720 Myr; CAHEN, 1963d).

Two uraninites and a curite from Katanga (Musoshi, Kamoto, and Kolwezi), two uraninites from Nkana and a brannerite from Kansanshi, all in Zambia, give mainly concordant apparent ages approximating (520 ± 20) Myr.

The 620-Myr-old uraninites postdate the last phase of the Katangan Orogeny, which is younger than all the Katangan, with the possible but improbable exception of the topmost strata. The uranium mineralization is followed by very weak crustal movements. The 520-Myr-old mineralization appears to be entirely posttectonic.

The Katangan is thus older than about 620 Myr. It is, however, probable that there was not a long time interval between the deposition of at least its upper part and the emplacement of the 620-Myr-old uranium minerals be-

---

[1] The following decay constants were used in dating. For the uranium–lead and thorium–lead methods the constants used by STIEFF and his associates (1959) are $\lambda_{238\text{-U}}$, 0.15369×10^{-9} yr^{-1}; $\lambda_{235\text{-U}}$, 0.97216×10^{-9} yr^{-1}; $\lambda_{232\text{-Th}}$, 0.0488×10^{-9} yr^{-1}; $^{238}\text{U}/^{235}\text{U} = 137.7$. For the common-lead method the decay constants used by MOORBATH (1959), which are very similar, are $\lambda_{238\text{-U}}$, 0.1541×10^{-9} yr^{-1}; $\lambda_{235\text{-U}}$, 0.972×10^{-9} yr^{-1}; $^{238}\text{U}/^{235}\text{U} = 137.8$. For the isotopic constitution of original and present-day lead, the values given by PATTERSON (1956) and PATTERSON, GOLDBERG, and INGHRAM (1953) were used; see also the unpublished tables by POCKLEY (1961). For the rubidium–strontium method the constants are $\lambda_{87\text{-Rb}} = 1.47 \times 10^{-11}$ yr^{-1} (FLYNN and GLENDENIN, 1959); $^{86}\text{Sr}/^{87}\text{Sr}$, 0.709. For the potassium–argon method the decay constants are $\lambda_K = 0.585 \times 10^{-10}$ yr^{-1} and $\lambda_\beta = 4.72 \times 10^{-10}$ yr^{-1} (ALDRICH and others, 1958).

cause the uranium mineralization preceded the movements which seem to be the last phases of an orogeny whose earlier phases accompanied the deposition of the Kundelungu sediments which form the upper part of the Katangan.

Besides these reliably dated uranium mineralizations there is a large number of lead deposits, mostly postdating the main phase of movement, which have yielded model ages comparable to the ages of the uraninites.

The older phase, about 720 Myr ago, is verified not only by the oldest uranium mineralization in Katanga but also by an old lead mineralization and, probably, a granite, all in the Broken Hill and Lusaka areas in Zambia (CAHEN, 1963d; SNELLING, 1963).

Outside the Katangan chain and its foreland, galena veins, which notably affect the Kibaran Belt, have similar model ages and indicate Katangan hydrothermal activity.

2.2.3. The West Congolian

Of all the different strata that have been correlated with the Katangan, only the West Congolian yields a fairly large number of geochronological data.

There are four groups of results pertaining to the West Congolian, as follows: seven conventional ages of galena leads have a mean value of (740 ± 12) Myr. They are the six datings from Niari, Congo (Brazzaville; DURAND and LAY, 1960) and one from Bamba Kilenda, Congo (Léopold-ville; see Fig. 23). Most of the former galenas belong to sheet mineraliza-tions found near the top of the *Schisto-calcaire* in the neighbourhood of large faults (see Table 21). The Bamba Kilenda galena is associated with a fault cutting the *Schisto-calcaire*, the Mpioka, and the Inkisi (see Table 21) and occurs in all these rocks. The interpretation of this group of ages was discussed by CAHEN and his associates (1963), who showed that the lead at Bamba Kilenda is reworked from an older source which may be either a post-*Schisto-calcaire* and pre-Mpioka epigenetic mineralization or an Upper *Schisto-calcaire* syngenetic mineralization. In either case the age of the *Schisto-calcaire* is not less than about 740 Myr.

The metamorphism, migmatites and certain intrusions pertaining to the West Congolian orogeny have an apparent rubidium–strontium age of about 625 Myr (CAHEN and others, 1963).

Other apparent rubidium–strontium ages, determined on microcline and muscovite, are about 525 Myr. These ages are characteristic of certain cross-cutting pegmatites in the pre-West Congolian Mayumbian Complex of the Boma region (CAHEN and others, 1963).

The youngest ages of (465 ± 35) Myr are potassium–argon and rubidium–strontium ages of biotites and microclines from discordant pegmatites and veins in the Lower Mayumbian of Boma, and common-lead ages of galena veins from the *Schisto-calcaire* towards the foreland (CAHEN and others, 1963).

Thus several episodes in the West Congolian cycle are dated, viz., (1) an intra-West Congolian pretectonic episode showing that the age of the upper beds of the *Schisto-calcaire* is equal to, or a little older than, 740 Myr; (2) the orogeny dated at about 625 Myr; (3) posttectonic episodes between 525 Myr and 465 Myr ago.

2.2.4. The Lindian

Lead from a galena vein cutting the *Mont des Homa* formation (see p. 262) gave a conventional age limit for a part of the Lindian at 750 Myr. Another lead from a neighbouring vein cutting older rocks yielded the same age.

2.2.5. General conclusions on the age of the Katangan

To summarize, many events of the Katangan Cycle appear to be definable by ages and conventional ages. About 720 Myr–740 Myr ago, there was a probably intra-Katangan orogenic episode. The West Congolian orogeny occurred about 625 Myr ago, and at about 620 Myr ago the uranium mineralization postdating the main phase of the Katangan orogeny in Katanga originated. About 525 Myr ago posttectonic, cross-cutting pegmatites were intruded in the Lower Congo, and (520 ± 20) Myr ago the entirely posttectonic uranium mineralization originated in Katanga and in Rhodesia, where it was accompanied by metasomatic metamorphism. Finally, about (465 ± 35) Myr ago, the posttectonic veins of the Lower Congo and Zambia were emplaced (CAHEN, 1963d).

2.2.6. The Kibaran–Burundian Belt

A dating programme for this belt (see p. 197) is now being carried out (MONTEYNE-POULAERT, DELWICHE, and CAHEN 1963; MONTEYNE-POU- LAERT and others, 1963; MONTEYNE-POULAERT and CAHEN, 1964, and unpublished). The results obtained so far concern Katanga, Kivu, Rwanda, and Burundi, and deal with posttectonic episodes with ages ranging from 1,120 Myr to 845 Myr, obtained on the minerals of four tin granites and more than thirty granite pegmatites and veins dated by the uranium– lead, common-lead, rubidium–strontium, and potassium–argon methods. Moreover, syntectonic events have been dated by the rubidium–strontium method on whole rocks. The age of the Kibaro–Burundian orogeny in Katanga can provisionally be stated as (1240 ± 70) Myr (CAHEN, DELHAL, and MONTEYNE–POULAERT, 1965).

2.2.7. The Ruzizian Belt

Several apparent and conventional ages have been obtained from Kivu, Rwanda, and Burundi within the Ruzizian Belt and from the Ubendian, its southeastern continuation in Tanzania, viz., apparent ages on muscovites and microclines of granite pegmatites from Kivu and northeastern Katanga (LEDENT and CAHEN, 1964) and conventional ages of galena leads from

Gakara, Burundi (see pp. 187 and 188), and Mpanda, Tanzania, and its neighbourhood (see Fig. 7). One of the conventional ages is taken from RUSSELL and FARQUHAR (1960, p. 160).

These ages fall within the range 1,650 Myr–1,850 Myr, which is suggested to mark late events in the history of the Ruzizian Belt. A Pb^{206}/Pb^{207} apparent age of $(2,100 \pm 250)$ Myr might indicate an earlier event which might even be pre-Ruzizian. It was obtained on alluvial monazite (Runinya River, southwest of Butare, formerly Astrida, Rwanda), derived from pre-Burundian monazite pegmatites and granites (see p. 187).

The complete geological interpretation of the ages listed is still impossible. The data available indicate an age for the rocks included in the "Ruzizian" (see p. 186) clearly older than the ages of the Kibaran and Burundian rocks.

2.2.8. The Mayumbian Complex [1]

For the rocks of the Lower Congo older than the West Congolian, only very imprecise and scanty age determinations are available. One cannot, therefore, draw any definite stratigraphical conclusions. Three zircons treated by the lead–alpha method (BESSOLES and others, 1956; M. ROQUES, unpublished; see CAHEN and others, 1963) yielded the ages 1,182 Myr, 1,250 Myr, and 1,483 Myr, respectively. The first and last of these apparent ages refer to two facies of the Lufu microgranite, Lower Congo (see p. 196 and Fig. 23), and the second age refers to the Saras quartz diorite of Congo (Brazzaville). All these rocks are part of the Upper Mayumbian (see Table 5) and are older than the Sansikwa and thus older than all the West Congolian. The indicated apparent ages seem to exclude the possibility that these zircons might be detrital, derived from Lower Mayumbian rocks, which are much older. In fact, the range of the apparent ages agrees well with the stratigraphical position of the Upper Mayumbian, which is intercalated between rocks older than 2,500 Myr (see below) and the West Congolian, folded about 625 Myr ago. The interpretation of these ages is uncertain. If one supposes that the discordance is caused solely by the loss of lead, then the highest apparent age is probably the best approximation. It has already been suggested (CAHEN, 1961a) that the ages of the order of 1,790 Myr (on zircons and galenas by the lead–alpha and common-lead methods, respectively) obtained from the northern part of the Mayumbe in Congo (Brazzaville), might similarly belong to the Upper Mayumbian.

There are a number of indications tending to show that the lower part of the Mayumbian Complex is older than 2,500 Myr (CAHEN and others, 1963). This problem will be discussed on p. 193.

2.2.9. The formations of northern Congo

It is known that at least two, and probably three, superposed groups make up the basement of northern Congo (see pp. 162 and 168).

In the eastern part the Kibalian rests unconformably on the West Nile

[1] See footnote on p. 193.

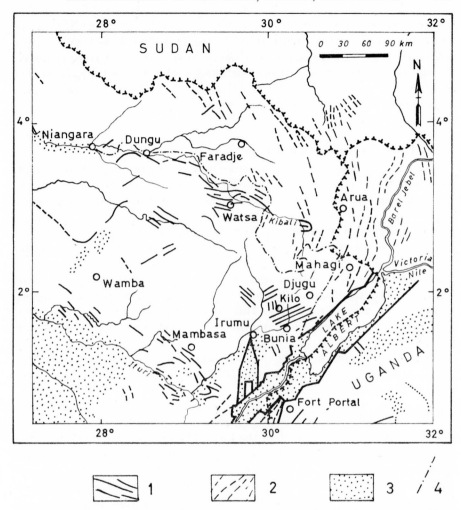

FIG. 4. Tectonic sketch map of northeastern Congo and adjoining areas. 1, Main trends in the Kibalian. 2, Main trends in the West Nile Complex. 3, Lindian (Late Precambrian) and younger rocks. 4, Tentative boundary between the Kibalian and the West Nile Complex. Modified from CAHEN (1954).

Complex. The lead from gold veins of the Watsa region (see Fig. 4) and the muscovites and microclines from pegmatites of a much larger area yield conventional ages and apparent rubidium–strontium ages which fall in the range 1,830 Myr–2,075 Myr. The veins and pegmatites are either connected with, or younger than, a granite which is younger than the Kibalian and must surely be older than $(2,075 \pm 60)$ Myr (see p. 165). The rubidium–strontium ages were published by LEDENT and CAHEN (1964).

In the central part of northern Congo, gold-bearing sulfide veins cut the Ganguan (see p. 170). The conventional age of the lead of two galenas is $(3,490 \pm 100)$ Myr. The Ganguan rests unconformably on the Bomu

Complex. However, if one admits that the lead of the post-Ganguan veins was remobilized from an earlier mineralization—a hypothesis that does not seem likely, since the galena is very rich in silver and other trace elements (CAHEN and others, 1958)—then their likely provenance is from the underlying Bomu Complex, and it follows that the Bomu Complex and its probable lateral equivalent, the West Nile Complex, are almost certainly older than 3,500 Myr.

2.2.10. The Kasai–Lomami–Lulua area

This region consists of very old rocks now being studied. Several events have been dated (LEDENT, LAY and DELHAL, 1963; DELHAL and LEDENT, in press). The microcline of a very old gneiss (the Upper Luanyi gneisses) yielded minimum rubidium–strontium age of 3,280 Myr. The charnockitization affecting the Kasai–Lomami Norite–Gabbro and Charnockite Complex has been dated by several apparent rubidium–strontium ages suggesting the age of the charnockitization at around 2,650 Myr. Furthermore, several apparent rubidium–strontium ages on muscovite date the metamorphism connected with the orogeny that affected the Luiza Metasediment Complex (see p. 178) at around 2,125 Myr. This same age, determined on microcline, was obtained for a young pegmatite in the Dibaya Granite–Migmatite Complex.

Finally, in an area in the south, spreading to the Upper Lulua region, rubidium–strontium ages of about 1,850 Myr characterize granites and date a pegmatite which sets an upper limit to the age of the Lukoshi Complex.

2.2.11. Provisional geochronological synthesis

Table 1 gives a summary of all the known facts. The ages quoted for the various dated events derive from a consideration of the body of data previously discussed.

Those dates that are based on conventional common-lead ages or on apparent lead–alpha ages, without verification by other methods, are given in parentheses.

3. The pre-Kibaran–Burundian formations: the basement of northern Congo and of the Kasai–Lomami–Lulua region

3.1. *Introduction*

The relatively well-known Ruzizian and Mayumbian Belts will be discussed on pp. 183–8. The other pre-Kibaran–Burundian formations that are certainly older, and those whose age is more or less uncertain will be described in this section. They occur in two main regions (see Figs. 1 and 3) which comprise: (1) northern Congo, where they are the continuation of the basement rocks of the Central African Republic, Sudan, and Uganda; and

(2) a vast region in southern Congo between Lat. 5° S. and Lat. 11° S. and Long. 20° E. and Long. 25° E. which is called in this paper the Kasai–Lomami–Lulua region and occupies the Upper Kasai, Lulua, Upper Lubilash, and Upper Lomami Basins.

Outside these two regions, formations of the same facies occur in the south of the Kwango, where they take the form of valley inliers and, perhaps, in northern Katanga, a still inadequately known region, where beds older than the Kibaran and the Ruzizian may possibly crop out. The Ruwenzori Massif, in eastern Congo, may be connected, at least in part, with the northern Congo formations.

Rocks of the same general age (older than 2,400 Myr) as those of the major parts of the basement described in this section seem to occur in the Mayumbian Complex. In view of the absence of a sufficient number of age determinations and of the complicated evolution of this area, it seems preferable to describe these rocks in connection with the Mayumbian Complex (see p. 193).

The ages of the formations described in this section have not yet been precisely determined everywhere. In northern Congo, two groups of ages are known (see p. 159), about 1,850 Myr–2,075 Myr and (3,490 ± 100) Myr, respectively. In the Kasai–Lomami–Lulua region, the geochronological data allow the distinction of at least four groups of ages (see p. 176), viz. around 1,850 Myr, 2,125 Myr, 2,650 Myr, and 3,280 Myr. These age data, and the following facts may be used to place these rocks in the general stratigraphical succession for Central Africa: (1) in northern Congo the Lindian and Ubangian, and in Ubangi the Liki–Bembian, a probable equivalent of the Sansikwa, rest with a major unconformity on the basement; (2) in the eastern part of the Kasai–Lomami–Lulua region, the basement is unconformably overlain by the Kibaran.

Strictly speaking, only events dated as 2,400 Myr old or older should be examined in this section. However, the description of undated events and of some younger events is included, and thus the relations these rock sequences have among themselves and with the oldest rocks of the African continent may be brought out, as well as the differences that allow them to be distinguished from the belts studied on pp. 182 ff.

Descriptions will be given by regions. Within each region the lithological properties that allow the distinction of units and the relationships that these units have with one another and with those of adjacent regions will be discussed. Numerous data still remain controversial, however. It has not been possible to expound the present-day knowledge as thoroughly as for the rocks studied on pp. 197–279. The descriptions and interpretations are based on a number of publications which frequently include chemical analyses and detailed petrographic studies. These are not reproduced here, because they would expand the text unnecessarily.

3.2. *Northern Congo*

3.2.1. Historical survey

The study of the metamorphic and igneous rocks of northern Congo has not yet been carried very far, and consequently the state of the present-day knowledge varies from region to region in accordance with their economic geological importance.

The reconnaissances of the first geologists to work in northern Congo L. DEWEZ in 1910, J. HENRY in 1924, and F. F. MATHIEU and L. DE DORLODOT in 1927 and 1931, were carried out in the eastern part of northern Congo. These geologists grouped the rocks into two categories, viz., "slightly" metamorphic rocks, on the one hand, and mica schists and gneiss, on the other hand. Their distinction is based entirely on an evolutionary difference. They also described large granite massifs.

Later, geologists working for the *Société des Mines d'Or de Kilo-Moto*, namely, F. BRUYNINCKX in 1924, R. ANTHOINE in 1922 and 1937, A. MOUREAU in 1939, M. LEGRAYE in 1940, P. MICHOT in 1942, and P. DUHOUX in 1950, studied in greater or lesser detail certain parts of the concession which occupies the eastern part of northern Congo. L. CAHEN in 1952 published a general tectonic sketch and synthesized the knowledge available at that time. He confirmed the existence of two superposed sequences, viz., the Kibali Group and the Western Nile Formation. Subsequently, many detailed studies accompanied by geological mapping and checked by borings helped to increase the knowledge of the Kibali Group in the Kilo area (STEENSTRA, 1954; WOODTLI, 1954, 1957a, b). CRUYSSAERT (1962) studied the region covered by the West Nile Complex near the northern end of Lake Albert.

The other regions of northern Congo have, in general, only been the subject of less detailed studies. The central, or the Lower Uele, region is known through the work of POLINARD (1935) and ADERCA (1952) and an unpublished account of LORMAND (1955), while for the eastern, or the Ubangi, region there exist the studies of ADERCA (1950) and GÉRARD, GÉRARD, and HUGÉ (1951). In the central region, the Gangu System resting unconformably on a mica schist and gneiss series, and in the Ubangi region the Banzyville System and mica schist and gneiss series have been distinguished, but their relationships are inadequately known.

Because the stratigraphical correlations among the three regions have not been determined, each of them will be treated separately. Hypotheses concerning their stratigraphical correlations and the relationships with adjacent areas will be discussed on p. 172.

3.2.2. General account of the eastern region (Upper Uele, Kibali, and Ituri)

The eastern region is bounded, on the one hand, by Long. 27° E. and the Equator and, on the other hand, by the Sudan and Uganda borders (see

Fig. 4). It consists essentially of metamorphic rocks, and of granites, which occupy a large area, mainly in the southeast. In the south, and locally elsewhere, these rocks are overlain with great unconformity by the Lindian (see p. 262) and by the Lukuga Series (Upper Carboniferous and Lower Permian). In the east they are interrupted by the Nile (Bar el Jebel)–Lake Albert–Semliki Rift, which contains Cenozoic lacustrine beds.

In this region one can recognize two groups of differing lithological composition and degree of metamorphism, namely the West Nile Complex (formerly Western Nile Formation) of deep mesozonal and catazonal metamorphic facies, affected by a gneissic granite, and the Kibalian of lower epizonal or upper mesozonal facies, affected by a nongneissic granite. The construction of a structural sketch, reproduced in Fig. 4, allowed CAHEN (1954, p. 156) to prove that the Kibalian and the West Nile Complex are two distinct sequences, and that the Kibalian is the younger of the two.

In Uganda near the Congo border, in the southwestern part of the West Nile district, an unconformity has been surmised between a sequence of hornblende–epidote schists equated with the Kibalian and three other groups which together are equivalent to the West Nile Complex of northeastern Congo (HEPWORTH, 1962, 1964).

3.2.3. The West Nile Complex

The West Nile Complex occupies a vast area in northeastern Congo and in adjacent parts of the Sudan and of Uganda (see Fig. 4). It has scarcely been studied in Congo, the stratigraphy has not been worked out, and it is only possible to list the main rock types that occur. They are mainly gneiss, amphibole gneiss, and mica schist, with some quartzite, quartz phyllite, and crystalline limestone. Some of the rocks affected by the granite gneisses and migmatites were clearly recognized as being of sedimentary origin by F. BRUYNINCKX in 1924, L. DE DORLODOT and F. F. MATHIEU in 1928–1930, P. MICHOT in 1933 and M. LEGRAYE in 1940 (see also CAHEN, 1954, p. 154).

The study of the West Nile Complex in Uganda between the Nile and the Congo border shows that it consists of three distinct groups, which are, in increasing order of age: (1) the Eastern Grey Gneiss; (2) the Western Grey Gneiss; and (3) the Granulite Group (HEPWORTH, 1964). The Eastern Grey Gneiss consists of gneisses, amphibolites, kyanite schist, and quartz–muscovite schists and is of epidote–amphibolite and amphibolite facies. The Western Grey Gneiss, of amphibolite facies, consists of gneisses, amphibolites, and fuchsite-bearing quartzites. The Granulite Group comprises silicic and mafic granulites, charnockites, garnet-kyanite quartzites, and other rocks. All these groups represent "events of orogenic status" (HEPWORTH, 1964).

When traced across the Uganda–Congo border, these groups form jointly the West Nile Complex of northeastern Congo. They have been penetrated twice by pegmatites and quartz–calcite veins. The first pegmatite group is parallel to the foliation of the rocks, the second cuts across both the foliation and the older pegmatites (see CAHEN, 1954, p. 154, and ANON., 1957, pp. 6, 23; ANON., 1958, pp. 4, 19; ANON., 1959, pp. 4, 19; ANON., 1960, pp. 4, 17; HEPWORTH, 1962; CRUYSSAERT, 1962).

3.2.4. The Kibalian

No stratigraphic sequence has been established for the Kibalian, and agreement is far from being reached concerning the origin of its constituent rocks. They have been the subject of numerous studies, viz., by R. ANTHOINE in 1922 and 1937, P. MICHOT in 1933 and 1942, E. POLINARD in 1936, P. DUHOUX in 1950, C. SOROTCHINSKY in 1953, and L. CAHEN in 1952 (see also LEGRAYE, 1940; CAHEN, 1954 pp. 154–156, 161; STEENSTRA, 1954; and WOODTLI, 1954, 1957a, b). The most detailed field studies and the most thorough petrographical investigations have been carried out in the Kilo region. On this basis the Kibalian, which consists of more or less drawn out patches of schistose rocks, surrounded on all sides by granites (see Fig. 4), will be described. A zonal arrangement, that appears to be fairly constant, exists between the centres of the granite massifs and the least disturbed of the Kibalian rocks. They are arranged as follows (WOODTLI, 1957b).

Granite massif

This massif contains, from the centre outwards: (1) alkalic granite with microcline (rarely orthoclase), subordinate albite, quartz, and biotite, with or without muscovite, and rarely hornblende; (2) akeritic granite with microcline (rarely orthoclase) and oligoclase (or sometimes andesine), quartz, biotite, and hornblende; (3) sodic granite with albite, oligoclase, or, sometimes, potassium feldspar, quartz and biotite, with or without musco- vite, and often with hornblende or chlorite; (4) coarse-grained albitite with variable proportions of albite, quartz, biotite, hornblende, and chlorite; (5) diorite, quartz-bearing or not, with oligoclase–andesine, andesine, and even labradorite, generally hornblende-bearing.

The succession of types (2)–(5) is not always regular. Certain rocks may be either repeated or omitted.

Amphibolite cover

The amphibolites form a discontinuous cover over the granitic rocks that, in places, reaches a thickness of 400 m. The amphibolites are generally fine-grained hornblende- and feldspar-bearing rocks that are often saussuri- tized, and frequently contain quartz, epidote, and zoisite. Either within the amphibolite or at its contact against the granite, there exist layers of horn- blende epidotite, microdiorite, amphibolite gneiss rich in feldspar and fine-grained albitite which is gneissic at the granite contact. This contact is not faulted and often corresponds to a zone of migmatites that may reach a thickness of 100 m.

Schists

Schistose rocks overlie the amphibolites and apparently have a conformable contact with them. They consist of actinolite schists, talc schists, sericite schists, and albite schists with some chlorite schists, biotite schists, and black schists, whose colour is caused by graphite, tourmaline, fine-grained pyrite, magnetite, or usually dark chlorite. All these rocks are often rich in carbonate minerals, mainly ankerite, which sometimes forms large masses, but also dolomite rich in ankerite and, in small amounts, calcite.

Itabirites frequently occur in the Kibalian. Associated with them are quartzites and cherts. These rocks pass downwards into siderite.

Dolerite dykes cut both the granite and its amphibolite and schist cover. Sheets of dolerite appear to rest on the Kibalian (WOODTLI, 1954, 1957b), but might only be sills resistant to erosion (STEENSTRA, 1954).

Various opinions have been presented about the geological history of the Kibalian. WOODTLI (1954) and SOROTCHINSKY (1953)[1] thought that, except for certain rocks that might be of volcanic origin, the amphibolites of the Kibalian are largely of sedimentary origin with limestones and dolomites predominating.

Previously (see CAHEN, 1954, pp. 154–155), other authors thought that at least some of the Kibalian rocks were of volcanic origin. STEENSTRA (1954) reached the same conclusion but believed that in the Kilo region it is the greater part of the Kibalian that is made up of more or less metamorphosed extrusive rocks, many of which are only slightly schistose. He distinguished two groups of rocks within the Kibalian. One, corresponding to the schists of WOODTLI (1957b), includes spilites, keratophyres, and other rare rocks which are more or less altered by a low-grade regional metamorphism and hydrothermal metasomatism. The other group, corresponding to the amphibolite cover, consists of various hornfelses which are more or less schistose, hornfels schists, gneisses, and amphibolites. This group has suffered a thermal metamorphism.

STEENSTRA (1954) believed that ankerite and the other carbonate minerals were products of hypothermal mineralization and doubted the presence of calcareous sediments in the Kibalian. He reconstructed the geological history of the Kilo region as follows: (1) volcanic activity accompanied by sedimentation and by intrusion of dolerites; (2) regional metamorphism; (3) emplacement of granites and diorites and thermal metamorphism; (4) mineralization and hypothermal alteration; (5) dolerite intrusions.

The age and the lithology of the dolerites have been much discussed. WOODTLI (1954, 1957b) believed them to be dykes and lava flows connected with Cenozoic movements. STEENSTRA (1954) remarked that the dolerite sheets might be sills in the Kibalian. LEPERSONNE (1956) showed that a post-Upper Carboniferous emplacement is very unlikely.

---

[1] According to SOROTCHINSKY, all the rocks were derived from calcitic and dolomitic limestones.

3.2.5. Age of the Kibalian

Minerals from veins and pegmatites have conventional and apparent ages that fall in the range 2,075 Myr–1,850 Myr. The Kibalian is thus older than 2,075 Myr.

3.2.6. Structural geology of the eastern region

The West Nile Complex forms a large arc which is concave towards the southwest (see p. 163 and Fig. 4). The sedimentary origin of at least a part of the complex validates the conclusion that the observed strikes are indeed those of bedding and, consequently, that the general arcuate shape can be interpreted as one belonging to a fold belt. However, there are no studies in the Congo that afford details of the tectonic structure. In Uganda the structural history is very complex (HEPWORTH, 1964), and the West Nile Complex bears the marks of several phases of folding, the latest of which may be Late Precambrian.

The absence in the Kibalian of any rocks definitely recognizable as being of sedimentary origin makes the evaluation of tectonic structures difficult. The structural data are based on the presence of faulted contacts between the major units defined on pp. 164–5, observations of fractures, infrequent mylonite zones, displacement of dolerite dykes, and the boundaries of certain units (STEENSTRA, 1954; WOODTLI, 1954, 1957b).

When placed in chronological order, from the oldest to the youngest, the structures may be grouped as follows: (1) Schistosity of a variable strike, most clearly observable in weathered rocks but obscured by thermal metamorphism, and thus definitely older than the emplacement of the granites. (2) Low-angle thrusting with at least one thrust affecting the granite, thus postdating the granite; the presence of a gold mineralization in quartz lenticles of one of the mylonite zones might suggest that the mylonitization was accompanied by mineralization. (3) Radial faulting, clearly younger than the emplacement of the granites and the gold mineralization, of three ages, one or two of which are certainly Precambrian.

3.2.7. Mineralization of the eastern region

Gold

The only mineral exploited in the eastern part of northern Congo is gold. The principal gold mines are located in the Watsa region in the north and in the Kilo region in the south. Other, less important, deposits are located in the Aruwimi–Ituri and the Lindi basins. The gold mineralization is connected with the granites that penetrate the Kibalian, the lodes forming belts in the Kibalian near its contact with the granites (see CAHEN, 1954, p. 510; STEENSTRA, 1954; WOODTLI, 1957a). There are rare lodes in the region of the West Nile Complex which seem to be related to granites of the same type, and probably of the same age, as those that penetrate the Kibalian (LEGRAYE, 1940).

The Kibalian deposits are distributed as follows (WOODTLI, 1957a). All the principal deposits occur in the Kibalian proper, a certain number in the diorite facies or in the transitional zone at the margins of the granites and rarely in the amphibolite covering the massifs, but no deposit is known from within the granite bodies. The gold occurs in usually lenticular quartz veins, silicified albitites, itabirites, mylonites, complex matrix of the shear zones, as films or sheets in the sericite or carbonate-mineral-rich schists, and in the hematite and magnetite veins. It is sometimes associated with pyrite, more rarely with pyrrhotite, arsenopyrite, or chalcopyrite, and seldom with galena or sphalerite. The silver content never exceeds 25% (STEENSTRA, 1954; WOODTLI, 1957a). It appears that the mineralization occurs in the zones where solutions could readily circulate, and is especially controlled by tangential faults (overthrusts) affecting both the granites and the Kibalian. The mineralization therefore postdates the emplacement of the granite bodies.

The origin of the mineralization has been the subject of many hypotheses (see CAHEN, 1954, p. 510). LEGRAYE (1940) thought that it was hypabyssal, produced by differentiation from the granite batholith and that it had traversed the more or less solidified granitic crust to be deposited either in the granite or in the adjacent Kibalian rocks. According to DUHOUX (1950), the gold originally occurred in small quantities throughout the Kibalian sediments. During the granitization it was concentrated into zones surrounding the granite bodies. SOROTCHINSKY (1953) suggested that the gold is of sedimentary origin and was concentrated by circulating ground water.

STEENSTRA (1954) noted that the gold-bearing zones are characterized by hydrothermal activity giving rise to a gold–quartz–ankerite–albite–tourmaline–magnetite association, often in the vicinity of small granite cupolas. He concluded that the paragenesis corresponds to that of the hypo-thermal gold deposits of the classification of EMMONS (1937). The occurrence of ankerite in mineralized belts seemed especially typical to STEENSTRA, and explained the occurrence of gold in some itabirites by the fact, often proved by diamond drilling, that the itabirites pass in depth into masses of ankerite, and thus are the result of superficial alteration of gold-bearing ankerite.

Albitization and sericitization of the Kibalian rocks and of the external margins of the granite bodies are probably connected with the gold mineralization. These processes are probably connected, in some way or other, with the secondary granite domes that project from the top of the batholith underlying the Kibalian. The mineralization affects the solidified margins of the domes. WOODTLI (1957a), however, believed that the mineralization is later than the albitization because the gold is often connected with silicified albitites.

The various opinions suggest that the gold mineralization is controlled by the granites that penetrate the Kibalian rocks, that it took place after the intrusion of the main granite phase, and that it was partly contemporaneous with or slightly later than the tangential crustal movements.

Diamond

A small quantity of diamonds is recovered from many of the gold workings. Their origin is unknown.

Iron

At many places, the Kibalian includes workable beds of iron ore of the itabirite or banded ironstone types (see LEGRAYE, 1940; DUHOUX, 1950; ANCION and CAHEN, 1952). These rocks are most abundant in the Lower and Upper Uele and in the Kibali–Ituri regions. They form large, elongated outcrops that follow the general schistosity. As a consequence of their hardness and resistance to erosion, they form isolated monadnocks which reach a length of 10 km and a thickness of 500 m. The reserves of iron ore are estimated as several thousand million tons containing 45%–70% Fe and 0%–30% SiO_2. The main minerals are hematite and magnetite, but siderite, ankerite, chlorite, pyrite, and arsenopyrite occur as accessories. SOROTCHINSKY (1953) and WOODTLI (1954, 1955, 1959, 1961) showed that certain itabirites of the Kilo and Watsa regions are derived by the silicification and oxidation of iron carbonate.

3.2.8. General account of the central region (Lower Uele)

The central region lies between Long. 22° E. and Long. 24° E. and is bounded in the north by the Bomu River, marking the frontier between Congo and the Central African Republic (see Fig. 5). In the south, the Lindian rests with marked unconformity on the basement, which consists of two sequences, viz., the Bomu Complex and the Ganguan (the Mica Schist and Gneiss Series and the Gangu Series of ADERCA, 1952).

Before ADERCA (1952) recognized the existence of two superposed rock sequences, several petrographic descriptions of the Lower Uele rocks had been made, by L. DE DORLODOT in 1923 and 1931, L. DE DORLODOT and F. F. MATHIEU in 1927, and E. POLINARD in 1935. The Ganguan is underlain by the Bomu Complex, from which it is separated by its lithological and tectonic properties. No unconformity has been observed, but the gentle folding of the Ganguan, the occurrence of arenaceous rocks at its base, and the appearance of the junction on maps rule out the possibility of a faulted contact and demonstrate the existence of two unconformable units.

The general orientation of the Bomu Complex, south of Bomu River, is W.S.W.–E.N.E.; it is intruded by a migmatitic granite. The orientation of the Ganguan is N.N.E.–S.S.W.; it has not been affected by the granitization, but might have been influenced by a younger granite, called the Bondo Granite.

3.2.9. The Bomu Complex

The Bomu Complex consists essentially of gneisses of two principal types, viz., amphibole gneiss, generally garnet-bearing, less frequently pyroxene-bearing, and a biotite gneiss or two-mica gneiss. The amphibole gneiss is

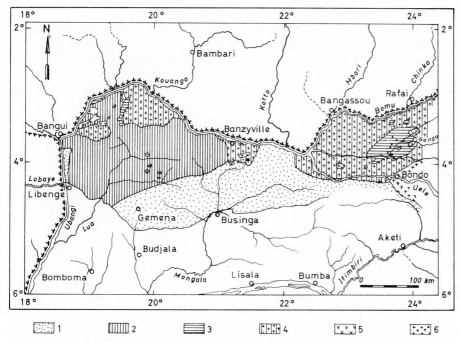

FIG. 5. Precambrian of Ubangi and Uele (northern Congo). 1, Ubangian and Lindian. 2, Liki–Bembian. 3, Ganguan. 4, Bomu and other "basement" rocks. 5, Dolerite (lava?). 6, Granite. Modified from ADERCA (1950, 1952).

composed of hornblende, often partly uralitized pyroxene, calcic-sodic plagioclase and quartz; garnet is nearly always present. The pyroxene is often augite. With an increase in the hornblende content the rock passes into an amphibolite or an amphibole schist made up almost completely of hornblende. With an increase in the pyroxene content the rock changes into pyroxenite. It seems that at least some of the amphibole gneisses derive from igneous rocks, no doubt mainly gabbros. The biotite and two-mica gneisses appear to be derived mainly from granites. Granite and pegmatite veins are frequently present in the gneisses, and there are many transitions between the veins and the gneisses. The granites are generally calc-alkalic, with a transition to quartz plagioclasites.

In addition to the main types described above, there are mica schists and completely recrystallized quartzites with abundant accessory minerals, kyanite being most frequent. There are numerous intrusions of gabbro and dolerite which appear to postdate the granitization, at least some of which are post-Ganguan (see p. 170). The feldspars of some of the gabbros have been altered to scapolite. ADERCA (1952) ascribed the scapolitization to the influence of pneumatolytic and hydrothermal solutions connected with the emplacement of the youngest granites.

The Bomu Complex is a deep mesozonal or a catazonal complex. Rocks recognizably of sedimentary origin are few and have been subjected to the general granitization. The occurrence of hypersthene granite has been noted (LORMAND, 1955), and the presence of charnockite is not excluded.

The Bomu Complex has been strongly compressed into tight, often isoclinal folds. The usual fold trend is W.S.W.–E.N.E., but locally this trend is interrupted by the S.E.–N.W. orientation of an amphibole gneiss massif of the same composition as the amphibole gneisses of the complex. It is uncertain whether this S.E.–N.W.-trending amphibole gneiss is of a different age or a part of the Bomu Complex displaced by thrusting.

3.2.10. The Ganguan

The facies of the Ganguan is essentially epizonal. The Ganguan is divided in two parts, the lower part consisting mainly of quartzites, the upper one of schists (ADERCA, 1952). The quartzites are sericitic, fine-grained, or very fine-grained and pass into schistose sericite quartzites and quartz–sericite schists which are often nodular. Iron-bearing zoned quartzites containing magnetite are also present. The upper, schistose part consists of sericite schists, sometimes chloritoid-bearing, talc schists with feldspar layers, chlorite schists, black schists, probably graphitic, and, less frequently, quartz–sericite schists.

The folding of the Ganguan is far less marked than that of the Bomu Complex. There exist open anticlines and synclines with dips of from 15° to 25° in the quartzites and up to 50° in the schists.

The Ganguan is locally cut by aplite veins and is pierced by many small augite gabbro massifs in which the ophitic texture is still recognizable but the pyroxenes are more or less uralitized and the feldspars are sericitized.

3.2.11. Age of the formations in the central region

The lead from galena veins cutting the Ganguan has a conventional age of (3,490 $\pm$ 100) Myr. It appears that one might consider the Bomu Complex as certainly, and the Ganguan as probably, older than this galena lead (see p. 160).

3.2.12. Granitic rocks of the central region

Granites are known to occur only in the Bomu Complex. They are of two types, viz., a diffuse, gneissic granite and one with well-defined margins characterized by the nonorientation of its constituent minerals. The granite gneisses are calc-alkalic and may pass into granodiorites or quartz plagio-clasites (POLINARD, 1935). The texture is very variable—oriented, bedded, lenticular, or banded (GÉRARD, 1958). Cataclastic zones and mylonite horizons occur (LORMAND, 1955), and pegmatite and aplite veins are frequent.

The nonoriented granite forms one large massif, the Bondo Granite, and probably other smaller massifs which have not been certainly distinguished from the older granites. The presence of slight traces of shearing shows that the Bondo granite predates the last deformation to affect rocks of the region (POLINARD, 1935). The chemical and mineralogical composition of the Bondo Granite is similar to that of the granite gneisses; the rock belongs to the monzonitic granites.

The granite gneisses belong to the Bomu Complex, but the age of the Bondo Granite is open to discussion. Its position within the Bomu Complex and its chemical and mineralogical composition, analogous to that of the granites of that complex, might lead one to consider it late syntectonic with respect to the orogeny that affected the complex. However, ADERCA (1952) believed that its emplacement was more recent, postdating the Ganguan. His opinion was based on the fact that in the Ganguan north of Bondo there are aplite veins and gold mineralization; that the quartzites have been silicified and recrystallized and the schists tourmalinized; and that the scapolitization of the feldspars of certain gabbros may also be connected with the Bondo granitization.

3.2.13. Mineralization of the central region

In all the region north of Bondo that it occupies (see Fig. 5), the Ganguan contains a gold mineralization of little economic importance. The gold occurs in quartz veins and is sometimes associated with sulfide minerals, mainly pyrite and galena, also in the recrystallized, silicified quartzites at whose contact the schists are often strongly tourmalinized, and in certain gabbros. ADERCA (1952) believed that the mineralization is connected with the hydrothermal–pneumatolytic phenomena associated with the emplacement of the Bondo Granite, that affected the Ganguan rocks.

Small quantities of diamonds are recovered with the gold. Their origin is unknown.

3.2.14. General account of the western region (Ubangi)

The basement of the Ubangi is divided into three groups (see Fig. 5), viz., the Ubangian, an equivalent of the Lindian; the Liki–Bembian; and a metamorphic basement. The feebly metamorphic and little-folded Liki–Bembian rests unconformably on the metamorphic basement. Its age is indeterminate, but its lithological analogy with the Sansikwa of the western Congo and an almost continuous chain of connecting links across the Republic of the Congo (Brazzaville) make it appropriate to deal with both the Liki–Bembian and the Sansikwa in Section 5.

The pre-Liki–Bembian metamorphic rocks were divided by ADERCA (1950) into two units, namely, the Banzyville System and the Mica Schist and Gneiss System. They are distinguished essentially on a lithological basis because no unconformity between them has been observed. French geologists who studied the continuation of these formations in the Central African Republic recognized the same lithological division, but concluded that there is a single concordant unit. We agree with their opinion (GÉRARD, 1958).

3.2.15. The pre-Liki–Bembian Complex

The upper sequence consists mainly of sericite quartzites, less frequently chlorite- or muscovite-bearing, and sericite schists. The lower sequence is made up of biotite gneiss, mica schists, and laminated biotite quartzites (ADERCA, 1950). The folding of the mica schists and the gneiss is intense, but the sericite quartzites are less strongly folded. The trend of the two groups is the same, close to north–south (see CAHEN, 1954, p. 192). In places the lower sequence is affected by migmatization (GÉRARD, GÉRARD, and HUGÉ, 1951). This granitization touches no part of the upper sequence. No geochronological data are yet available, and no mineralization has been observed.

3.2.16. Correlation between the various regions of northern Congo and with adjacent areas

The absence of definite links between the formations of the eastern and central parts of northern Congo is caused by the lack of systematic geological investigations. In the intervening area only the results of reconnaissance surveys are available. They show that the West Nile Complex and the Bomu Complex are certainly continuous and that the large granite batholiths continue towards the west but become less important. Also within the interlying area there are various patches of epimetamorphic rocks that appear to rest on the basement. It is not known whether they belong to the Ganguan, or to the Kibalian, or make up a separate group.

Geochronological data (see p. 159) indicate the existence of at least two gold mineralizations. Their age is different, and, if the genetic relationship assumed by many geologists to exist between the granites and the mineralizations is real, the Bondo granite and the Kibalian granite are not coeval.

The lack of connection between the basement of the Lower Uele and that of the Ubangi is caused by the presence of a sheet of Ubangian. The correlation of the pre-Liki–Bembian Complex with the Bomu Complex is nevertheless generally admitted by geologists who have worked in Congo and by those who prepared the maps of the Central African Republic. In particular, French geologists have been able to establish a connection between the two complexes by means of a long detour to the north. ADERCA (1952) equated the upper part of the pre-Liki–Bembian Complex in Ubangi with the Ganguan. This correlation has not been validated, but if it is true it would indicate that sequences that are concordant in the west become discordant towards the east.

Correlations with the sequences recognized by French geologists in the Central African Republic can be made without difficulty, as follows. The West Nile Complex, the Bomu Complex, and the Mica Schist and Gneiss Series of Ubangi are equivalent to the Lower Pelitic Series of the Basement Complex (Lower Precambrian), and the Banzyville of ADERCA and possibly the Ganguan are related to the Upper Detrital Series of the Basement

Complex in the Central African Republic. A comparison of the geological maps shows the very great extent of the amphibole–pyroxene gneiss of the Bomu Complex in the Central African Republic.

With regard to correlations with regions east of northern Congo, the West Nile Complex and the Kibalian will be discussed separately. The West Nile Complex continues into Uganda west of the Rift Valley. The Kibalian now known in the West Nile District of Uganda (HEPWORTH, 1964) has been equated with the Toro "System" of Uganda and the Nyanzian "System" of Kenya (CAHEN, 1954, p. 266). Recent data allow further discussion of this correlation (CAHEN, 1961a). Ages of about 1,850 Myr–1,800 Myr for granites and pegmatites cutting the Buganda and Toro Systems of Uganda are similar to those found for the post-Kibalian veins and pegmatites of northeastern Congo (see p. 159). Consequently, in the regions considered, the latest intrusive activity took place at about 1,850 Myr–1,800 Myr ago. The Kibalian may be much older than this, and thus the correlation formerly proposed is neither confirmed nor denied. However, it is now known that the Nyanzian is much older than the ages obtained in the Kibalian and in the Buganda-Toro of Uganda would indicate (SNELLING, 1964). In view of the fact that no ages of the same magnitude have been obtained in the Buganda-Toro–Kibali areas, it is thought that the Kibalian is more likely to belong to the Buganda-Toro belt than to the Nyanzian. It is certainly older than the Karagwe–Ankolean and the Burundian.

South of the gold-mine region of Kilo, the Kibalian and the West Nile Complex continue so that one ought to be able to determine their relationships to the Burundian and the Ruzizian. At the present time, the absence of systematic studies does not allow this to be done. Available geochronological data (see pp. 157 and 159) show definitely that the Burundian is younger than the other sequences but do not indicate the time relations between the Kibalian and the Ruzizian.

3.3. *The Kasai–Lomami–Lulua region*

3.3.1. Historical survey

The first geological reconnaissance survey of the northeastern part of the Kasai–Lomami–Lulua region (see Fig. 6) dates from 1891–1893 and was carried out by the Belgian geologist, J. CORNET. Later, R. KOSTKA in 1912 and S. H. BALL and M. K. SHALER in 1912 published the results of a more detailed investigation, and A. LEDOUX, in 1913, made the first petrographical study of the granitic rocks of Kasai.

Between 1920 and 1940, the geologists and prospectors of the *Société Internationale Forestière et Minière du Congo ("Forminière")* explored the country in a systematic way, but only a small part of their results was published, and those mainly in the form of petrographic studies of some specimens, such as those published by E. POLINARD in 1925–1949, by J. THOREAU in 1935, and by C. FRIEDLAENDER in 1942. These studies led to the recognition of a basement where gneisses and granites preponderate and, in the Luiza gold-bearing region, to the establishment of three sequences, viz., the *"Système schisto-phylladique"*, later called the Lulua Group, consisting of only slightly metamorphosed rocks, and at the present called the Lulua Sedimentary and Volcanic Complex; a complex of mica schists and gneisses, now called the Luiza Metasedimentary Complex; and the Lulua–Bushimay Norite–Gabbro Massif, now called the Kasai–Lomami Norite–Gabbro and Charnockite Complex, which was previously considered to be of Katangan age.

In 1946, geologists of the *Comité Spécial du Katanga* working in the eastern part of the region gave the name "Kalundwe Formation" to a part of the pre-Kibaran basement on the basis of its lithological composition (see CAHEN, 1954, pp. 240–241). In the extreme south the Lukoshi Formation was similarly recognized, consisting of intensely metamorphosed sedimentary rocks that probably rest unconformably on a granite and gneiss basement (see CAHEN, 1954, pp. 240–241) and which are certainly pre-Kibaran (MOUREAU, 1960).

Since 1950, officers of the Geological Survey of the Congo have made detailed studies of the Dibaya and Luiza quadrangles and of parts of the Luluabourg and Bakwanga quadrangles. From 1956 to 1960 a *Forminière* group under the direction of P. RAUCQ has extended their studies to a much larger area covering parts of the regions cited above. These studies have resulted in various preliminary publications (LEGRAND, 1955; LEGRAND and RAUCQ, 1957; MORELLI and RAUCQ, 1961; RAUCQ, 1961) and in some detailed memoirs (DELHAL, 1957a,b, 1963a) on the Kasai–Lomami Norite–Gabbro and Charnockite Complex, and the "basement" of the Luiza region. Further, we have been able to use some, as yet unpublished, geological maps, field notes, and the preliminary results of petrological studies that J. THOREAU of the University of Louvain and P. RAUCQ, J. DELHAL, and H. LADMIRANT at the *Musée royal de l'Afrique centrale* have made with a view to revising the geological maps, and their descriptions of the rocks and mineralizations.

The eastward continuation of the Kasai–Lomami Norite–Gabbro and Charnockite Complex into the region of Long. 24° E. was the subject of a study of BEUGNIES (1953; see DELHAL and FIEREMANS, 1964).

3.3.2. General account

The major part of the vast Kasai–Lomami–Lulua region consists of a complex of metamorphic and igneous rocks, whose study is made difficult by the presence of an extensive Mesozoic and Cenozoic cover (see Fig. 6). Most of the published investigations (see p. 173) deal with small areas. They consist of detailed petrographical descriptions, often accompanied by chemical analyses, but do not allow one to get a general view of the geological history of the whole region. Nevertheless, the area bounded by Lat. 6° S. and Lat. 8° S. and Long 22° E. and Long. 24° E. has been studied in great

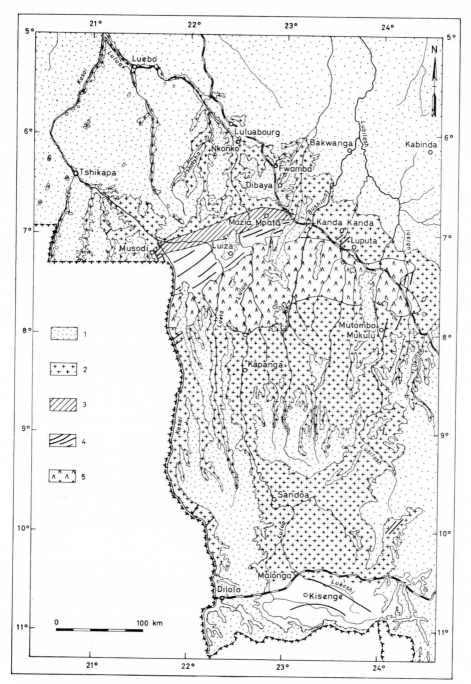

FIG. 6. Pre-Bushimay formations of Kasai. 1, Bushimay (Late Precambrian) and
Upper Palaeozoic, Mesozoic and Cenozoic cover. 2, Mainly migmatites, including
the Dibaya Granite–Migmatite Complex (near Dibaya) and the Upper Luanyi
gneiss (between the two charnockitic complexes). 3, Lulua Sedimentary and
Volcanic Complex. 4, Luiza Metasedimentary Complex (near Luiza); Lukoshi
complex (near Dilolo); direction of metasedimentary rocks within the Migmatitic
Complex (2) (other places). 5, Charnockitic Complex.

detail, and it is possible to define the major geological units and to study their evolution. It is, however, necessary to divide the area into two parts, namely, the region referred to above, which will be called the Dibaya, Luiza, and Kanda Kanda Region, and the other areas of the Kasai–Lomami–Lulua.

3.3.3. The Dibaya, Luiza, and Kanda Kanda region (see Fig. 6)

The partly unpublished results of field work and petrological studies, and geochronological data (LEDENT, LAY, and DELHAL, 1963; DELHAL and LEDENT, in press) permit the subdivision of the formations of this region as follows (Table 2).

TABLE 2

Succession of events in the Dibaya, Luiza, and Kanda Kanda region

Lulua Sedimentary and Volcanic Complex	
————————————————————————	Presumed unconformity
Synorogenic metamorphism about 2,125 Myr ago	
Luiza Metasedimentary Complex	
Presumed unconformity ————————————————————————	Unconformity
(Dibaya quadrangle)	(Luiza quadrangle)
Migmatitization older than 2,500 Myr	Charnockitization about 2,650 Myr ago
Dibaya Complex	Kasai–Lomami Norite–Gabbro and Charnockite Complex
————————————————————————	Presumed unconformity
Metamorphism about 3,280 Myr ago. Upper Luanyi Gneisses	

Not all events in this area have been summarized in Table 2, as some are still tentatively dated or of unknown age.

The Upper Luanyi Gneisses

The gneisses consist of quartz, plagioclase, biotite, and some microcline. Their areal extent is badly known, and their relationship with the Kasai–Lomami Norite–Gabbro and Charnockite Complex, with which they are in contact, has not yet been determined. However, their mineralogical composition and age suggest that they form the substratum from which the charnockites were derived by catazonal metamorphism. Towards the south, the Upper Luanyi Gneisses are affected by a granitization directly linked to a vast complex of granites and migmatites extending to south of Lat. 8° S.

The Kasai–Lomami Norite–Gabbro and Charnockite Complex

The norite–gabbro massif and the "granites" that succeed it to the south were described by E. POLINARD in 1944 and 1949, by J. THOREAU in 1933 and by FRIEDLAENDER in 1942. Their continuation to the east was studied by BEUGNIES (1953), who called them the Inter Lubilash–Lubishi Magmatic Complex. None of these authors had recognized the charnockitic nature of this complex which was established by DELHAL (1957a,b, 1958a), who found it necessary to disregard partly the interpretation given in previous papers and included numerous petrographical descriptions and chemical analyses. The charnockitic complex forms an east–west-trending band, with several interruptions, stretching for nearly 300 km from the Congo–Angola border to the Lubilash River and having a width of up to 80 km.

In the Luiza quadrangle area the main massif consists of four parts, namely: (1) a northern norite–gabbro zone (gabbros, norite–gabbros, garnet gabbros with or without hypersthene, anorthosites, and amphibolites); (2) a southern charnockite zone (rocks ranging from granitic to tonalitic containing hypersthene—charnockites and enderbites—which are sometimes garnetiferous, and quartz-feldspar rocks containing garnet and sillimanite—granulites) with patches of norite–gabbro, intermediate charnockites, aplites and pegmatites, and quartz veins; (3) an eastern amphibolite gneiss zone consisting of gneisses with or without microcline; biotite, amphibole, epidote, and garnet gneisses; zoisite amphibolites and garnet amphibolites, and epidotites; and (4) a zone called the Lueta Massif, north of the norite–gabbro zone and separated from it by the Luiza Metasedimentary Complex, which consists mainly of amphibolites with some norite–gabbro and garnet gneiss.

The evolution of the charnockite massif appears to consist of three phases, namely: (1) the presence of a complex basement, probably granitic and gneissose but in places very rich in aluminum, which is, probably, a part of the Upper Luanyi Gneiss; (2) the emplacement of norite–gabbros by means of an intrusive magmatic process and the formation of the charnockite zone by metamorphism and granitization in the catazone; (3) tectonic activity with cataclasis in the catazone.

In the eastern amphibolite–gneiss zone, the successive phases are deformation and mesozonal metamorphism accompanied by migmatization which was followed by epizonal hydrothermal alteration.

In the Lueta Massif, the charnockite complex has suffered retrograde metamorphism in mesozonal and, later, in epizonal conditions; no migmatites have been observed, however. In the north of the amphibolite–gneiss zone and at the border of the Lueta Massif, the deformation and upper mesozonal metamorphism of the Luizan Orogeny superimpose their effects on those of previous events, causing an alteration of the amphibolites derived from gabbros into amphibolite schists (DELHAL, 1963a).

The Dibaya Granite–Migmatite Complex

The granitic rocks occupy a vast area which extends beyond the limits of the true Dibaya area, mainly towards the west, the north, and the east. The migmatitic character of these rocks can often be observed in the field, but the nature of their substratum, which appears to comprise amphibolites and pyroxene-bearing rocks, is generally impossible to define. Petrographic studies and chemical analyses show that the rocks are alkalic or calc-alkalic granites, monzonitic granites, akeritic granites, and granodiorites (CAHEN, 1954, pp. 24–48).

In the Dibaya quadrangle area, petrographic studies that are still in progress (THOREAU, 1960; J. DELHAL, B. EGOROFF, and P. THONNART, personal communications) show that the granitization has a probably lower mesozonal or even upper catazonal character, and that it was followed by movements consisting of one or more phases (LEDENT, LAY, and DELHAL, 1963) that caused a cataclasis that can pass into mylonitization. These events are accompanied or followed by recrystallization, perhaps including some metasomatism. The clearest, and doubtless the most recent, of these changes belong to the upper mesozone or to the lower epizone. In addition, the plagioclases are saussuritized.

The granite–migmatite complex contains several types of pyroxene-bearing intrusive rocks. The most important among them are the Lutshatsha enstatitite and serpentinite, the Nkonko serpentinite, and the Fwamba diallagite massifs (LEGRAND, LOHEST, and RAUCQ, 1958; RAUCQ, 1961). There are also dolerite dykes (CAHEN, 1954, p. 246) and rocks resembling lavas (J. DELHAL, personal communication). Some of these rocks predate the migmatitization, while others are younger but are older than Cretaceous.

The granitization in the Dibaya Complex is approximately the same age as the charnockitization of the Kasai–Lomami Complex. Field and petro-logical observations suggesting this age relationship are borne out by radiometric ages (DELHAL and LEDENT, in press). The granitization is of migmatitic type in the northern part of the Dibaya quadrangle and of more homogeneous type in the southern part.

The Luiza Metasedimentary Complex

The Luiza metasedimentary complex forms a W.S.W.–E.N.E.-trending band which lies between the Lulua Complex in the north and the Kasai–Lomami Complex and the Luanyi Gneiss in the south. Its contact against the Lulua Complex and against the Upper Luanyi Gneiss is faulted. Against the Kasai–Lomami Complex the contact is either faulted or unconformable, varying from region to region. The dip of the beds is generally between 60° and 90°, and the dip of the fault planes seems to be about the same size. The complex consists of rocks of sedimentary origin—quartzites, micaceous quartzites, muscovite, sericite, and tremolite schists, and itabirites; and rocks of magmatic origin—granite gneiss and granite pegmatites. All these rocks are affected by the deformation and upper mesozonal metamorphism that characterizes the Luizian Orogeny. Radiometric ages (DELHAL and LEDENT, in press) indicate that some of the granites belong to the pre-Luiza basement but crop out in anticlines of the Luiza Complex. Others are pre-sumed to be remobilized from the basement and injected into the Luiza

Complex itself. The amphibole schists, that might be thought to form a part of the Luiza Complex, in fact belong to the Kasai–Lomami norite–gabbro (see p. 176) and probably represent the axial zones of anticlinal folds (LEGRAND, 1955, DELHAL, 1957a, 1963). The synorogenic metamorphism which affected the Luiza Complex has been dated at about 2,125 Myr (see p. 160).

In the Kanda Kanda region there are small patches of micaceous quartzite, muscovite schist, and metamorphosed conglomerate (MORELLI and RAUCQ, 1961) which are lithologically similar to, and have the same tectonic orientation as, the corresponding rocks of the Luiza Complex. The age of 2,135 Myr of mica from a conglomerate completes the correlation. These patches seem to rest unconformably on the crystalline basement, which is the eastward continuation of the Charnockite Complex (MORELLI and RAUCQ, 1961).

The Lulua Sedimentary and Volcanic complex

This only feebly metamorphosed complex rests unconformably on the Dibaya Complex (FIEREMANS, 1959). The age of the Lulua Complex is unknown, but its lithological properties suggest correlation with the Kibaran–Burundian. It will be described in Section 5.

3.3.4. Other parts of the Kasai–Lomami–Lulua area

Among all the igneous and metamorphic rocks in the other parts of the Kasai–Lomami–Lulua area (see Fig. 6) only two sequences have been distinguished, viz., the Kalundwe Complex and the Lukoshi Complex, both unconformably overlain by the Kibaran.

The Kalundwe Complex was first observed in the Mutombo Mukulu region, east of Long. 24° E. (CAHEN, 1954, p. 240). The complex is certainly pre-Kibaran, but its age has not been determined and its stratigraphical relationships with the formations of the Dibaya, Luiza, and Kanda Kanda regions are unknown.

The Lukoshi Complex crops out in the Upper Lulua Basin in the extreme south of the Kasai–Lomami–Lulua region. It consists of phyllites, sericite schists and talc schists, sericitic quartzites, arkoses, and metamorphosed conglomerates (CAHEN, 1954, pp. 240–241). The amphibole rocks in contact with these rocks may also belong to the complex. The rocks are intensely sheared. The beds are folded with strikes varying between 250° and 280° and between 340° and 350° and with dips directed towards the south. The conglomerates contain pebbles of granite and pegmatite in a feldspar-bearing matrix. The conglomerates are thus younger than the granite but are themselves migmatized. The age relations between the granite and the migmatites of this region and the granites and migmatites of the north (see p. 177) have not yet been determined. The age of 1,845 Myr (see p. 160) sets a younger age limit to the Lukoshi Complex. Ages of similar magnitude characterize the granitic and migmatitic rocks mentioned on p. 176.

3.3.5. Structural geology

The present-day knowledge is insufficient for outlining the tectonic geology in detail. There is a certain similarity of the general trends of rock masses, of migmatitic zonation, and of the foliation of crystalline schists, but there are differences in detail. The rocks generally strike between E.W. and N.E.–S.W. However, there are strikes approaching N.–S. or even N.W.–S.E. in many areas, particularly in the Kanda Kanda, Mutombo Mukulu, and Kapanga regions.

The evolution of the Dibaya, Luiza, and Kanda Kanda region suggests the existence of at least three main orogenies (DELHAL, 1963a; LEDENT, LAY, and DELHAL, 1963), namely: (1) the oldest orogeny corresponding to the formation of the Luanyi Gneiss; (2) one corresponding to the intrusion of the norite–gabbro and the charnockitization, and probably to the Dibaya Complex; and (3) the orogeny of the Luiza Complex. Events postdating the last of these three main orogenies must be taken into consideration, even though they are dated unreliably or not at all. Among them are mentioned the formation of certain mylonites of the Dibaya Complex (see p. 177) and epizonal hydrothermal alteration facilitated by a network of narrow fissures that penetrate, in a very irregular way, all the formations of the basement. The fissures may represent a superficial tectonic phase. The structural evolution of the region ended with a period of faulting, the main faults postdating the Lulua Complex (see p. 220).

The Lukoshi Complex forms an arc, concave towards the south, that seems to be the remains of a fold chain that disappears, towards the southeast, under the N.E.-trending Kibaran Belt that rests unconformably on the Complex (MOUREAU, 1960).

3.3.6. Mineralization

Gold

Gold has been recovered from many alluvial or eluvial deposits of low yield, now worked out, which are distributed, from the north to the south: in the Luiza Complex; in the Norite–Gabbro and Charnockite Complex which follows towards the south; in the region of amphibole rocks, gneisses, and migmatites making up a part of the Lulua Basin between Kapanga and Sandoa, and in the basins of many affluents of the Upper Lulua, south of the Katanga–Dilolo–Angola railway, a region occupied by the Lukoshi Complex, amphibole rocks, and migmatites.

The only deposits studied in detail are those of the Norite–Gabbro and Charnockite Complex (THOREAU, 1935; FRIEDLAENDER, 1942). There, the gold occurs, always in small quantities, in charnockite, in mesothermal quartz and feldspar veins, in quartz veins, and as an accessory mineral in quartz–feldspar–garnet rocks (granulites) of the charnockite zone, biotite- and garnet-bearing pegmatite veins, and dolerite dykes. Several phases of mineralization exist, possibly related to the same intrusive cycle.

In the other deposits, gold appears to be most abundant in the rocks of the amphibole zone; gold occurs in vein quartz, sometimes associated with tourmaline (LEPERSONNE, 1941). A deposit on the Upper Lulua contains gold associated with cassiterite in pegmatite and in greisen. It is not known if the gold, which occurs in quartz veins, is of the same age as the tin, which might be of Kibaran age.

Manganese

A large deposit of manganese is mined at Kisenge, not far from the gold–tin zone of the Upper Lulua Basin. By 1960, the annual production had reached 390,000 tons of ore containing more than 48% Mn. The deposit, described by MARCHANDISE (1958), consists of several layers of manganese oxides (cryptomelane, pyrolusite, lithiophorite?) interstratified with slates that are often very rich in garnet and sometimes contain graphite. Associated with the slates there are gondites which form a part of the zone of sericite schists and accessory quartzites of the Lukoshi Complex. These rocks have an E.–W. strike and dip south at 45°–70°. Boreholes have revealed the presence in depth of manganese carbonate. The garnet contains about 35% MnO and is almost pure spessartine.

For a considerable thickness from the surface, the deposit is the result of concentration of products of lateritic alteration of manganese-bearing rocks; the alteration of the garnet is particularly noticeable. The passage in depth of the oxide minerals into carbonate rock also containing garnet (P. GROSE- MANS, unpublished information) suggests that the carbonate rock might be the main source of the manganese, and that the oxides were derived from it.

The Kisenge deposit may be compared with the manganese deposits of India, Ghana, and Brazil. A deposit of the same type, whose economical importance is still unknown, was discovered in the Luputa region of eastern Kasai, associated with patches of metamorphic rocks (MORELLI and RAUCQ, 1961).

Chromium, nickel, and iron

In the Lutshatsha and Nkonko serpentinites which crop out in the granite– migmatite complex of the Dibaya region (see p. 178), chromite (LEGRAND, LOHEST and RAUCQ, 1958; HERMAN and RAUCQ, 1961) and nickel (RAUCQ, 1961) deposits occur. The serpentinites contain generally less than 1% Cr, the chromite being very finely dispersed, and 0.2%–0.3% Ni. Finally, the itabirite massifs that exist in many parts of the Kasai–Lomami–Lulua region contain reserves of iron ore amounting to hundreds of millions of tons, with 40%–65% Fe. The origin of the itabirites has been the subject of numerous studies (THOREAU, 1935; CAHEN, 1948; MORELLI and RAUCQ, 1962).

3.4. *Common characteristics of basement rocks of northern Congo and of the Kasai–Lomami–Lulua region*

The basement rocks of northern Congo and of the Kasai–Lomami–Lulua region are similar to the majority of basement rocks of central and southern Africa. There are vast areas of granite and migmatitic gneiss, and within them occur patches of metamorphic rocks of sedimentary or volcanic origin whose relations with one another and with the gneisses are difficult to establish, and amphibole rocks derived by the metamorphism of intrusive rocks, lavas, and sediments are abundant. Mesozonal metamorphism is most common, but some large areas are either epizonal or catazonal and often belong to the charnockite facies.

The strikes of zonation, of foliation, and, even though it is rarely observable, of stratification are very irregular. However, general trends of regional extent are often discernible.

In northern Congo, there occur two or three superposed groups, and it is certain that the area was affected by several orogenies. In the south, traces of three orogenic cycles are at present distinguished, and there are two additional complexes that are still inadequately defined.

Within each of these major complexes, the elements characteristic of the development of a folded belt of geosynclinal origin cannot always be observed. A. M. MacGREGOR, who has worked on the Precambrian of Rhodesia which is of the same type, reached the following conclusion: "The structure of the gold belts suggests gravitational subsidence of a thin crust in a lighter medium, and appears to be determined not by the intersection of orogenic belts, but by the location of gregarious ovoidal batholiths (gneiss domes), between which the schists have a synclinal structure often cleaved by cupolas or triangular in shape. In dealing with rocks formed when the world was less than half its present age, a strict adherence to the doctrine of uniformitarianism is considered unjustified." (MacGREGOR, 1951, p. XXVII).

It seems, however, that this opinion must be modified. Some of the oldest rock sequences in Central Africa, for instance the North Congo Shield, which is partly probably older than 3,500 Myr, include a notable quantity of metasediments and have the general form of a folded belt. The same is true of some very old rocks of Kasai. It seems, therefore, that even in the Early Precambrian times the sedimentation and tectonics were those characteristic of folded belts.

4. The Pre-Kibaran–Burundian formations: the Ruzizian and the Mayumbian Complex[1]

4.1. *Introduction*

The Ruzizian and at least part of the Mayumbian Complex are younger than most of the rocks dealt with in Section 3, but like them are older than

[1] See footnote on p. 193.

the Kibaran–Burundian (see Section 5). However, the Ruzizian and the Mayumbian, like the Kibaran–Burundian, are the readily recognizable remains of ancient denuded mountain chains, with all the characteristics of a normal geosynclinal evolution.

The contact of the Ruzizian and the Mayumbian with their basement is inadequately known. They are overlain with great unconformity by the Kibaran–Burundian, by formations comparable to the latter, and by still younger formations.

4.2. *The Ruzizian*

4.2.1. General account

The Ruzizian forms a notable folded belt at least 250 km wide. This belt occurs in eastern Congo and in Tanzania on both sides of Lake Tanganyika, where it has a S.E.–N.W. trend. In northern Burundi and in southern Kivu it turns north, then west across Kivu and Maniema to disappear under the rocks of the Congo Basin. The Ruzizian continues into Tanzania as the Ubendian (CAHEN, 1954, p. 121).

4.2.2. Historical survey

The Urundian and the Ruzizian "Systems" were defined by F. DELHAYE and A. SALÉE in 1928 and 1932 in the course of their work in Rwanda and Burundi. Up till 1939, various geologists—N. BOUTAKOFF in 1939, J. DE LA VALLÉE POUSSIN in 1939, and E. ASSELBERGHS in 1939—applied the stratigraphic scale established by DELHAYE and SALÉE to Kivu without any modification. However, the difficulty in distinguishing the unconformity between the Urundian and the Ruzizian led them to consider these two "Systems" as a single major unit in spite of local disharmony in their folding.

Since 1946, many papers have been published giving stratigraphical details and some that demonstrated the occurrence of a notable discordance within the Urundian–Ruzizian sequence. These investigations are those of A. LHOEST in 1946, R. DE DYCKER in 1948, P. GROSEMANS in 1949, A. JAMOTTE in 1949, and A. SAFIANNIKOFF in 1950. In 1952, L. CAHEN (see CAHEN, 1954, pp. 120–122) produced a tectonic sketch and, synthesizing the available data, showed that there were two independent folded belts which agreed closely with the original definitions of DELHAYE and SALÉE. He was thus able to redefine the Urundian (now spelled Burundian) and the Ruzizian (see Fig. 7). Finally, some unpublished works (ANTUN, 1961b; DE BOURNONVILLE, 1961) give details of the contact between the Burundian and the Ruzizian in Burundi.

4.2.3. Stratigraphy

CAHEN (1954, p. 137) established a stratigraphic sequence for the Ruzizian on the basis of numerous sections in various regions of Tanzania, North Katanga, Kivu, and Maniema. He (CAHEN, 1954, p. 126) showed that in

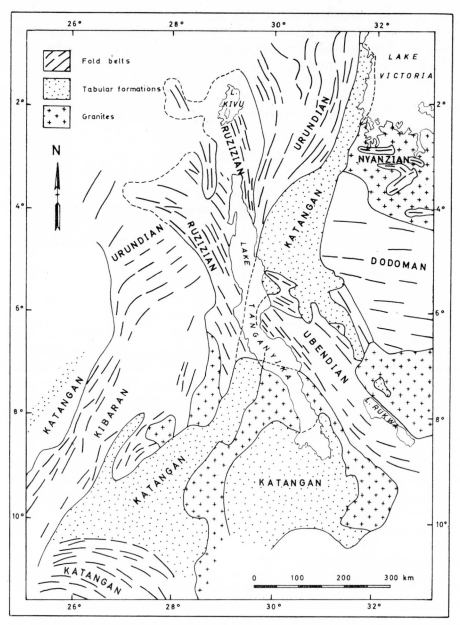

Fig. 7. Tectonic sketch map showing relations between the Kibarian–Urundian and the Ubendian–Ruzizian. Modified from QUENNELL and HALDEMANN (1960).

the type area, located in Burundi east of Lake Tanganyika and the Ruzizi Valley (see Fig. 11), where F. DELHAYE and A. SALÉE had defined the *"Système de la Ruzizi"*, a section can be incorporated in the general stratigraphic scale. Some partly unpublished data later than CAHEN's work confirms that the formations of this region that LENK-CHEVITCH (1948), and PEETERS (1956) attributed to the Burundian are indeed Ruzizian. However, some modifications in the stratigraphic sequence proposed by CAHEN are necessary.

The unconformity between the Burundian and the Ruzizian is observed on both sides of the type area (see Fig. 11). First, in the west, in the Itombwe region southwest of Lake Kivu, the Burundian forms a syncline resting unconformably on gneiss, amphibolite, mica schist, and micaceous quartzite (CAHEN, 1954, p. 121; LHOEST, 1964, and personal communication). Secondly, in the east, the Burundian rests unconformably on analogous formations. The unconformity follows the Congo–Nile ridge and crops out in the region between Muramvia and Ndora (ANTUN, 1961b) and in the south of Burundi near Nyanza (personal communication from the Geological Survey of Burundi). In the Ruzizian zone thus defined (see Figs 7 and 11), and in its continuation in Tanzania, datings have yielded ages definitely older than those of the Burundian (see p. 186).

A critical examination of the published data (LENK-CHEVITCH, 1948; CAHEN, 1954, p. 126; PEETERS, 1956; WEIS, 1959) in the light of more recent but still unpublished information (MINÉTAIN, 1958; ANTUN, 1961b) allows the establishment of the stratigraphical succession for the Ruzizian of the type area given in Table 3. This replaces the succession given by CAHEN.

TABLE 3

Stratigraphy of the Ruzizian in the type area

Lithological description	Thickness, m
(4) Schists, phyllites, and sericite schists with quartzites and quartz phyllites in the lower part	500–1,000
(3) Schists, phyllites, and sericite schists with large lenses of calcitic and dolomitic limestone, passing into mica schists and amphibolites	1,500
(2) Quartzites, locally arkosic or conglomeratic, with interbedded slates, passing into mica schists and sericite quartzites	500–1,000
(1) Slates, frequently graphite-bearing, passing into biotite, sericite, and chlorite schists; passing into or overlain by gneiss, mica schists, amphibolites, and micaceous quartzites, all intruded by granite	

On the basis of sections in the Ruzizian of northern Katanga, Kivu, and Maniema, CAHEN (1954, p. 137) established the stratigraphical succession given in Table 4.

A comparison of the succession given above with that of the type region

G

TABLE 4

General stratigraphy of the Ruzizian

Upper sequence (from top to bottom)

(5) Various schists, phyllites, and quartzites that may pass laterally, by metamorphism, into mica schists, amphibole schists, amphibolites, and quartzites

(4) Phyllitic conglomerate, very thick, sometimes with limestone pebbles; may pass laterally, by metamorphism, into a biotite schist with drawn-out lenses of calcitic limestone, amphibole schists, and amphibolites

Lower sequence (from top to bottom)

(3) Mica schists and phyllites, often graphite-bearing, with lenses and beds of fine-grained, crystalline calcitic limestone

(2) Quartzites, arkoses, and dark-coloured phyllitic schists

(1) Schists, often graphite-bearing, quartz phyllites and quartzites

When metamorphosed, the lower beds pass into sericite schists, chlorite schists, and amphibole schists, amphibolites, and gneisses

---

shows that the rocks of the type region probably belong to the lower sequence. The total thickness of the Ruzizian cannot be determined precisely, but is certainly very considerable.

4.2.4. Age, relationships with younger and older groups, and relationships with adjacent regions

The datings that assign an age of about 1,240 Myr (see p. 157) to the Burundian Orogeny, and an age exceeding 1,850 Myr (see p. 158) to the Ruzizian Orogeny, agree with the unconformity observed in the field.

The ages of 1,850 Myr–1,650 Myr were obtained on rocks from the type area of the Ruzizian and in the area of northern Katanga ascribed to the Ruzizian. They confirm the placing of formations in these two regions into the same pre-Burundian group (CAHEN, 1954, pp. 122–126). A somewhat imprecise age of (2,100 ± 250) Myr (see p. 158) pertains to some granite gneisses ascribed to the Ruzizian, from the Runinya River, 24 km W.S.W. of Astrida (Rwanda; see Fig. 11). This age might belong to the Ruzizian cycle, but it might also indicate that the gneiss is pre-Ruzizian. Apart from this possibility, which should be reinvestigated, nothing is known in the Congo, Rwanda, and Burundi of the relationship of the Ruzizian to older rocks (CAHEN, 1954, pp. 260–266; 1963a).

CAHEN (1954, pp. 122–124) showed that the Ruzizian is the equivalent of those rocks in Tanzania which occur in the continuation of the Ruzizian tectonic trend and are, at the present, placed in the Ubendian System (QUENNELL, McKINLAY and AITKEN, 1956). Ages in the same time range have been obtained for some of these rocks (see p. 158).

4.2.5. Tectonics

The general form of the Ruzizian Belt was described on p. 183. The extent of this folded belt and the lithological constitution and thickness of the constituent rocks demonstrate that it is a product of geosynclinal evolution. The data available are altogether too fragmentary to permit description of this evolution in detail and to define the tectonic structures. It is only possible to state that the beds are folded, often forming large monoclinal groupings, with dips of 50°–70°, in which one might suspect the presence of isoclinal folding. In the region between Albertville and Lat. 5° S., the folds are overturned towards the northeast (CAHEN, 1954, p. 138; SCHAAR, 1959).

4.2.6. Metamorphism

The degree of metamorphism of the Ruzizian varies from region to region, and within one region it varies according to the proximity of granite massifs. It is not at present possible to distinguish between regional and contact metamorphism. It can only be said that the rocks described range from epizonal to mesozonal and that no facies that could be called catazonal has, as yet, been found. The presence of more or less crystalline calcitic and dolomitic limestones and of marbles is a frequent characteristic of the Ruzizian, but it seems that nowhere do these rocks form large masses.

4.2.7. Plutonic activity

Granite massifs occupy a considerable part of the outcrop area of the Ruzizian, and their gneissose or migmatitic character has frequently been noted. The pertinent granitizations belong to at least two periods. First, the Burundian granites (see p. 212) have affected the Ruzizian of Rwanda, Burundi, Kivu, and Maniema, where the two belts either are, or were, superposed. Tin, tungsten, and niobium–tantalum mineralizations are connected with these granites. Secondly, it seems certain that there are Ruzizian granites which occur in at least the following three areas.

On both sides of the southern end of the Itombe synclinorium, probably Burundian (SAFIANNIKOFF, 1950; PEETERS, 1956), there are below the unconformity, granites that pass into gneisses and migmatites, then into mica schists. These granites have not affected the rocks of the synclinorium. In addition pebbles of granite occur in the basal conglomerate of the Burundian of the synclinorium (LHOEST, 1946).

The second region is the northeast of Katanga, and there a granite has been dated at (1,690 ± 170) Myr.

The third region is located west of Butare (formerly Astrida, Rwanda), and there an age of (2,100 ± 250) Myr has been obtained (see p. 158) which might even be pre-Ruzizian (see p. 186). This zone of old granites lies east of the region where a stratigraphic succession for the Ruzizian was established (see p. 185).

4.2.8. Mineralization

Because the Ruzizian was frequently the site of mineralizations connected with the Burundian granites, it is difficult to distinguish the mineralizations belonging to the Ruzizian Cycle. The occurrence of pegmatites or granites with lanthanide minerals, mainly monazite, is characteristic of the pre-Burundian rocks of many regions. Some deposits have been exploited, such as the bastnäsite deposits at Karonge, southeast of Bujumbura (formerly Usumbura; see Fig. 11) in Ruzizian rocks (THOREAU, ADERCA and VAN WAMBEKE, 1958). These deposits consist of veinlets of bastnäsite sometimes associated with quartz, and faults and joints filled by a gangue breccia of partly silicified barite which contains fragments of bastnäsite and sometimes sulfide minerals, viz., pyrite and galena. The faults and joints are younger than the post-Burundian pegmatites with an age of 970 Myr (MME DOLLY LEDENT, in MONTEYNE-POULAERT, DELWICHE, and CAHEN, 1963), but the breccia includes older materials such as galena with an age of 1,650 Myr (see p. 158), which belongs to the Ruzizian. Consequently, it appears that, like the galena, the bastnäsite of the breccia is derived from Ruzizian veins or veinlets.

Besides the lanthanide mineralizations, it seems that certain gold mineralizations of Maniema, Rwanda, Burundi, and northern Katanga are Ruzizian, as well as the corundum of Kivu (CAHEN, 1954, pp. 141, 512–515).

4.3. *The Mayumbian Complex*[1]

4.3.1. Geographical setting and general stratigraphical relationships

The Mayumbian Complex runs nearly parallel to the Atlantic coast, from which it is usually separated by a 100-km-wide strip of Mesozoic and Tertiary strata (see Fig. 8). These rocks are of marine or continental origin, are little disturbed, and rest unconformably on the Mayumbian. The Mayumbian crops out, from the north to the south, in the Gabon Republic, the Congo Republic (Brazzaville), the Cabinda Enclave, the Lower Congo (Congo Republic, Léopoldville), and north of Angola.

In Lower Congo, the Mayumbian forms a band, 80–100 km wide, running parallel to the coast, and reappears farther in the east as two windows, namely, the Sansikwa Massif near the Angola frontier and, in the north, the Kimuaka Massif, which lies between the Congo River and the frontier of the Congo Republic (Brazzaville).

The Mayumbian is unconformably overlain by the Sansikwa (see p. 221). The structural geology of Lower Congo is extremely complex (see p. 193).

4.3.2. Historical survey

The first data on the Mayumbian, then called Archean, were assembled by E. DUPONT in 1889, J. CORNET in 1896, and V. BRIEN in 1910. The name "Mayumbe System" was introduced by L. CAHEN in 1945. The present-day information is due to the investigations of L. CAHEN in 1945 and 1948 (see CAHEN, 1954), CORIN (1946, 1948), THONNART (1955, 1956), BERTOSSA and THONNART (1957), and unpublished observations of L. CAHEN and P.

[1] See footnote on p. 193.

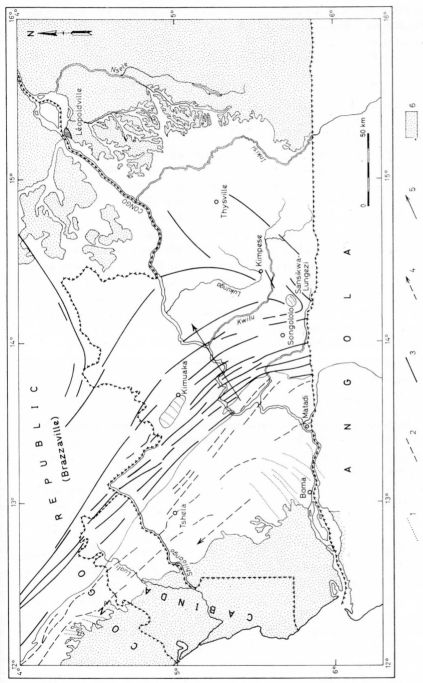

FIG. 8. Tectonic sketch map of Lower Congo. 1, Lower Mayumbian fold axes and trends. 2, Mayumbian and West Congolian fold axes and trends superimposed on older rocks. 3, West Congolian fold axes and trends (towards the foreland of the West Congolian fold belt, the West Congolian trends are influenced by older Mayumbian structures). 4, Presumed direction of foreland of the Lower Mayumbian belt. 5, Direction of foreland of West Congolian belt. 6, Mesozoic, Cenozoic, and Recent cover.

THONNART in 1958. The major unconformity at the top of the Mayumbian, suspected to exist by E. DUPONT in 1889 and L. CAHEN in 1948, was verified by LEPERSONNE (1951) and ANTUN (1961a).

Outside Lower Congo, the same rocks have been the subject of studies in the Congo Republic (Brazzaville) by COSSON (1953, 1955), and in the Gabon Republic by DÉVIGNE (1959), who divided the beds corresponding to the Mayumbian of Lower Congo into two independent sequences called the Pre-Mayombe and the Mayombe Systems. Towards the south, the Mayumbian passes into Angola, where its upper part is included within an extension of the Sansikwa, and its lower part is called the "Basement Complex" (KORPERSHOEK, 1960; SCHERMERHORN, 1960).

In this paper, the names "Mayumbian Complex" and "Mayumbian" are used in the same sense as the "Mayumbe System" of L. CAHEN in 1945 (see CAHEN, 1954). It is now certain that this complex must be subdivided in two more or less completely independent units. However, in view of current discussions on the nature and stratigraphical position of the intra-Mayumbian unconformity (see p. 193) and of the fact that this unconformity appears to be less visible in Lower Congo than in the neighbouring areas, we have refrained from giving new names to these units, which are here respectively called the Upper Mayumbian and the Lower Mayumbian (see CAHEN 1963c). All or a part of the Lower Mayumbian is of the same age as some of the older formations of the Kasai basement and, were the stratigraphy better known, should have been described in Section 3.

4.3.3. Stratigraphy

Lithological successions

Two successions have been established, one in the region of the railway from Boma to Tshela and the other in the Matadi–Inga region. The first of them remains essentially as described by CAHEN in 1945 and 1948 (see CAHEN, 1954, p. 204); the more detailed later observations of B. STEENSTRA are not yet available in their entirety. The second succession is based on a modification of CAHEN's original sequence, and in its present form includes the observations of BERTOSSA and THONNART (1957) and L. CAHEN and P. THONNART (unpublished; see Table 5, Columns 3 and 4).

It is certain that the Inga sequence forms a part of the Duizi sequence, but the relationship between the Tshela sequence and the Gangila Greenstone Complex has given rise to discussion. In Lower Congo and in Congo (Brazzaville) available evidence seems to favour the correlation of the Tshela sequence with the Yelala Conglomerate. It appears, however, that in Angola the evidence suggests that the Tshela sequence corresponds to the Gangila Greenstone Complex (see CAHEN, 1963c).

Table 5 shows, besides the Congo successions, those observed by DÉVIGNE (1959) in the Gabon Republic and by COSSON (1955) in Congo (Brazzaville). It should be noted that columns 1–3 represent successions that are

FIG. 9. Stromatolitic bioherm in Sekelolo limestone ("Lamba Rocks"). Near Kimpese, Lower Congo. Contact of bedded formation with the bioherm can be seen on lower left and mounts gradually towards the right, to disappear in the middle of the photograph, the right-hand portion of which is completely made up of stromatolitic material. The bioherm is approximately 300 m across and 50 m high. (The Sekelolo limestone belongs to the West Congolian (see p. 268). Photo, J. Lepersonne.

TABLE 5

Regional stratigraphy of the Mayumbian Complex
(CAHEN, 1954)

Western Gabon DÉVIGNE (1959)	Congo Republic, Brazzaville COSSON (1955)	Boma–Tshela Railway region (CAHEN, 1948b, 1954)	Matadi–Inga region (BERTOSSA and THONNART, 1957; CAHEN, 1963; L. CAHEN and P. THONNART, unpublished)
Mayombe System	Loukoula sequence. Upper Group:	Duizi sequence:	Inga sequence.
Sounda sequence: Slates, crystalline limestones, quartzites, volcanic rocks	In the south, "*schistes lustrés*", often pyrite-bearing, black or dark grey; phyllites, sandstones and mica- and graphite-bearing quartzites	Sericite, talc, and chlorite schists, augen schists passing locally into gneiss, sericite quartzites, grits, laminated rhyolites, partly porphyritic, ? crystalline calcitic limestones	Mount Lungu formation: Micaceous and schistose quartzites, sericite–chlorite schists, talc schists, black schists, laminated rhyolites; locally, conglomerate horizon at the base
Loukoula sequence: Chlorite schists, mica schists, and tuffaceous schists, volcanic rocks (including rhyolites)	In the north, quartzites Lower Group: Complex of chlorite-bearing mica schists and rhyolite schists; sporadic basal conglomerate with a matrix of mica schist		Sikila Formation: Laminated, metamorphosed rhyolites and pyroclastics; laminated, porphyritic granite; local quartzite horizons
Pre-Mayombe System	Bikossi sequence. Upper Group or greenstone complex: green schists: complex in which rocks of magmatic origin seem to be subordinate to parametamorphic rocks	(Locally: greenstones)	Gangila Greenstone Complex: Amygdaloidal amphibolites, amphibole, biotite, and chlorite schists, epidosites, dolerites and microdolerites
Douigni sequence: Mica schists, amphibolites, porphyroids			
	Lower Group or muscovite quartzites: graphite schists	Tshela sequence: Graphite schists and quartzites; sandstones and quartzites, partly feldspar-bearing	
Kouboula Mountains sequence: Quartzites, micaceous quartzites	Muscovite quartzites with frequent magnetite; subordinate mica schists; conglomerate facies with pebbles of quartzite drawn out to an almond shape	Matadi and Palabala sequence: Conglomerates, muscovite quartzites well developed in the Boma area, less crystalline towards the north; rare mica schists	Matadi and Palabala sequence: Yelala Conglomerate (quartz and quartzite pebbles in a quartzitic matrix)
			Matadi Formation: Quartzites and grey schistose quartzites containing sericite and often magnetite; mica schists
Doussa sequence: Plagioclase–muscovite–biotite gneisses	Loémé sequence: Mica schists and two-mica gneisses	Quartzitic mica schists containing biotite, and, less frequently, muscovite; micaceous quartzites; intense migmatization	Palabala Formation: Quartzitic mica schists with quartzites and amphibolites; gneisses

nearly continuous from north-northwest to south-southeast. The correlation of Columns 1 and 2 is that of Dévigne (1959).

Subdivision of the lithological sequence

The lithological subdivision of the Mayumbian Complex was discussed by Cahen (1963c). In Lower Congo, no major break within the complex has ever been recorded, even though the existence of a break of some magnitude has been suspected (Cahen, 1954, p. 233; Bertossa and Thonnart, 1957). In the north [Congo (Brazzaville) and Gabon], evidence is more definite, pointing to a major unconformity in Gabon (see Table 5, Column 1), allowing Dévigne (1959) to distinguish a "Mayombe System" and a "Pre-Mayombe System". This major break corresponds with the suspected break in Lower Congo. The Duizi–Inga sequence (or Upper Mayumbian) is, in Angola, considered a part of the extended Sansikwa (Korpershoek, 1960; Schermerhorn, 1960, and personal communication) and rests with a major unconformity on a "Basement Complex" (Schermerhorn and Stanton, 1963b). This unconformity confirms the existence of an important, perhaps major, break below the Duizi–Inga sequence.

Geochronological evidence (see p. 158) and tectonic evidence (see p. 194) also favour the division of the Mayumbian Complex into two distinct orogenic cycles. Cahen (1963c; Cahen and others, 1963) gave reasons supporting the location of a major break beneath the Duizi–Inga sequence (Upper Mayumbian).[1]

4.3.4. Tectonics

At first sight, the geological map of the Lower Congo (see Fig. 8) seems to show a N.N.W.-running main trend of folding in all rocks except in the quasi-tabular portions of the *"Schisto-calcaire"* and *"Schisto-gréseux"* (see p. 265). Also, nearly all the folds are overturned towards the east, and the variations in the degree of metamorphism are fairly gradual. This broad uniformity has, for a long time, hindered the unravelling of the tectonics of Lower Congo. It was not until 1947 that M. C. Brandes and C. Kool (quoted in Cahen, 1948b; see Cahen, 1954, p. 212) observed the first major unconformity. Their observation was followed by other more precise ones (Lepersonne, 1951; Antun, 1961a). The existence of two major orogenies was demonstrated, but a number of observations remained unexplained.

In fact, two principal trends appear in the Mayumbe Region (see Fig. 8),

---

[1] *Note added in proof.* L. Cahen and J. Lepersonne (*Compt. Rend.*, **262**, 1184, 1966) definitely showed that three superposed orogenies exist in Lower Congo. The unconformities have been mapped across the whole country. The lowermost stratigraphical unit that comprises what was hitherto called "Lower Mayumbian" plus some beds previously considered "Upper Mayumbian", is now called the Zadinian; the middle unit, which comprises the "Upper Mayumbian" less the aforementioned beds, but to which recently individual beds have been added, is now called the Mayumbian. The West Congolian forms the uppermost unit.

viz., a dominant N.N.W. trend, and one that is more local, varying from N.N.E. to N.E., and, as regards the trend of true folds, occurs only in the Mayumbian Complex. It also occurs as the trend of faults and undulations in the foreland part of the West Congolian belt. The N.N.W. trend is the only trend of true folding in the West Congolian of Lower Congo and occurs also in the Mayumbian Complex. Furthermore, it has been proved that a number of N.E.-trending folds in the Mayumbian have been subsequently deformed during the N.N.W.-directed phase of folding. Thus the conclusion follows that the N.E. trend is older than the N.N.W. trend. Dévigne (1959) had already noted these two trends of folding and referred the first trend to Pre-Mayombian folding and the second one to Mayombian folding. In Lower Congo the N.E. trend affects the Lower Mayumbian; and a N.W. trend the Upper Mayumbian, which corresponds to Dévigne's Mayombian.

One of the best-known tectonic features is the anticlinorial zone of Matadi. The original trend of at least the Palabala, Matadi, and Yelala formations was E.N.E. This was succeeded by the present N.N.W. trend of the anticlinorial zone which is overturned towards the east. This zone is a part of a more complex structural unit involving both Upper and Lower Mayumbian which is overturned on inverted Sansikwa beds. Whatever the nature of the contact between this structural complex and the Sansikwa, whether a normal contact or a thrust zone, it dates from a violent post-Sansikwa tectonic phase. Because the Sansikwa was involved in the West Congolian movements (see p. 273), the N.N.W.-trending structure that affects Lower Mayumbian rocks does not belong only to the Mayumbian but also to the West Congolian Orogeny. The influence of this orogeny is confirmed by the West Congolian Boma migmatites and pegmatites and by the similarly West Congolian main metamorphism of the Boma region (Cahen and others, 1963; see p. 195).

Within the Mayumbian the distribution of the N.E. trends with respect to the N.N.W. trends is significant. The former are preserved mainly in the Boma region or farther in the west and in the anticlinal windows, exposed far in the east beneath a post-Mayumbian cover. The most definite among the N.N.W. trends occur between the two groups of N.E. trends.

The greatest depth of the N.N.W.-trending West Congolian Geosyncline was without doubt attained west of Matadi, and it is there that the pre-West Congolian rocks were depressed to their greatest depth and were thus most intensely affected by the second orogeny. In the regions depressed to a lesser depth the original trends are preserved. In the direction of the hinterland (Boma and farther west) they are only partly preserved, but towards the foreland (anticlines of the Kimuaka and the Sansikwa Massifs) they are much more completely preserved.

The facts mentioned in the preceding paragraphs were considered by Cahen (1963c), who, however, overrated the regularity of the N.E. trends in the Upper Mayumbian. These trends certainly exist mainly outside Lower Congo, where N.W. trends are dominant which are not ascribable to the N.N.W. direction of the West Congolian folding. Moreover, petro-graphical evidence (DELHAL, 1964a) confirms the independent evolution of the Upper Mayumbian with respect to the West Congolian.

Taking these new facts into account, the following conclusions, slightly modifying those of CAHEN (1963c), may be drawn for Lower Congo.

(1) The original fold trend of the Lower Mayumbian wherever visible is northeasterly. The original trend of the Upper Mayumbian folding in Lower Congo is northwesterly.

(2) The N.N.W. trend is that of the West Congolian folding. In the fore-land of the West Congolian the undulating cover of the older belt(s) is modelled on the N.E.–E.N.E. trend visible in the older belts.

(3) The present-day distribution of trends is only partly original and is largely caused by the superposition of the West Congolian orogeny on the older belt(s).

4.3.5. Metamorphism

The metamorphism of the Mayumbian rocks is very complex. To the pre-West Congolian metamorphic effects must be added those of the West Congolian Orogeny and the by no means negligible contact metamorphism. The oldest strata of the Lower Mayumbian seem to have been metamor-phosed low in the mesozone, whereas the depth zone of the metamorphism of the Upper Mayumbian is scarcely deeper than the lower epizone.

4.3.6. Plutonic activity

In the Boma region, there is a group of migmatitic gneisses, pegmatites, and aplites which have affected the mica schists and amphibolites of the Matadi–Palabala sequence. Farther in the north, the same migmatites have affected the fine-grained granites at km 29–40 along the Mayumbe Railway (see CAHEN, 1954, p. 207; DELHAL, 1958c; CAHEN and others, 1963). There exist, therefore, two distinct phenomena. Firstly, the granites at km 29–40, which were emplaced during the Lower Mayumbian time, have undoubtedly been tectonized, but it is not certain whether their tectonization took place during the post-Lower Mayumbian or the post-Upper Mayumbian phase. Secondly, the migmatites and the associated pegmatites are clearly of West Congolian or post-West Congolian age (see p. 156).

The migmatitic gneisses and pegmatites of the M'Pozo region near Matadi have, since J. CORNET's investigations in 1896, been considered to be related to those of Boma. Like the Boma gneisses and pegmatites, they were emplaced in the Matadi–Palabala sequence and have similar chemical and mineralogical properties. Nevertheless, they bear the marks of an orogeny postdating their time of formation. An admittedly imprecise age of $(2,970 \pm 470)$ Myr makes them definitely older than the Boma mig-matites (see p. 156).

FIG. 10. The Inga rapids on the Congo (Lower Congo). The foreground and the middle ground are made up of schists and metamorphic rhyolites of the Duizi–Inga series of the Mayumbian. In the background, Lufu microgranite. A large hydro-electric plant is planned at the site illustrated. Photo, C. Lamote.

The Lufu Microgranite Massif, among other similar massifs, is definitely of Mayumbian, pre-Sansikwa, age, and thus belongs to the Upper Mayumbian. The age of this massif, which is fairly shallow and is probably connected with the rhyolite extrusions of the Sikila Formation (BERTOSSA and THONNART, 1957), seems to be of the order of 1,500 Myr or older (see Fig. 10 and p. 158).

Finally, the emplacement of the alkalic Noqui Granite, which contains riebeckite and aegirite, postdates the formation of the Matadi anticline (see p. 194). It appears to be very similar to the so-called "Older Granites" of Nigeria, whose age is around 500 Myr.

Several beds of extrusive rocks are known. The Palabala beds include stratified greenstones which are probably lavas. The Gangila Greenstone Complex contains abundant amygdaloidal amphibolitized lavas which probably end the Lower Mayumbian phase. Finally, a notable part of the Upper Mayumbian consists of rhyolites.

4.3.7. Mineralization

The only economic mineral connected with the Mayumbian is gold, but it occurs only in small quantities, and some deposits are clearly veins of uncertain age. There are also traces of copper, iron, manganese, and tin, the latter connected with the Noqui Granite.

4.3.8. Conclusions

The present-day evidence clearly favours the existence, in Lower Congo, of three superposed orogenies. The first orogeny with an age of the order of $(2,970 \pm 470)$ Myr most probably affected the sequence here called the Lower Mayumbian. This was involved in the formation of a mainly northeast-trending chain which was followed by the deposition of the Upper Mayumbian sequence, which was folded probably more than 1,500 Myr ago. The Upper Mayumbian folding was succeeded by the formation of a large geosyncline with a N.N.W. trend, viz., the West Congolian geosyncline, and its main folding phase, at about 625 Myr ago, gave the beds already affected by the previous periods of deformation their present-day appearance.

5. The Kibaran–Burundian and comparable sequences

5.1. *Introduction*

The rock sequences which are here discussed, namely, the Kibaran and Burundian (see Fig. 11), the Lulua Sedimentary and Volcanic Complex (see Fig. 6) and the Sansikwa and Liki–Bembian (see Fig. 15) are younger than those dealt with in Section 4. For some of them geochronological data are available which allow their ages to be placed between about 1,850 Myr and 1,240 Myr (see p. 157), and the field relations of the others suggest that they date from the same interval of time. In general, these sequences rest, with a major unconformity, on their basements and are overlain, with a marked unconformity, by the Katangan and its equivalents (see Section 6). Locally, these boundary unconformities are less obvious but are always observable. The state of the present-day knowledge varies greatly from region to region; much is known of a large part of the Burundian, of most of the Kibaran, of the Lulua Complex, and of the Sansikwa; but very little of the Liki–Bembian.

5.2. *The Kibaran*

5.2.1. General survey

The very thick Kibaran sequence which occupies a vast area, crops out in a S.W.–N.E. direction across Katanga from the Nzilo Gorges to near Lat. 5° S. (see Fig. 11). The southern half of the area has been studied in some detail. Some less systematic studies show that the beds continue, always with the same general strike, across the northern frontier of Katanga, where they are called the Burundian (see p. 152). The Kibaran and part of the Burundian form a single belt that was deposited in the same geosyncline. Nevertheless, the inadequate state of the present-day knowledge and the

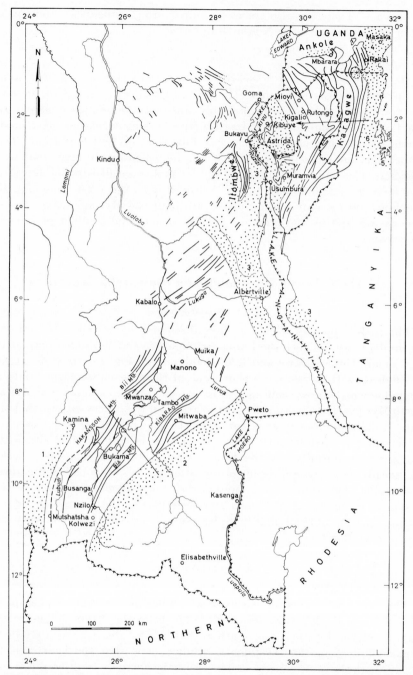

FIG. 11. Sketch map of the Kibaran–Burundian geosyncline. 1, Kasai Shield (foreland of the Kibaran). 2, Hinterland of the Kibaran, covered by the Katangan.
3, The Ubendian–Ruzizian geanticline. 4, 5, 6, Hinterland of the Burundian
(4, Toro; 5, Toro or Nyanzian or both covered by the Bukoban; 6, Nyanzian).

fact that there is an important gap in observations between the type regions of the two justify their separate treatment.

5.2.2. Historical survey

The rocks which make up the Kibaran were studied by J. CORNET in 1897, F. E. STUDT in 1908, and F. F. MATHIEU in 1913, and were divided into various "systems" on the basis of their degree of metamorphism. The name "Kibara System" was coined by M. ROBERT in 1931 and defined in the area of Kibara Mountains. In 1935, I. DE MAGNÉE established the stratigraphical sequence of the type area; it was only slightly modified in later years.

5.2.3. Stratigraphy

The territory now known in detail is extensive. For various parts of this area, geologists have produced stratigraphic successions and have proposed correlations between adjacent regions or with the general successions established before their work, but still no general summary based on the latest investigations has been published. A comparison of the various regional successions shows that a stratigraphical summary is indeed possible, but must be considered provisional because a detailed study of the available unpublished information has not been completed, and it is known that some of the regional sequences are not entirely correct as published.

The general stratigraphical sequence given in Table 6 results from a comparison of successions from the following regions: (1) Lugenda–Lubudi, southwest of Katanga (MOUREAU, 1960); (2) central Lubudi (DUMONT, 1952); (3) Lower Lubudi, Bukama, and the country south of the Hakansson Mountains (MORTELMANS, 1939); (4) the country north of the Hakansson Mountains, south of Mwanza (VAN DE WALLE, 1960); (5) Bii and Sangwa Mountains, north of Mwanza (VAN DE WALLE, 1960); (6) Nzilo region, southwestern Katanga (MOUREAU, 1960); (7) Bia Mountains (MORTELMANS, 1939); (8) Kibara Mountains (RORIVE, 1954; VAN DE WALLE, 1960). This comparison (see Fig. 12) shows that in its major features the lithological succession is the same nearly everywhere with the exception of some marked, but perhaps local, differences in region (5) and that in the western part of the Kibaran Belt (regions 1–3) the upper part of the lithological successions is more varied and more complete than in the eastern part (regions 6–8). This conclusion, illustrated in Fig. 12, appears to end the uncertainty concerning the correlation of the upper part of the successions in the Kibara Mountains (region 8) with that of the Lower Lubudi (region 3; see CAHEN and LEPERSONNE, 1956, p. 39).

The regional stratigraphical correlations used in the construction of Table 6 and Fig. 10 are based on either the correlation of one area with the next adjacent area or the presence of lithologically characteristic strata.

TABLE 6

Stratigraphy of the Kibaran

Sequences	Lithostratigraphic subdivisions	Lithological description	Thickness, m	
Sequence IV	K 5	Calcitic and dolomitic limestones, often silicified, stromatolite limestones	100–1,000	Regions (2) and (3) 1,500–1,850
	K 4b	Graphite slates, locally argillaceous grits or quartzites Dark, feldspar-bearing quartzites, arkoses, conglomeratic horizons or lenses	500–850	
Sequence III	K 4a	Schists, graphite schists, dark quartzites	500–1,500	1,900–4,000
	K 3	Schists and phyllites with thin intercalations of quartzite and quartz phyllite; feldspar-bearing quartzite intercalations in the lower part	1,000–2,500	
	K 2b	Light-coloured quartzites, locally dark and feldspar-bearing, conglomerates	450–900	
Sequence II	K 2a	In the east (regions 4–8): quartzites, locally phyllites, quartz phyllites; conglomerate horizons in the lower part In the west (regions 1–3): quartzites, quartz phyllites and phyllites; dolerites in the upper part and conglomerate horizons in the lower part. No dolerite in region (2); lenses of limestone at the top	1,000–3,600	1,500–5,600
	K 1b	Phyllites, quartz phyllites and quartzites; frequent intercalations of conglomerate and coarse-grained quartzite in the lower part; in regions (2) and (3) lenses of limestone in the upper part	500–2,000	
Sequence I	K 1a	Phyllites, quartz phyllites, sericite schists, chlorite schists; locally (in regions 4 and 8) rhyolite at the top; locally (in regions 1, 5, 6, 7) intercalations of crystalline calcitic and dolomitic limestone; locally (in regions 4, 5, 7) intercalations of quartzite and conglomerate in the lower half; locally (in regions 4, 5, 6, 7, 8) mica schists and amphibolites at base. Basal conglomerate resting unconformably on a crystalline basement (in region 1 only)	1,700–4,300	

NOTE: The "K" divisions usually correspond to formations.

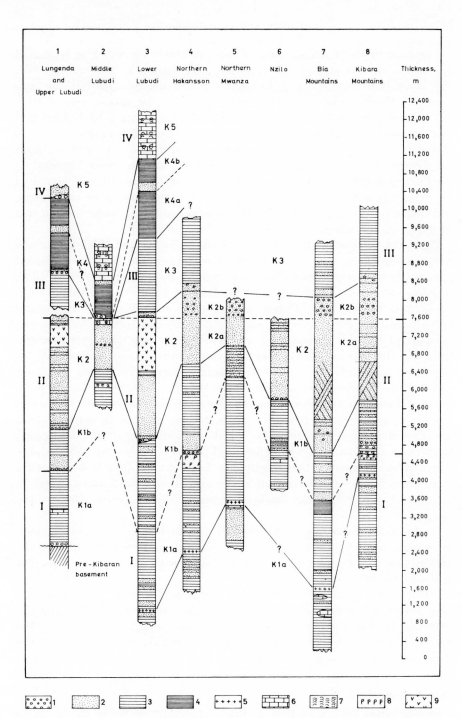

Fig. 12. Stratigraphy of the Kibaran. 1, Conglomerates and coarse-grained arkoses. 2, Quartzites. 3, Schists, slates, and shales. 4, Black shales and slates. 5, Zone of development of chloritoid. 6, Calcitic and dolomitic limestones, dolomites. 7, Stromatolites. 8, Silicic lavas. 9. Mafic lavas.

The base of the Kibaran resting unconformably on an older basement has been observed only in the Lugenda area (region 1; MOUREAU, 1960). The correlation between the different sections makes apparent the constancy of three strata of conglomerate, quartzite, or arkose, representing sedimentary breaks by means of which the Kibaran may be divided into four sequences in the sense given on p. 150. The break between Sequences II and III seems to be the most important, and it has been used to divide the Kibaran into a lower "system", or the Nzilo, and an upper "system" or the Lubudi (CAHEN, 1954, pp. 40–46). The present state of knowledge does not definitely show that this break is more important than the two others, and thus a provisional subdivision into four sequences is preferred, but it is advisable to give them no names.

Figure 12 illustrates the main variations in facies and thickness of the Kibaran sequences. However, it must be borne in mind that the indicated thicknesses have not always been determined with comparable precision. One fact, however, stands out, that is, definite diminution in thickness in the central Lubudi area. During a part of its sedimentation the central Lubudi area and the country immediately to the east seem to have played the part of a ridge separating a western trough from an eastern trough. It is still difficult to decide whether the eastern trough was simple, or whether it was divided into several troughs separated by ridges.

Along the southeastern margin of the Kibaran belt, subdivisions K 1a and K 1b contain numerous quartzite intercalations whose thickness and number at first decrease towards the northwest and then increase again in the same direction. Similarly, the basal conglomerate of the subdivision K 1b reaches its maximum thickness and contains its largest pebbles near Mitwaba but disappears towards the northwest to reappear in the Mwanza area. These facies variations confirm the existence of the eastern trough in the central part, where the thicknesses are markedly greater than at the margins.

In the western trough, of which only the eastern part is known, conglomerates are abundant and the lithological units are thinner in the westernmost known part of the belt compared with what is known farther in the east.

When these lithological differences and some tectonic differences are considered, viz., overturning of the folds towards the northwest, and the existence of less disturbed, sometimes gently undulating, beds in the western part of the chain (see p. 203), it appears that the hinterland of the Kibaran Belt was located in the southeast and its foreland in the northwest.

5.2.4. Palaeontology

Stromatolites are known from at least three horizons in the stratigraphic column, viz., in divisions K 1b, K 2a, and K 5 (see CAHEN, 1954, p. 46).

5.2.5. Tectonics

By and large, the Kibaran tectonics display a relatively simple folding. Large anticlinorial and synclinorial zones are arranged in quasi-parallel bands with a S.W.–N.E. trend. Overturning towards the northwest is the rule except, it seems, in the Upper Lubudi region, where several overfolds towards the east were observed by V. OBOLENSKY in 1940. In each region that has been studied in detail, various tectonic units are distinguished, but the lack of a precise map of those parts of the Kibaran Belt that have been studied so far hinders the definitive correlation of the regional units. A provisional attempt at this has been made, however (CAHEN, 1954, pp. 46, 47).

In the eastern part of the chain, in the Kibara Mountains, the folds are very tight and have an isoclinal appearance, especially in the synclinorial areas and in pelitic rocks. Farther towards the west, in the Lower and central Lubudi areas, the folds are more open, but it seems that in the western trough, in the Upper Lubudi area, the isoclinal style of folding reappears.

The lithological succession shows that there were a number of tectonic phases before the main Kibaran Orogeny.

5.2.6. Metamorphism

Regional metamorphism is not of very high grade, and in the region studied so far, the Kibaran has been metamorphosed at most in the lower epizone. Apart from quartz, the constituent minerals of the rocks are sericite, muscovite, zoisite, chlorite, and chloritoid, which does not appear to have been formed above a relatively low level in the stratigraphic succession (VAN DE STEEN, 1959). Contact metamorphism has frequently produced aureoles, all limited to the characteristic parageneses of the lower epizone. Biotite schists are exceptional (VAN DE STEEN, 1959).

5.2.7. Plutonic activity

With respect to the main phase of folding, pretectonic, syntectonic, and posttectonic plutonic activity is distinguished (CAHEN, 1954, pp. 47–49; VAN DE STEEN, 1959; CAHEN, DELHAL, and MONTEYNE-POULAERT, 1965).

The results of the pretectonic plutonic activity appear in the form of dolerites and rhyolites and gabbro and dolerite sills, notably in the Kibara Mountains and in the Mwanza region (VAN DE WALLE, 1960). These rocks are interstratified with beds of Sequence I, the rhyolites ending the deposition of this sequence. Some other pretectonic lavas, generally doleritic, occur in the Hakansson Mountains and in the Bukama region. Their stratigraphical position above the subdivision K2a in the upper part of Sequence II is now in doubt (P. DUMONT, unpublished information).

Still pretectonic or perhaps early tectonic plutonic activity is represented by biotite-bearing calc-alkalic granites or granodiorites, often porphyroidal and generally gneissose; the microcline porphyroblasts are set in a ground mass of quartz, orthoclase, oligoclase or andesine, and abundant biotite. These granites are (1,310 ± 40) Myr old.

Syntectonic granitization, producing gneissic biotite or biotite-muscovite granites, occurred somewhat later and is provisionally dated at (1,240 ± 70) Myr (CAHEN, DELHAL, and MONTEYNE-POULAERT, in press).

The posttectonic plutonic activity consists of the emplacement: (1) pegmatites and quartz veins, 1,120 Myr old; (2) equigranular granites containing biotite, muscovite, or both, about 1,000 Myr old; and (3) pegmatites, aplites, and quartz veins derived from them, from 1,000 Myr to 850 Myr old (see p. 157).

Finally, the posttectonic dolerites and gabbros, frequently pigeonite-bearing, are intrusive in all Kibaran beds. They might represent the last stage of Kibaran plutonic activity or be attributed to later activity. The first hypothesis is favoured by the fact that these rocks follow the Kibaran structural trend.

5.2.8. Mineralization

Connected with and following the late syntectonic or posttectonic granites with an age of about 1,000 Myr is a suite of pegmatites and mineral veins which contain important tin, niobium, tantalum, and tungsten mineralizations (CAHEN, 1954, pp. 517, 520–522). Some deposits are pegmatites, e.g., those at Manono and Muika, while others are veins, such as those at Busanga and Mitwaba.

In the veins of the Mitwaba region, the mineralization consists of quartz, cassiterite, arsenopyrite, pyrite, sphalerite, galena, chalcopyrite, and molybdenite; beryl is always present. In the adjacent Mandwe region there are pegmatite veins passing into a tin-bearing greisen containing columbite and cassiterite.

The Muika pegmatites contain cassiterite and columbite–tantalite, accompanied by beryl and amblygonite.

The most important tin and columbite–tantalite deposit in Katanga, at Manono, consists of two pegmatite laccoliths, each outcropping over a distance of 5 km and having a mean width of about 400 m. Several types of pegmatites are known which, along with common pegmatite minerals, contain apatite, lepidolite, lithian muscovite, spodumene, fluorite, zircon, rutile, cassiterite, columbite, tantalite, thoreaulite, loellingite, arsenopyrite, pyrite, ilmenite, oxide minerals of iron and manganese, and traces of autunite. Cassiterite is dispersed in a fairly homogeneous manner throughout the pegmatite. There are also greisens containing cassiterite and columbite–tantalite and quartz veins carrying thoreaulite, tantalite, and wolframite.

5.2.9. Geological evolution

At the present time the geology of the hinterland of the Kibaran geosyncline (see p. 202) is almost unknown because the area is covered almost totally by the Katangan of the type region. However, certain rocks are known as enclaves of the kimberlite pipes of the Kundelungu Plateau, and a small stretch might crop out between the Lukumbi and Lufonzo Rivers, both affluents of the Luvua River, in northern Katanga (CAHEN, 1954, pp. 18, 50). By contrast, the foreland, which forms a part of the Kasai–Lomami–Lulua Basement (see p. 173) is well exposed, and the unconformable contact of the Kibaran with its foreland is observable in the Lugenda Basin west of Mutshatsha (MOUREAU, 1960); its course has been plotted in the vicinity of Kamina (CAHEN, 1954, p. 240).

Between these two basement areas there is a geosyncline with a S.W.–N.E. trend, of which the part studied on pp. 199–206 has a length greater than 500 km, representing nearly a quarter of the Kibaran–Burundian Geosyncline (see p. 227). The area on which the belt crops out is at most 250 km wide.

The strata of Sequence I (see Table 6) seem to indicate a fairly regular subsidence. The strata are notably thicker in the eastern (internal) trough than in the western (external) trough; the axis of subsidence might have been situated in the Bia Mountains. In the eastern trough, the original predominantly argillaceous sediments associated with arenaceous and calcareous sediments are accompanied by a suite of volcanic flows that are mainly doleritic. The subsidence and sedimentation were interrupted by a tectonic event accompanied by the effusion of rhyolite flows. The movements caused, at least locally, an emergence marked by conglomerates on both sides of the eastern trough and in the western trough, but not along the axis of the eastern trough. It seems that this tectonic phase was accompanied by a notable uplift of the hinterland.

The tectonic event was followed by the deposition of the sediments of Sequence II, which marks the filling of the eastern trough by sediments which became progressively more arenaceous. The axis of maximum subsidence seems to have been located in the Kibara Mountains. During this time the Central Lubudi Ridge separating the western external trough from the eastern internal trough was formed. A new tectonic episode ended the deposition of the sediments of Sequence II by causing the uplift of the margins of the geosyncline and, probably, the arching of the hinterland.

This uplift of the hinterland caused the deposition of coarser-grained arenaceous and frequently conglomeratic and arkosic sediments which, particularly in the eastern trough, form the base of Sequence III. They were followed by the thick and regular deposits of pelitic sediments of this sequence, again with an axis in the Kibara Mountains.

The geological history of Sequences III and IV can be studied only in the region of the Central Lubudi Ridge and in the immediately adjacent areas on its both sides. The ridge persisted throughout the time of deposition of the sediments of Sequence III and, less certainly, at the beginning of deposition of those of Sequence IV. Both sequences were affected by several tectonic episodes, among which the one that separates the two sequences seems to have caused a local emergence.

The main phase of the Kibaran Orogeny began after the deposition of all the Kibaran sediments. It was accompanied, in the eastern trough, by syntectonic granitization and was followed by the intrusion of granites younger than the last folding.

During the last stages of geosynclinal evolution, three troughs formed, within, behind, and in front of the Kibaran Belt. They were filled with thick layers of terrigenous sediments of molasse type, lying definitely unconformably on the Kibaran, and making up the base of the Bushimay, the Nonda, and the Roan in the area between Mitwaba and Luvua (see p. 234).

Most of its properties (ophiolitic rocks, much plutonic activity and overthrusting towards the western external trough) suggest that the eastern trough was eugeosynclinal, and that the western trough, of which only a part is known, was miogeosynclinal.

5.3. *The Burundian*

5.3.1. General account

In eastern Congo, Rwanda, and Burundi, the Burundian (see Fig. 11) forms a great S.W.–N.E.-trending folded belt which connects the Kibaran of Katanga with the Karagwe–Ankolean of northwestern Tanzania and southwestern Uganda (see p. 152). At the latitude of Lake Kivu, the strike of the beds turns first north and then northwest, and a noteworthy branch of the belt with this trend crosses Maniema and finally disappears under the cover rocks of the Congo Basin. The branch which continues northwards into Uganda is soon interrupted by outcropping older rocks which display the unconformity of the Karagwe–Ankolean at several points (PHILLIPS, 1959; REECE, 1960).

The distinction of the Burundian from the Ruzizian was established without great difficulty in Burundi and southwest of Lake Kivu (see p. 183). Elsewhere, it has usually not been possible to determine the precise contact between these two groups.

5.3.2. Historical survey

An account of the development of knowledge concerning the Burundian and Ruzizian was given on p. 183. To the papers already cited are here added those of PEETERS (1952, 1955, 1956) and LHOEST (1957a, b, 1961) describing the stratigraphy and numerous sections of the Burundian. The Burundian pegmatites and mineralizations were studied by DE DYCKER (1949), SAFIANNIKOFF (1950, 1954), VARLAMOFF (1953, 1954, 1957, 1958a, b, 1959), AGASSIZ (1954), DE KUN (1954, 1959), and still other geologists.

5.3.3. Stratigraphy

On the basis of a series of locally observed sections, CAHEN (1954, pp. 127–129, 133–134, 137–138) established the following general stratigraphical succession for the Burundian (from top to bottom):

(7) Dark grey schists, almost without quartzites.

(6) Quartzites, arkoses, and conglomerates. Probable gap in the observations.

(5) Schists with rare thin marble lenticles and with conglomerate lenses, displaying most of the lithological properties of tillite.

(4) Group of black schists and banded schists, with rare thin quartzite lenticles.

(3) Banded schists and black schists, quartz phyllites, alternating with thick quartzite beds.

(2) Banded schists and black schists, quartz phyllites alternating with numerous thin beds of quartzite; thin marble lenticles.

(1) Arkoses and conglomerates, with local phyllite intercalations.

A sequence in northern Rwanda, the Miovi (now spelled Miyove) Formation (see CAHEN, 1954, p. 149) is omitted from this succession because N. VARLAMOFF, who, in, 1952, was the first to establish it, considered it to rest unconformably on the Burundian. LHOEST (1961), however, considered this unconformity improbable; detailed investigation (GÉRARDS and LEPERSONNE, 1964) confirmed its existence in various regions. Because the Miyove sequence was affected by the Burundian orogeny and is traversed by reliably dated Burundian pegmatites, it must be included in the Burundian.

The investigations of PEETERS (1955, 1956), LHOEST (1957b), and ANTUN (1961b) provided details of the Burundian successions of the various parts of Kivu, Rwanda, and Burundi. PEETERS (1956) attempted to establish a general scale for the Burundian including a division into five sequences with a total thickness approaching 22,000 m. We do not believe it possible to adopt his interpretation. In fact, at least a part of the rocks placed in the Burundian belong to the Ruzizian (see p. 185). Furthermore, it seems that several correlations are open to discussion and that PEETERS did not adequately consider the possibility of faulted contacts.

According to the present-day knowledge, no single stratigraphic scale can be proposed for the Burundian. Two main areas must be considered, namely, (1) the eastern area comprising the northeastern half of Rwanda and the eastern half of Burundi, where the stratigraphy of the Burundian is well known, even though its basis has not been observed, and which is the type region; (2) the western area consisting of the Nile–Congo watershed in Burundi and the Itombwe syncline, southwest of Lake Kivu. In both these areas the basal unconformity has been observed, and higher up in the succession a tillite or a tilloid, unknown in the eastern area, is present. The strata of the Nile–Congo watershed which lie below this tilloid are traced into the type area. This is not the case for the strata exposed in the Itombwe syncline, which are correlated with the Burundian on lithological and tectonic grounds.

Table 7 gives an outline of a section in the type region, based on work by

TABLE 7

Stratigraphy of the Burundian in the eastern part of Rwanda and Burundi

Lithological description	Thickness, m
Miyove sequence	
(10) Siliceous slates and phyllites with intercalations of quartzite and psammitic sandstones and intercalations of coarse-grained arkose at the base	∼1,300–1,400
(9) Fine-grained–coarse-grained grit with conglomerates in the upper part	∼140
Slight unconformity	
Byumba sequence	
(8) Dark phyllites and quartz phyllites with intercalations of quartzite and psammitic sandstone	∼1,200
(7) Coarse-grained quartzites with intercalations of banded phyllites; basal conglomerate with small pebbles of quartz and quartzite	1,000
Lower sequence	
(6) Dark schists and phyllites with rare intercalations of quartzite; dark quartz phyllites at the base	2,000
(5) Nduba quartzite	30
(4) Phyllites, quartz phyllites, grits and quartzites; basal quartzite passing into a conglomerate with small pebbles of quartz and quartzite	1,300
(3) Alternating schists, phyllites, grits, and quartzites	1,200
(2) Rutongo sandstones and quartzites, locally coarse-grained	130
(1) Alternating quartzites and phyllites, passing in the lower part into muscovite schists and crystalline quartzites by contact metamorphism caused by granite	1,000
Base not observed	

LHOEST (1957b, 1961) and on later detailed geological maps (GÉRARDS and LEPERSONNE, 1964a, b) which have shown the validity of LHOEST's succession for a vast area in northern and eastern Rwanda and which have also made possible the subdivision of the Burundian succession into three sequences, which are, from top to bottom, the Miyove sequence, the Byumba sequence, and the Lower sequence, or sequences. The Lower sequence is still incompletely known and may be composite.

Table 8 presents an outline of a section of the western region constructed from a section in the Itombwe Synclinorium southwest of Lake Kivu (LHOEST, 1964, personal communication; PEETERS, 1955, 1956), covering formations (1) through (5), and a section from the Dendezi–Nyamasheke region on the eastern shore of Lake Kivu in Rwanda (L. PEETERS, personal communication), covering formations (3) through (7). The correlation between the two sections rests on the recognition of formations (3) and (5) in both sections where they occur with the same facies. In Burundi, north and west of Kayanza, ANTUN (1961b, personal communication) observed a succession of beds similar to units (1) through (5) of Table 8. The basal

TABLE 8

Stratigraphy of the Burundian in the western area (western Rwanda and Burundi and southern Kivu)

Sequence	Lithological description	Thickness, m
Burundian	(7) Slates with quartzite lenses	600
	(6) Quartzite	40–800
	(5) Black and banded slates; thin marble lenses and sometimes thick conglomerate lenses with an argillaceous matrix (tilloid)	up to 2,000
	(4) Banded slates, often black, with thin rare quartzite lenses	200–1,000
	(3) Quartzites, feldspar-bearing and conglomeratic in the lower part, with intercalations of schists and quartz phyllite	600–1,000
	(2) Phyllites and dark sericite schists with local crystalline limestones	600–1,000
	(1) Quartzites and conglomerates	50–200
	Unconformity	
Ruzizian		

beds (1), which rest unconformably on the Ruzizian in the neighbourhood of Kayanza, consist of quartzites, 300 m thick. The schists which succeed them are thicker than sequence (2) and include dolerite sills passing into lava flows in their lower part and quartzites near their central part.

5.3.4. Relationships between the sequences of the western and eastern regions and with the Karagwe–Ankolean

Unpublished geological maps (*Musée royal de l'Afrique centrale*) show that the correlation of formation (7) in the eastern section with formation (3) in the western section is extremely probable (see p. 208). This formation common to the two regions has a relatively constant lithological composition characterized by a coarse-grained, often conglomeratic, arenaceous facies. The deposition of coarse-grained material, abruptly following the deposition of pelitic sediments, marks a renewal of erosion which justifies the distinction of the Byumba sequence as being independent of the Lower sequence. The deposits of the Lower sequence are much thicker and much more differentiated in the eastern region than in the western region (see Tables 7 and 8, and Fig. 13). The formations younger than formation (1) in the eastern section have lithofacies different from that of those younger than formation (3) in the western section, and their correlation is still impossible, except for formations (5), (6), and (7) in the western region, which might correspond to formations (8), (9), and (10) in the eastern region (see Tables 7 and 8).

In order to determine the variations of lithofacies and the thickness of the Burundian (see Fig. 13) it is necessary to examine the correlation of the succession of the eastern region (see Table 7) with successions in the

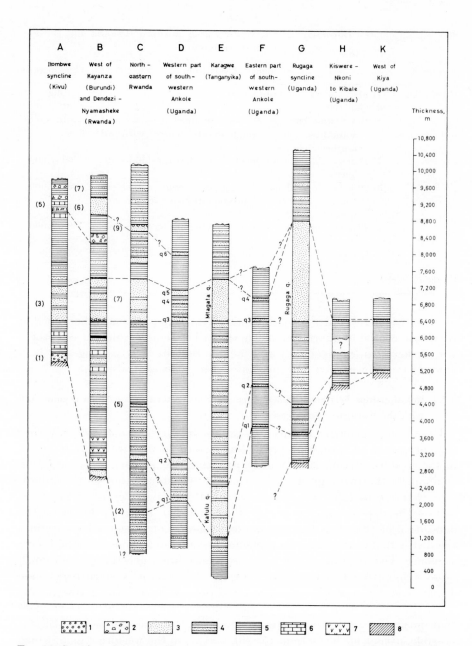

Fig. 13. Stratigraphy of the Burundian. 1, Conglomerates. 2, Tillites. 3, Quartzites. 4, Schists, slates, and shales with impersistent quartzites. 5, Schists, slates, and shales. 6, Metamorphic limestones. 7, Mafic lavas. 8, Pre-Burundian basement.

Karagwe–Ankolean of adjacent areas in Uganda (COMBE, 1932; PHILLIPS, 1959) and in Tanzania (STOCKLEY and WILLIAMS, 1938). These correlations can be safely made by following the same beds on both sides of the frontier. The correlation between the successions established by COMBE and by STOCKLEY and WILLIAMS, on the one hand, and by PHILLIPS, on the other hand, is less certain, since there is a gap between the area they studied. Figure 13 shows the various sections from the southwest (Itombwe, Kivu) to the northeast (Rakai, Uganda). The thicknesses are those given by the pertinent authors except for the lower half of Section B, for which approximate thicknesses were calculated from geological maps. Figure 13 shows the presence of a trough with a notable subsidence in western Uganda and Tanzania, and in eastern Rwanda and Burundi. On both sides of this trough the pre-Burundian basement rises rapidly. West of the elevation, southwest of Lake Kivu, the Burundian is again present in Kivu and Maniema, but neither its lithological composition nor its thickness is known. The elevated zone coincides with the Rift Valley, south of Lake Kivu, occupied by the Ruzizi River, and with the marginal ridges on both sides. This zone might be the very old forerunner of the elevation that preceded the formation of the Rift Valley in Tertiary or Quaternary time.

5.3.5. Relationships with older and younger rocks

The Burundian rests unconformably on the Ruzizian of southern Burundi and of Kivu (see pp. 183, 185). A little to the north of the Rwanda–Uganda border, the Karagwe–Ankolean lies unconformably on the Igara Group (REECE, 1960) and on the Toro "System" and the Basement Complex (PHILLIPS, 1959). These three sequences were considered by McCONNELL (1959) to belong to the same sequence, called the Buganda Group. In southern Burundi the Burundian is unconformably overlain by the Malagarasian and, in Maniema, by patches of the Lindian, both formations being correlated with the Katangan.

5.3.6. Tectonics

The general form of the Burundian fold belt was described on p. 206. The details of the known sections show that the beds are strongly folded in Kivu, Rwanda, and Burundi, while in Maniema they appear to undulate (VARLAMOFF, 1950). The folds do not show a marked virgation; north of Kigali (in Rwanda), LHOEST (1957a, b) noted sharp overturning towards the west and thrust planes dipping towards the east. In the Itombwe Synclinorium, PEETERS (1952) observed faults, probably thrusts, suggesting transport from the east towards the west. The existence of pronounced transverse warping is marked by the rapid dying-out of some folds in Rwanda and in Burundi.

5.3.7. Metamorphism

In many regions, the distinction between the Burundian and the Ruzizian cannot be made, or, when possible, is subject to arguments. Consequently, there is some doubt as to the degree of metamorphism to be assigned to each sequence. Nevertheless, it seems that, in general, outside the areas affected by granite intrusions, the metamorphism of the Burundian was always feeble (PEETERS, 1952, 1956; VARLAMOFF, 1957). The argillaceous sediments have been metamorphosed into slates, sericite schists, and chlorite schists. In the more strongly metamorphosed zones, small flakes of biotite are abundant and, in Rwanda and Burundi, there are local muscovite schists. The arenaceous sediments now occur as quartzites, sometimes sericite- or feldspar-bearing. The dolomitic and calcitic limestones, which are known to occur only in the western region, are crystalline, and often contain metamorphic silicate minerals. Amphibolites are rare and seem to be more often ortho-amphibolites than para-amphibolites.

The intensity of metamorphism caused by granite massifs differs from region to region (VARLAMOFF, 1957). In Maniema, the metamorphic aureoles are no wider than 100 m–200 m and are characterized by the presence of muscovite and amphibole. A more or less intense tourmalinization is associated with the formation of quartz veins. In northern Maniema, andalusite, staurolite, and garnet schists occur, and in them muscovite replaces andalusite and staurolite at the granite contact. In Kivu, the metamorphic aureoles are wider, and the degree of metamorphism is higher, having caused the formation of garnet, staurolite, and andalusite. In Rwanda and in Burundi, the metamorphic aureoles reach a width of many hundreds of metres.

5.3.8. Plutonic activity

The Burundian granites are calc-alkalic (usually monzonites or akerites) and alkalic rocks (CAHEN, 1954, p. 130). Many geologists (J. THOREAU in 1930 and 1936, A. COMBE in 1932 and 1939, A. KAZMITCHEFF in 1935, and N. BOUTAKOFF in 1939; see CAHEN, 1954, pp. 130, 136) believed they could distinguish two granite types, called G2 and G3, one syntectonic and the other late syntectonic or posttectonic, but others (F. BLAISE and N. BOUTAKOFF in 1933, M. E. DENAEYER in 1950, and N. VARLAMOFF in 1952; see CAHEN, 1954, p. 136) showed that the two types occur in the same massifs and that there is a continuous transition from one to the other. SAFIANNIKOFF (1950), VARLAMOFF (1953, 1957), and PEETERS (1956) agreed that the emplacement of the granite postdates the main phase of Burundian folding, but was either accompanied or followed by movements that caused reorientation of the minerals in certain parts of the massifs.

In northeastern Rwanda (DELHAL, 1964), two types of granites have been distinguished: (1) granite gneiss containing biotite alone, biotite and muscovite, or, locally, muscovite and tourmaline; (2) muscovite granites, subequigranular and containing some tourmaline and biotite. The first granites are syntectonic, while the second are younger and probably post-tectonic.

VARLAMOFF (1953, 1957) described a system of zones in the granite massifs of Maniema. They occur in the following order, starting at the centre: pegmatite with giant microcline crystals, large plagioclase and quartz crystals, and biotite; transition to a porphyritic zone in which rounded microcline crystals are set in a granitic matrix containing very fine-grained biotite; medium-grained and fine-grained granite either containing biotite alone or biotite and muscovite; and muscovite granite, both medium-grained and coarse-grained. The study of the Kivu granites is less advanced, and VARLAMOFF (1953), following the comments of SAFIANNIKOFF (1950), admitted that the existence of several successive granite phases cannot be excluded.

Generally, but not invariably, the granites are emplaced in anticlines. This is particularly so in Maniema, where the beds are gently folded and the granites cause a doming of the country rocks. The same fact is observed in eastern Rwanda.

The emplacement of a suite of aplites, pegmatites, and quartz veins is linked with the granites. The pegmatites and the quartz veins, with which tin, tantalum, niobium, tungsten, and, sometimes, gold mineralizations are associated, have been the subject of numerous studies, the most important being those by VARLAMOFF (1953, 1954, 1957, 1958a, b, 1959; see also CAHEN, 1954, pp. 517–519). The conclusions of these studies may be summarized as follows.

The emplacement of these rocks is posttectonic and took place in the joints that cut granite and country rock alike; the joints are best developed in the apical parts of the granite massifs. The pegmatites and quartz veins have often undergone fracturing, allowing the emplacement of successive layers. The jointing and filling of joints occur in a regular way, which is always the same, as if there were a deep-lying magma which, while slowly cooling, gave rise successively to the aplites, pegmatites, and quartz veins, and to the various mineralizations.

Taking A. E. FERSMAN's pegmatite classification as a basis, VARLAMOFF showed that, with some modification, it can be applied to Maniema, Rwanda, and Burundi. Finally, he (VARLAMOFF, 1959) established a zonal scheme for the Central African pegmatites based on mineralogical composition, which reflects the temperature of crystallization. The classification comprises nine types, characterized by the presence of biotite, microcline, plagioclase, tourmaline, muscovite, beryl, albite, cleavelandite, and quartz.

Many other minerals also occur in the pegmatites, notably amblygonite, spodumene, topaz, rubellite, lithium micas, triphylite, lithiophilite, hureaulite (THOREAU and SAFIANNIKOFF, 1957), variscite, and fluorite.

With respect to the contact between the granite and the country rock, different types occur in different regions. Figure 14, reproduced from VARLAMOFF (1959), shows their distribution. It would seem that the pegmatites of Maniema were emplaced under a thinner sedimentary cover than those of Kivu and Rwanda.

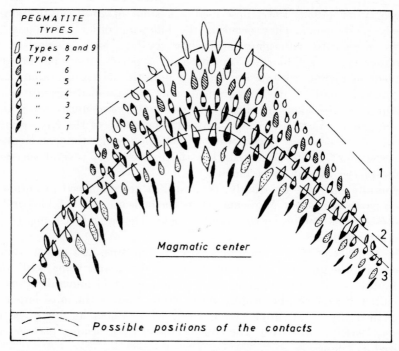

FIG. 14. Relative position of different pegmatite types with respect to a magmatic centre from which they derive. Position of the contacts: 1, in Maniema; 2, in Kivu; 3, in Rwanda. Modified from VARLAMOFF (1959).

Regarding the pegmatites and mineral veins of Kivu, SAFIANNIKOFF (1954) remarked that the zonation is more complex than VARLAMOFF (1954) had supposed, and commented on the frequency of condensed sequences. VARLAMOFF (1957) admitted the possibility of successive phases, but felt that the present state of knowledge does not allow the problems posed in Kivu to be solved.

Some datings (see p. 157) made since the publication of the papers of VARLAMOFF and SAFIANNIKOFF show that among different pegmatites and veins the ages can differ by as much as 250 Myr (MONTEYNE-POULAERT and others, 1963). The occurrence of several successive pegmatites postulated by SAFIANNIKOFF is thus confirmed.

To conclude the list of intrusive rocks that affect the Burundian, mention is made of various types which make only small massifs and whose age is usually in doubt. They are dolerites and amphibolites, perhaps derived from gabbros (CAHEN, 1954, pp. 131, 132), and syenites and nepheline syenites (CAHEN, 1954, p. 131; DENAEYER, 1959), which are definitely posttectonic and possibly considerably younger than the Burundian. Connected with the syenite massifs in Kivu are the Lueshe carbonatite (DE BÉTHUNE and MEYER, 1956) and a riebeckite granite (THOREAU, 1956).

Sills of dolerite associated with interstratified lava are known from the Lower sequence of the Burundian in Burundi (ANTUN, 1961b) and in southeastern Rwanda (V. PETRICEC, personal communication).

5.3.9. Mineralization

The mineral deposits exploited in Maniema, Kivu, Rwanda, and Burundi, which are either certainly or probably connected with the Burundian, contain tin, tantalum, niobium, tungsten, and gold (see CAHEN, 1954, pp. 512, 514, 517–519). A brief general description of the deposits is given in the following paragraphs.

Cassiterite and columbite–tantalite occur either together or separately in pegmatites and quartz veins. VARLAMOFF (1959) defined their position in the zonal scheme he established (see p. 213 and Fig. 14). The paragenesis was described by VARLAMOFF in 1950 and SAFIANNIKOFF (1950); the cassiterite and columbite–tantalite are accompanied by wolframite, native bismuth, stannite, varlamoffite, chalcopyrite, molybdenite, pyrite, sphalerite, galena, marcasite, graphite, and traces of gold.

The tungsten deposits are divided into two types, viz., those that contain well-crystallized wolframite with more than 2% MnO and those which include ferberite with less than 1% MnO (VARLAMOFF, 1958b). The workable wolframite deposits are located in Maniema; the wolframite occurs in greisen or in quartz veins in the granites or near their contact. It is associated with cassiterite, arsenopyrite, stannite, pyrite, chalcopyrite, sphalerite, and galena. The MnO content varies from 2% to 17% (VARLAMOFF, 1958b). The ferberite deposits are located in Maniema and in Rwanda. They occur frequently in the anticlines and are always associated with graphite-bearing schists and quartzites. The ferberite occurs in quartz veins, generally as pseudomorphs after scheelite; it is frequently associated with anthoinite, cassiterite, tourmaline, and arsenopyrite. The MnO content is always less than 2% and rarely more than 1%.

In Maniema, the veins are clearly located above the contacts of the apical parts of the granite massifs. In Rwanda, the veins are very irregular and small and show no discernible relationship with the granite massifs. In view of the fact that the Rwanda tin mineralization occurs at a greater distance from the granite than in Maniema, VARLAMOFF (1958b) suggested that the tungsten mineralization is similarly connected with hidden deep-lying Burundian granites.

In both Maniema and Rwanda the main primary mineral is scheelite, successively replaced by ferberite, then by anthoinite; some gold seems to be associated with this mineralization. VARLAMOFF (1958b) showed that graphite, a characteristic constituent of the country rock, is epigenetic, thus connecting the graphitization with the mineralization.

The tungsten deposits of Rwanda were described by DE MAGNÉE and ADERCA (1960). They admitted that in the western Rwanda deposits the tungsten is related to granite, but pointed out that in eastern Rwanda tungsten is present, sometimes in notable quantities, in the Burundian slates and schists, and that there are traces of scheelite that have not been changed to ferberite in the veins. The study of these deposits led them to propose a syngenetic origin for the tungsten without, however, rejecting the possibility that its emplacement in the veins was caused by the intrusion of granite, which caused a concentration and a rearrangement of the sedimentary minerals into metalliferous aureoles. It seems difficult to reconcile some of VARLAMOFF's observations, not discussed by DE MAGNÉE and ADERCA, with the idea of a syngenetic origin for the tungsten, but some facts noted by DE MAGNÉE and ADERCA are difficult to explain on the basis of a purely epigenetic origin.

Some gold mineralizations are exploited in Kivu, Maniema, Rwanda, and Burundi. Only those in southern Kivu, the gold in a ferberite deposit in Rwanda, and traces of gold in a ferberite deposit in Maniema are definitely of Burundian or of post-Burundian age. In the other regions the gold is, or may be, of Ruzizian age (see p. 188). The gold mineralization of southern Kivu was described by SAFIANNIKOFF (1950). He considered it to be related to the tin-bearing granites and drew attention to the complexity of mineralization resulting from the occurrence of several phases of mineralization in the same vein. Datings (MONTEYNE-POULAERT and others, 1962b) confirm the connection of these veins with post-Burundian pegmatites. Some veins are of post-Katangan age.

5.3.10. Geological history

The Burundian consists essentially of rocks of pelitic and arenaceous origin. Limestones and conglomerates are much less abundant. In general, the total thickness of the pelites is much greater than that of the arenaceous rocks, apparently at least three or four times as great. The facies and thickness variations between the two types are rapid and, as a result, the sandstone, quartzite, or grit beds form lenticular bodies of various sizes (PEETERS, 1956). These variations are most marked in two areas where the base of the Burundian is known, namely, in the region south of Lake Kivu and in the southwestern part of Uganda (PHILLIPS, 1959; REECE, 1960). In these two regions the Burundian is strongly transgressive over its basement, and there are marked variations in the thickness of the arenaceous facies which may locally reach a thickness similar to that of the pelitic facies.

The existence of the Burundian Geosyncline is well shown by the trough of subsidence which occupied eastern Rwanda and Burundi and adjacent areas of Uganda and Tanzania. There, the total thickness of strata exceeds 9,000 m, the metamorphism is more thorough than elsewhere, and the relationships between the pegmatites, mineralizations, and granite massifs show that these were emplaced at a deeper level in the crust (see pp. 212, 213). West of the geanticline south of Lake Kivu, the tin region of central Maniema seems to be close to the ancient foreland. The tectonic style is simpler than in the eastern trough, the metamorphism is less marked, and the shallower level of intrusions and mineralizations (see p. 215) are all indications of the smaller thickness of the Burundian formations, as compared to their thickness in Rwanda and in Burundi.

In the present state of knowledge, it is not possible to determine what became of the axis of the eastern geosyncline in the regions north of Kivu and Maniema, where a branch of the Burundian Belt assumes a north-westerly trend.

5.4. *The Lulua Sedimentary and Volcanic Complex*

5.4.1. Introduction

Under the name "Lulua Sedimentary and Volcanic Complex" various lithological units are combined whose relationships have not been precisely determined in the field. They occur together in an area of elongated shape with a main E.N.E. direction, in part of Kasai situated either side of Lat. 7° S., between Long. 24° 30′ and Long. 23° E. This area is bounded nearly everywhere by faults which separate it from the Dibaya Granite–Migmatite Complex in the north and from the Luiza Metasedimentary Complex (see p. 178) in the south (see Fig. 6). The complex thus defined includes two main groups of rocks, viz., sedimentary rocks, feebly metamorphosed or non-metamorphosed, more or less folded, and greenstones of volcanic origin.

5.4.2. Historical survey

The sedimentary part of the Lulua Complex was described by POLINARD (1934) as *Système Schisto-phylladique*, or the Lulua System, which became the Lulua Group (COMMISSION DE GÉOLOGIE DU MINISTÈRE DES COLONIES, 1935). CAHEN (1954, pp. 242–244, 546) showed that the Lulua Group of the type area is probably older than the Bushimay of Kasai and Katanga and younger than the crystalline and metamorphic rocks of the Kasai basement, and might be an equivalent of the Kibaran. He also described the formations of the Lulua–Lubilash interfluve, between Lat. 9° S. and Lat. 10° S., the main features of which are dealt with in the paragraphs devoted to the Katangan of northeastern Katanga or Bushimay (Luamba Group, see p. 253).

Following field studies by the *Service géologique du Congo* in the Dibaya and Luiza–Musodi Quadrangles, various studies have completed the knowledge of the lithological composition and tectonics of the sedimentary rocks and the origin of the greenstones (LEGRAND, 1955; DELHAL and LEGRAND, 1957; LEGRAND and RAUCQ, 1957; DELHAL, 1958b, 1959). FIEREMANS (1959) published the results of his observations made west of the type area. The basis of the following account is an unpublished study of the stratigraphy, tectonics, and petrography of the Lulua Complex (DELHAL, LEPERSONNE, and RAUCQ, in press).

H

5.4.3. Stratigraphy

In the regions of the Dibaya and Luiza Quadrangles and in the eastern half of Musodi (see Fig. 6), the following lithological units have been distinguished (LEGRAND, 1955; DELHAL and LEGRAND, 1957; LEGRAND and RAUCQ, 1957): (1) a folded group of slates and quartzites, feebly metamorphosed or nonmetamorphosed, corresponding to the Lulua Group of previous authors; (2) some argillaceous sandstones, called "purple rocks" and thought to be younger than the preceding group; (3) greenstones (lavas) and pyroclastics, thought to be younger than group (1) but whose relationship with the "purple rocks" has not been established; (4) small patches of limestone or calcareous shale of doubtful stratigraphical position.

On the basis of new field observations by P. RAUCQ, made in 1956–1960, petrographic studies, and a photogeological revision of the geological map (DELHAL, LEPERSONNE, and RAUCQ, in press) showed that groups (1), (2), (3), and (4) belong to the same folded sedimentary and volcanic sequence.

These data allow the determination of the general stratigraphy of the Lulua Complex shown on Table 9. In Table 9, units (1)–(4) are based on

TABLE 9

Stratigraphy of the Lulua Sedimentary and Volcanic Complex

Lithological description	Thickness, m
(7) Shales and phyllites with local intercalations of silicified limestones, calcareous shales and pyroclastics	unknown
(6) Shales, phyllites, and quartzites with local intercalations of greenstones (lavas) and pyroclastics	unknown
(5) Greenstones and pyroclastics with local intercalations of shales	unknown
(4) Shales and phyllites with lenticular beds of quartzite and, locally, quartz phyllites	600
(3) Shales and phyllites, locally containing lenticles of black chert	160
(2) Shales and pelitic sandstones, quartzites	500
(1) Coarse-grained, feldspar-bearing quartzites with lenses of conglomerate	80

the study of FIEREMANS (1959) in the Kasadi Sadi area (see Fig. 6) east of Musodi at the extreme western end of the region occupied by the complex; the thickness data, however, might only indicate local values. The order of superposition of units (4)–(7) is derived from their succession on the geological map; the only superposition observed in the field is that unit (6) lies on unit (5) in the Mazia Mpata region at the extreme eastern end of the area occupied by the Lulua Complex. The thicknesses of units (5)–(7) cannot be determined. These comments show that the stratigraphy given in Table 9 is partly uncertain and must therefore be considered provisional.

5.4.4. Lithology and metamorphism

Apart from the coarse-grained feldspar-bearing quartzites and conglomerates of unit (1) of the Kasadi Sadi area, the metasedimentary rocks of the Lulua Complex are essentially of argillaceous and arenaceous origin. The argillaceous rocks are now mudstones or phyllites, rarely sericite schists; locally hematite-bearing slates exist (FIEREMANS, 1959). The arenaceous rocks are quartzites, rarely feldspar-bearing, and often fairly coarse-grained. In thin sections of the quartzites, a cataclastic texture is observed (DELHAL, LEPERSONNE, and RAUCQ, in press). The metamorphism affecting the Lulua Complex is of an upper epizonal character.

The greenstones of the Lulua Complex have been the subject of a thorough study based on petrographical examination and chemical analysis (DELHAL, 1958b, 1959). For the most part they are extrusive rocks, consisting of albite, amphibole, epidote, chlorite, sphene, leucoxene, ilmenite, and pyrite, and contain often amygdales of chlorite and epidote, or, less frequently, of quartz, calcite, and amphibole. The pyroxene-bearing rocks occur in the eastern part of the complex, whereas the rocks devoid of this mineral crop out in the western part, where the volcanic character is more obvious. Some types of albite-bearing trachyte-like rocks resemble certain keratophyres. There are some, not very frequent, rocks of uncertain extrusive origin. The chemical and mineralogical composition of the greenstones and their association with rocks resembling certain keratophyres and with siliceous rocks similar to phtanites suggest that the greenstones might be of spilitic origin. However, pillow structures have not been observed.

The mineralogical and structural properties of the greenstones show that they have undergone an epizonal metamorphism, which is ascribed partly to autometamorphism and partly to regional metamorphism which, subsequently, has affected the complex.

The deposits associated with the greenstones (DELHAL, 1959) comprise pyroclastics and various siliceous rocks derived, at least in part, from tuffs by silicification and chloritization.

5.4.5. Plutonic activity

Apart from the greenstones, the only extrusive rocks in the area covered by the Lulua Complex are some coarse-grained rocks composed of laths of red, albitized feldspar which are strongly altered and intensely coloured by hematite, and nests of green minerals, viz., pyroxene, chlorite, and hornblende, with sometimes a little quartz and biotite. The petrographic composition of these rocks places them into the group of syenodiorites (DELHAL, 1959; chemical analyses in DELHAL, 1958 b). They form an E.–W.-trending dyke, tens of metres broad and tens of kilometres long, and a more restricted set of unconnected outcrops emplaced in metasedimentary rocks and in greenstones of Mazia Mpata in the northeastern part of the Lulua Complex (DELHAL, LEPERSONNE, and RAUCQ, in press). These rocks that were certainly emplaced after the extrusion of the lavas have suffered changes comparable to those of the greenstones.

5.4.6. Age, and relationships with older and younger formations and with adjacent areas

In the Kasadi Sadi region, the Lulua Complex lies unconformably on the granites and migmatites of the Dibaya Complex (FIEREMANS, 1959).

The absence of rocks belonging to the Luiza Metasedimentary Complex between the Lulua and the Dibaya Complexes tends to show that the Lulua Complex is younger than the Luiza Complex and, with respect to the Kasai–Lomami–Lulua metamorphic and igneous basement, occupies a position analogous to that of the Kibaran (see p. 197) and of the Bushimay (see p. 252). If the Lulua Complex does not constitute a separate entity it is to be equated with one of these two units which follow chronologically with almost no gap (see p. 256). Thus, we return to the hypotheses of CAHEN (1954, pp. 243–244), which led to the assignment of a Kibaran age to this complex.

The Lulua Complex cannot be traced continuously into Angola, but LEGRAND and RAUCQ (1957) and FIEREMANS (1959) suggested its correlation with the Cartuchi and Camaungo Formations and with a part of the formations assigned to the Kibara in the neighbourhood of the Angola–Congo border.

5.4.7. Tectonics

The Lulua Complex is folded with a generally S.W.–N.E. trend. At the northern end, the beds have a very regular southerly dip of 10°–20°; towards the south, the dips become progressively steeper and may even be vertical. The occurrence of a number of folds can be deduced from the geological map, but, in the absence of direct observations, it is not possible to determine whether the predominantly southerly dip derives from monoclinal or isoclinal folds overturned towards the north. Dips are always steeper to the south than to the north and suggest pressures from the south towards the north.

The slates are only locally affected by a cleavage oblique to the stratification (LEGRAND, 1955), and the quartzites are frequently cataclastic (see p. 219). The greenstones do not seem to have been deformed except for local cataclasis and shearing (DELHAL, LEPERSONNE, and RAUCQ, in press).

Numerous faults affect the Lulua Complex. Some are longitudinal with a trend slightly oblique to the strike of the beds, and others are transverse and postdate the longitudinal faults. Two longitudinal faults are known, limiting the complex in the north and the south (see Fig. 6). The southern fault separates the Lulua Complex from the Luiza Metasedimentary Complex and has a W.S.W.–E.N.E. trend (DELHAL, LEPERSONNE, and RAUCQ, in press). At present it is not known whether the fault is normal or reverse. The northern, or the Malafudi Fault (LEGRAND and RAUCQ, 1957), separates the Lulua Complex from the Dibaya Migmatite Complex. It has an arcuate form, trending W.S.W.–E.N.E. in the west, but becoming first E.–W., then

N.W.–S.E., in the east. This fault has been particularly closely studied west of the Lulua River, where it throws greenstones against granite. Its dip is nearly vertical, and it has thus been considered a normal fault (DELHAL, LEPERSONNE, and RAUCQ, in press).

FIEREMANS (1959) showed that in the Kasadi Sadi area normal faults with a N.N.W.–S.S.E. trend cut the margin of the Lulua Complex causing a displacement from the north towards the south. Numerous faults of the same type occur throughout the area of the Lulua Complex. Wherever they cut the bounding faults the latter are displaced, and the former faults are therefore younger (DELHAL, LEPERSONNE, and RAUCQ, in press). The age of the various fault systems is certainly pre-Lower Cretaceous and probably much older because no original relief remains.

5.5. *The Sansikwa and the Liki–Bembian*

5.5.1. General account

Although the Sansikwa and the Liki–Bembian are so distant from each other (see Fig. 15), the first cropping out in the Lower Congo and the second in Ubangi, it is worthwhile to bring together accounts relative to both. These two units are, in fact, connected across the Congo Republic (Brazzaville) and the Central African Republic by a series of intermediate patches of similar rocks which make their correlation very likely.

5.5.2. The Sansikwa

Historical survey

The Sansikwa was distinguished by LEPERSONNE, in 1951, in the Sansikwa–Lungezi Massif, south of the Matadi–Léopoldville railway between the Songololo–Kimpese branch and the Angola frontier (see Figs. 8 and 23). Formerly, its constituent formations were placed in the Bembezi and Mount Bamba Stages of the Upper Shiloango System, as previously defined (CAHEN, 1954, p. 209).

Stratigraphy

The succession recognized in the Sansikwa Massif is given in column 1 of Table 10. Elsewhere in the region south of the Congo River, only a part of the Sansikwa is exposed. It is for this reason that in the N.N.W.-trending strip which rests directly and unconformably on the main outcrop of the Mayumbian (see p. 188 and Fig. 23), the Sansikwa is represented by a phyllite sequence which includes a quartzite horizon some tens of metres thick at the top and a basal conglomerate (BERTOSSA and THONNART, 1957), representing approximately the formations S 0, S 1, and S 2a of the sequence observed in the Sansikwa Massif (see Table 10).

North of the Congo River, the Sansikwa crops out abundantly, largely as a result of the dying-out of the folds towards the north. Here it has a lithological composition analogous to that of the Sansikwa–Lungezi Massif and

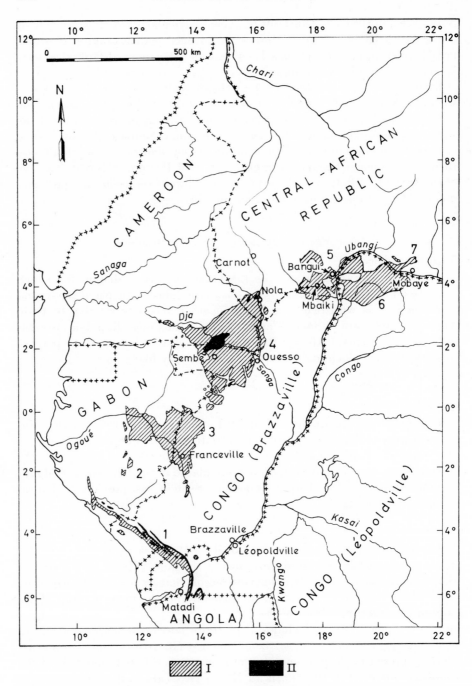

Fig. 15. Sketch map of the Sansikwa—Liki–Bembian. I: 1, Sansikwa; 2, Ouano; 3, Francevillian; 4, Sembe–Ouesso–Beuk-Nola; 5, Mbaiki; 6, Liki–Bembian; 7, Ouakini. II: Tillites.

TABLE 10

A comparison of the stratigraphic successions of the Sansikwa and the Liki-Bembian

Lower Congo. According to LEPERSONNE (1951). See CAHEN (1954, p. 212)			Ubangi. According to ADERCA (1950). See CAHEN (1954, p. 194)		
Stratigraphic unit	Lithological description	Thickness, m	Stratigraphic unit	Lithological description	Thickness, m
Lower Tillite of the Lower Congo	Glacial and interglacial formations, interbedded lavas				
Dolerite intrusions			Dolerite intrusions		
Sansikwa			Liki-Bembian		Unknown
S 2b	Coarse-grained feldspar-bearing quartzites with intercalated cherts and less frequently slates	Up to 1,375			
S 2a	Quartzites, micaceous slates, and phyllites with cherts and muddy limestones (?)	Up to 875	IIb	Phyllitic slates and phyllites; rare intercalations of conglomerate; calcareous shales and limestones in the upper part	Unknown
S 1	Phyllites, quartz phyllites, and micaceous shaly grits, some intercalated coarse-grained quartzites	Up to 500	IIa	Quartzites; rare intercalations of slate and phyllite; coarse-grained quartzites and conglomerates at the base	200–250
			Transgression		
S 0	Conglomerate with quartz and schist pebbles; intercalated phyllites and arkoses	4.50	I	Phyllites and phyllitic slates; quartzites and quartzite conglomerates	Unknown

comprises several hundred metres of phyllites resting on a basal conglomerate and succeeded by several hundred metres of generally feldspar-
bearing quartzites. Still farther north, in the Congo (Brazzaville), the
Sansikwa is represented by the Bamba Mountains "System" which consists
of two sequences, viz., the Mossouva sequence and the M'Vouti sequence.[1]
The relationship between the two sequences is uncertain (COSSON, 1955).

Upper and lower contacts

The Sansikwa rests with a major unconformity on the Mayumbian
Complex. This observation was made by J. LEPERSONNE in 1951 in the
Sansikwa–Lungezi Massif, and similar observations have been made in the
Kimuaka Massif, north of the Congo River (M. C. BRANDES and C. KOOL,
1947; see CAHEN, 1954, pp. 209–212; ANTUN, 1961a; CAHEN, 1963c). In
addition, the geological map brings out the existence of this unconformity
along the junction of the Sansikwa with the main outcrop of the Mayumbian; but here the strikes are often nearly parallel (see p. 193).

The geological map also brings out the unconformity at the top of the
Sansikwa in the Sansikwa–Lungezi Massif (see CAHEN, 1954, p. 213). The
Lower Tillite of Lower Congo rests there on different formations of the
Sansikwa and also includes numerous pebbles of Mayumbian rocks. Near
the eastern margin of the main Mayumbian outcrop, south of the Congo
River, the tillite rests on formation S 2a (see Table 10), and in the Sansikwa–
Lungezi Massif and north of the Congo River it rests on formation S 2b,
which is several hundred metres thick.

Tectonics

The major part of the Sansikwa has isopic lines with a N.N.W. trend, and
in the main the folds have the same trend. The tectonics of the Sansikwa
are characterized by a gentle, essentially N.N.W.–trending folding. The
Sansikwa was later involved in the strong West Congolian Orogeny.

Plutonic activity

The only plutonic rocks known from the Sansikwa consist of dolerite sills
(ANTUN, 1961a) and small patches of gabbro forming the roots of lava flows
that accompanied the deposition of the Lower Tillite of Lower Congo (see
p. 267), which forms the "roof" of the Sansikwa. The Sansikwa is also cut
by quartz veins.

5.5.3. Correlation of the Sansikwa and the Liki–Bembian

The Sansikwa and its continuation to the north, the Bamba Mountains
"System" as they were defined (see above) are essentially restricted to the

---

[1] *Note added in proof.* CAHEN and LEPERSONNE [*Compt. Rend.*, **262**, 1184 (1966)]
showed that the Mossouva Sequence alone corresponds to the Sansikwa.

western margin of the West Congolian fold belt. Between this region and the part of Ubangi occupied by the Liki–Bembian there are in the Congo Republic (Brazzaville) and in the Central African Republic (see Fig. 15) some more or less extensive outcrops of rocks analogous to the Sansikwa and the Liki–Bembian. They consist of the following sequences, quoted in order from the southwest to the northeast (GAZEL, HOURCQ, and NICKLÈS, 1956; GÉRARD, 1958): the "Intermediate Series", and in particular the Ouano sequence, of the western margin of the West Congolian fold belt and forming a part of its foreland; the Francevillian, which is continuous with a part of the "Intermediate Series"; the Sembe–Ouesso sequence, the Lower Dja sequence (in the Cameroons) and the Nola sequence, which are separated from the Francevillian by a gap of only 50 km and are probably its continuation under the Cretaceous or Tertiary cover; and, finally, the Mbaiki sequence, which is almost certainly continuous with the preceding sequences under the Cretaceous cover (the Carnot Sandstone). The Mbaiki sequence continues directly in Ubangi as the Liki–Bembian, which itself continues northeast in the Central African Republic as the Ouakini sequence.

Correlation was made between adjoining formations and stages by means of the following properties that they share and have in common with the Sansikwa. Their lithological properties are very similar; they all rest with an unconformity on a metamorphic or igneous basement; the only plutonic activity that has affected them consists of dolerite intrusions; the most southwesterly part of the "Intermediate Series" is succeeded, unconformably as it seems, by the Bouenzian, probably equivalent to the Upper Shiloango–Louila (GÉRARD, 1958; see p. 268); the Sembe–Ouesso, Lower Dja, and Nola sequences are surmounted by a tillite complex, probably accompanied by lavas, analogous to the Lower Tillite of Lower Congo; and, finally, the Liki–Bembian is succeeded in places by lavas and rocks of tillitic appearance, and elsewhere by the Ubangian, which, like the West Congolian, belongs to the Katangan.

The correlations among the different rock sequences reveal progressive facies variations which are displayed in the comparison of the Sansikwa and the Liki–Bembian in Table 10. The tectonic structure is correspondingly modified (see Fig. 15): the Ouano sequence, taken as a type for the "Intermediate Series", is preserved between faults and folded; the Francevillian is thrown into notable undulations; the Sembe–Ouesso and the most strongly folded sequences have a N.N.E. trend, and the intensity of folding increases from the west to the east. In the Mbaiki sequence the strikes swing so as to become close to the E.–W. strike of the Liki–Bembian.

5.5.4. The Liki–Bembian

Historical survey

The only description of the Liki–Bembian (see Figs. 5 and 15) is that of ADERCA (1950), who, under the name "Bembe Group", described a succession of three superposed "systems". Some complementary observations were made by GÉRARD, GÉRARD, and HUGÉ (1951). In order to avoid confusion with the Bembe System of Angola, the name was later changed to that of the Liki–Bembe Group, and a subdivision in better agreement with the observations was adopted (see CAHEN, 1954, p. 194).

Stratigraphy

The succession given on Table 10 must be divided into two sequences: the lower, consisting of Formation I, is overlain by the upper, consisting of Formations IIa and IIb, which possibly lies on a basal conglomerate overlying the pre-Liki–Bembian basement.

Upper and lower contacts

No normal contact with the pre-Liki–Bembian basement has been observed in Ubangi. As is the case for the Ouakini and Mbaiki Sequences, the presence of an unconformity can be inferred from the different fold trends and styles and from a difference in the degree of metamorphism. The upper contact of the Liki–Bembian possibly exists near the Batanga Rapids, where the Ubangian has been described as resting unconformably on folded Lower Liki–Bembian (ADERCA, 1950).

Tectonics

The Liki–Bembian has been strongly folded with a general trend ranging from N. 70° E. to N. 80° E. The folds are always asymmetrical and are sometimes overturned. The Liki–Bembian is often thrust over its basement, the contact, in this case, being flat-lying, undulating faults marked by tectonic breccias.

Plutonic activity

No granites are known, but the Liki–Bembian is cut by dolerites and gabbros and is locally covered by amygdaloidal doleritic lavas.

Mineralization

No mineralization is known in the Liki–Bembian, but in the Mbaiki sequence, which is its continuation in the Central African Republic, quartz veins carry sometimes gold, pyrite, galena, and arsenopyrite mineralizations.

5.5.5. Conclusions

The Sansikwa and the Liki–Bembian seem to correspond rather closely, contrary to previous correlations (see CAHEN, 1954, p. 226), which make the Liki–Bembian an equivalent not only of the Sansikwa but also of the Upper Shiloango–Louila of Lower Congo. The new correlation appears feasible on the basis of recent information gathered in the Congo Republic (Brazzaville) and in the Central African Republic. This correlation suggests that the relatively gentle post-Sansikwa, pre-Lower Tillite folding in Lower Congo, which at first seemed to be an early phase of the West Congolian orogeny, increases towards the north until, particularly in the Liki–Bembian, it becomes an important tectonic phase that is independent of the post-Ubangian folding (equivalent to the West Congolian Orogeny). It is one reason why we have dealt with these rocks in Section 5. They probably represent all or a part of that period of time which, in eastern Congo, covers the formation of the Kibaran and the Burundian (see p. 157).

5.6. *Summary*

5.6.1. The Kibaran–Burundian–Karagwe–Ankolean geosyncline

The unity of the Kibaran, the Burundian, and the Karagwe–Ankolean and their development in the same vast, complex geosyncline, which has for long been suspected, now appears certain.

The continuity of the Burundian and the Karagwe–Ankolean is gapless. There remains a gap between the Kibaran and the Burundian, partly caused by the lack of recent geological investigations in northern Katanga and partly by the existence of a transverse swell that brings the older Ruzizian to crop out. The certainty that one is dealing with the same assemblage comes from mineral and rock ages data pertaining to tectonics, stratigraphy, mineralizations, and plutonic activity.

The Kibaran, the Burundian, and the Karagwe–Ankolean rest unconformably on the Lukoshian, the Ruzizian, and the Toro assemblage, all of which are traversed by granites or pegmatites about 1,850 Myr old, which have not affected the Kibaran and the Burundian, for which numerous granites, pegmatites, and veins have yielded ages between 1,300 Myr and 845 Myr (CAHEN, 1954, p. 120; see also p. 204).

The thickness of the Kibaran is very close to that of the Burundian and amounts to more than 10,000 m. The sedimentation of both sequences seems to have taken place between about 1,850 Myr and 1,240 Myr. The predominantly pelitic and arenaceous sedimentation appears to be very similar in those parts of the two assemblages which correspond most closely, viz., the Kibara Mountains and the central parts of Rwanda and Burundi. Pelitic sedimentation was interspersed with arenaceous sedimentation episodes (Kibaran, 4,000 m–5,000 m; Burundian, 5,000 m–6,000 m), succeeded by an arenaceous sedimentation with only minor episodes of pelitic sedimentation (Kibaran, 1,200 m–2,450 m; Burundian, 1,000 m–2,500 m). After this arenaceous episode followed a pelitic sedimentation with arenaceous sedimentation episodes rare in the Kibaran but more numerous in the Burundian (Kibaran, up to 3,300 m; Burundian, 2,000 m).

Besides the general parallelism of sedimentation, the tectonic similarity of the two parts of this single unit must be emphasized. Both have a fold trend of a northeasterly orientation, except that the Burundian turns parallel to the Ruzizian towards the northwest. The Kibaran and a part of the Burundian are aligned. The vergence of the folds, more marked in the Kibaran than in the Burundian, the thrusting, and the transport are all the result of pressures from the southeast or the east towards the northwest or the west, except locally in the Burundian.

The metamorphism of the Kibaran and the Burundian bears witness to their development at a relatively shallow depth (see pp. 203 and 211). There is also a great similarity in their plutonic activity, and their mineralizations are almost identical (see pp. 203, 204, 212, 215).

In spite of some disparity in the knowledge of the two regions, it can be concluded that there existed, on the one hand, an eastern, eugeosynclinal trough in the Kibaran (see p. 205) and, on the other hand, a deep geosynclinal zone in central Rwanda and Burundi (see p. 209).

The conclusion follows that the subsidence, sedimentation, tectonic and metamorphic evolution, plutonic activity and paragenesis of the two aligned assemblages are highly comparable and that they developed in the same complex geosyncline whose subsidence began at about 1,850 Myr ago. The orogeny that concluded their formation is dated at about 1,240 Myr, and the younger, posttectonic granitic and pegmatitic episodes fall approximately between 1,120 Myr and 845 Myr (see p. 157).

5.6.2. Possible correlation of the Sansikwa, the Liki–Bembian and the Lulua Complex with the Kibaran–Burundian

The geological reasons for supposing that the Sansikwa and the Liki–Bembian are equivalents was discussed on p. 224. It is equally important to show that they are chronologically comparable to the Kibaran–Burundian. This similarity in age is brought out by the fact that both are unconformably overlain, more or less markedly, by equivalents of the Katangan (see pp. 224, 226), the West Congolian, and the Ubangian, respectively. The Sansikwa certainly lies unconformably on the Upper Mayumbian, which was folded roughly 1,500 Myr ago (see p. 158), and the excellent correlation between the Sansikwa and the Liki–Bembian is a suggestion that the same holds good for the latter. These sequences therefore seem to lie between the same time limits as part or all of the Kibaran–Burundian and might thus be the equivalent of the latter. However, they do not seem to have formed under similar conditions. At this time, there are only very hypothetical arguments which favour the incorporation of the Lulua Complex in the list of formations correlated in whole or in part with the Kibaran–Burundian (see p. 220).

6. The end of the Precambrian. The Katangan and its equivalents

6.1. *Introduction*

The rocks that are here reviewed crop out around much of the periphery of the Congo Basin and seem to underlie a large part of it (see Fig. 16). In

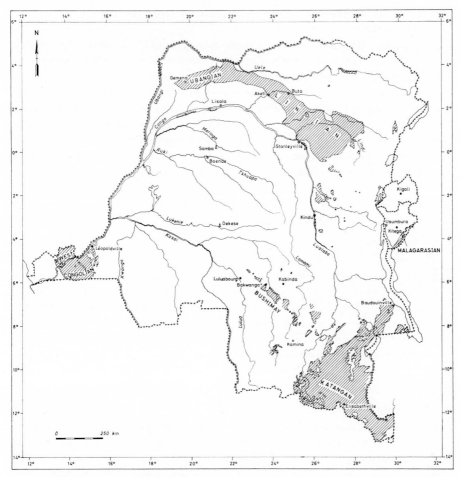

FIG. 16. Sketch map of the Katangan *sensu lato*, showing the following local entities: Katangan *sensu stricto*, Bushimay, Malagarasian, Lindian, Ubangian, and West Congolian.

most areas they consist of little folded or unfolded rocks, metamorphosed feebly or not at all, lying with a marked unconformity on older rocks and unconformably overlain by cover rocks. In southern Katanga and in western Lower Congo, the folding is clearly more marked than elsewhere and is intense. Everywhere, these groups are made up of two or more subdivisions, separated from one another by unconformities of secondary importance. In the broad view, there is a threefold division, namely, an arenaceous or an arenaceous–pelitic complex at the base; a calcareous or a calcareous–pelitic complex in the middle; and an arenaceous or an arenaceous–pelitic complex at the top, sometimes more or less calcareous and characterized by a generally red colour ("Old Red Sandstone" facies). Tillites occur in Katanga, Lower Congo and Ituri. Locally, especially in

Katanga, the succession is more complicated than the plan just outlined would indicate.

Except for the floor of the Congo Basin, which has recently become known through diamond drilling and geophysical surveys, these rocks have been known for a long time and are traditionally correlated on the basis of their lithological similarity, their property of being unfolded or little folded and unmetamorphosed or feebly metamorphosed, and their geographical distribution around the Congo Basin. At the present time, wherever datings have been made (see pp. 155, 156, 157) they confirm the traditional correlations and suggest a Precambrian age for all, or the greater part, of these assemblages. Only the youngest rocks might, perhaps, be Lower Palaeozoic.

6.2. *The Katangan of the type region*

6.2.1. Introduction

The complexity of the vast Katangan region dealt with here (see Fig. 17) demands the separate discussion of the Katangan of southern Katanga, here defined as covering the area between the southern and eastern frontiers and an oblique line drawn from the Kolwezi region in the southwest to the Pweto region, north of Lake Moero, in the northeast. The Katangan of northeastern Katanga and that of western Katanga with its continuation into southeastern Kasai will be discussed in Section 6.3. Southern Katanga is the type area of the Katangan.

6.2.2. Historical survey

Except for some small areas, the whole region consists of Katangan rocks, folded in the south and practically horizontal in the north. The early geologists, particularly J. CORNET in 1897 and F. E. STUDT in 1908, thought that the metamorphosed and folded formations in the south consist of several "systems" that are older than the horizontal Kundelungu rocks in the north. By 1913, F. E. STUDT had already combined several of the folded systems of southern Katanga, and, in 1914, F. DELHAYE showed that the horizontal beds pass into folded rocks. The main body of geological knowledge of southern Katanga is the result of work by the *Comité Spécial du Katanga* in collaboration with the *Union Minière du Haut Katanga*, mainly under the direction of M. ROBERT since 1920 (see ROBERT, 1940; CAHEN, 1954, pp. 55–117).

The subdivision and terminology of the Katangan have given rise to so much discussion that, in order to avoid confusion, the reader who studies early publications must consult, for instance, the *Lexique stratigraphique du Congo belge et du Ruanda–Urundi* (CAHEN and LEPERSONNE, 1956) or the book of CAHEN (1954, pp. 57–58).

Similarly, the age of the Katangan has been much discussed (see CAHEN, 1954, p. 261; ROBERT, 1956). At the moment it is known that the Katangan

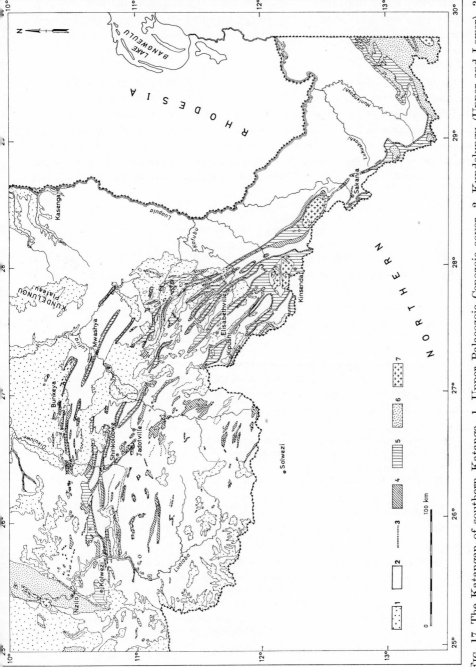

Fig. 17. The Katangan of southern Katanga. 1, Upper Palaeozoic–Cenozoic cover. 2, Kundelungu (Upper and Lower). 3, "Little Conglomerate". 4, "Great Conglomerate". 5, Mwashya and Roan. 6, Kibaran (near Kolwezi); Muva (in the south), 7, Granite.

is definitely older than (620 ± 20) Myr, with the possible but not probable exception of some hundred metres of the topmost strata (CAHEN and others, 1961; see p. 156).

6.2.3. Stratigraphy

Variations in facies and thickness are frequent and geologically important. Unfortunately, not all the beds can be observed everywhere. Table 11 gives the general succession of beds from top to bottom. The lithological composition of the Upper Kundelungu was determined in the northern part of the type area (north of Bunkeya), while that of the rest of the sequence was taken from the southern part. There are groups in some regions which can be safely attributed to a given major subdivision, but

TABLE 11

Stratigraphy of the Katangan

Upper Kundelungu (thickness 3,000 m in the fold belt, 1,500 m–1,800 m farther N.)

  Upper or Plateau Group (1,500 m in the fold belt, 550–800 m farther N.)

    (B) Red shale (>100 m in the N.)
    (A) Gritty and arkosic quartzite of the plateaus (450 m–550 m in the N.)

  Middle or Kyubo Group (1,500 m–2,000 m in the fold belt; 980 m–1,200 m farther N.)

    (D) Fine-grained quartzite, thick beds (100 m–200 m in the N.)
    (C) Micaceous shale (>300 m in the N.)
    (B) Shale and calcareous shale with chert (550 m–600 m in the N.)
    (A) Kyubo feldspar-bearing grit (15 m–75 m in the N.)

  Lower or Kalule Group (Middle Kundelungu of CAHEN and MORTELMANS, 1948; see p. 240)

    (E) Shale and calcareous shale (100 m in the N.)
    (D) Lubudi Cement Works Oolitic Limestone (10 m–45 m in the N.)
    (C) Kanianga Calcareous Sandstones (10 m–100 m in the N.)
    (B) "Pink" Dolomitic Limestone (20 m–45 m in the N.)
    (A) Conglomerate (>10 m)

Little Conglomerate

  Tillite with a calcareous-shale matrix (thickness outcrops at least 50 m)

Lower Kundelungu (thickness 0 m–2,000 m, major in the S.)

    (D) Nonwezi Sandstone and Quartzite (up to 1,000 m in the S.)
    (C) Shales and slates and calcareous shales and slates (up to 500 m in the S.)
    (B) Kakontwe Formation. Calcareous shales and slates, limestones and dolomites
        with stromatolites (up to 400 m in the S.)
    (A) Conglomerate. Absent in the S.; may reach a great thickness in the N., where
        it might be the only representative of the sequence

Great Conglomerate and Mwashya (thickness up to 1,100 m)

  Tillite, and periglacial deposits (up to 300 m)
  Mwashya sequence (600 m–800 m)
    Varved slates and phyllites, grits and feldspar-bearing quartzites, black phyllites,
    grey-green macigno, and tillite-like intercalations

Roan

Mofya group[a] (475 m): black, silicified oolites containing *Girvanella roberti* HAC-
   QUAERT, and associated jasper (25 m). Alternation of more or less magnesian limestones with micaceous silty phyllites (estimated 450 m)

Dipeta group (>400 m)[a]
   Alternating chlorite–talc schists, feldspar-bearing grits and siliceous, sometimes
      fetid dolomites (>60 m)
   Shaly and feldspar-bearing sandstones and grits, generally calcareous (200 m–
      350 m)

"Mine Series" group (>100 m)[b]
   (E) Dolomites (*C.M.N.*), grit, conglomeratic stromatolites (50 m–150 m)
   (D) Shales, usually dolomitic (*S.D.*) with massive dolomite (*B.O.M.Z.*), and
      stromatolites (35 m–90 m)
   (C) Siliceous dolomite with stromatolites (*R.S.C.*); (20 m)
   (B) Stratified, micaceous, silicified dolomite (*R.S.F.* and *D. strat*); (7 m–9 m)
   (A) Chloritic sandstone with a dolomitic cement (0.5 m–3 m)

Red, chloritic sandstones with dolomite cement (at least 225 m)

Base not seen in the type area

---

[a] Unpublished information from the *Union Minière du Haut Katanga* indicates that
these groups are more complex than here shown.

[b] Letters in parentheses are the conventional abbreviations used by geologists of the
Union Minière du Haut Katanga.

cannot be precisely correlated with the more detailed subdivisions in the
table.

Variations in facies and thickness, relationships between sequences, and
stratigraphically uncertain sequences will be dealt with on pp. 234–41.

This general stratigraphical sequence is a modification of one published
by CAHEN (1954, pp. 107, 113). It consists of five major divisions in place of
three, which brings it close to the sequence of VANDEN BRANDE (1937).
The stratigraphy of the "Mine Series" and underlying beds was summarized
from OOSTERBOSCH (1959).

The names "Great Conglomerate" (*Grand conglomérat*) and "Little
Conglomerate" (*Petit conglomérat*) are traditional in Katanga. The Great
Conglomerate is the thicker of the two.

The base of the Katangan

The base of the Katangan is known in the south, the north, and, probably,
the west of southern Katanga (see Figs. 17 and 26). In each of the three
regions, conglomerates or coarse-grained arkoses rest with a marked unconformity on the basement in the south, and on the Kibaran in the west
and the north. Even though in the south they certainly form the base of
the Roan, as is shown in Table 11, the exact position of conglomerates of
other regions in the stratigraphical table of the Roan is less certain.

West of the Nzilo massif, as in areas farther in the north, the autochtho-
nous Katangan is mainly represented by the upper divisions lying on the

Great Conglomerate; the latter lies unconformably on the Kibaran. Locally, between the Great Conglomerate and the Kibaran, there are conglomerates and coarse-grained arkosic rocks which also lie unconformably on the Kibaran and underlie, with a less marked unconformity, the Great Conglomerate. Near Lat. 9° S., in the areas south and southeast of Mitwaba, a group of rocks characteristic of the Roan (see p. 237) is intercalated between these conglomerate complexes and the Great Conglomerate.

The lower part of the Roan

In the region where the stratigraphical sequence given in Table 11 was established, the lower part of the Roan has not been observed. However, it is well known farther in the south in the Copper Belt of northern Zambia and in southeastern Katanga, largely in diamond drill holes in Katanga. Even though the facies variations appear to be fairly numerous, the general succession is well illustrated by Table 12, which gives a somewhat generalized succession at Kinsenda.

TABLE 12

Stratigraphy of the lower part of the Roan at Kinsenda

Lithological description	Thickness, m
(6) Dolomites and dolomitic shales, often micaceous	~400
(5) Gritty dolomites and dolomitic shales with intercalations of sandy shales	~250
(4) Feldspar-bearing and micaceous dolomitic shales	~100
(3) Feldspar-bearing grits, more or less schistose, with feldspar-bearing quartzites	~100
(2) Conglomeratic, feldspar-bearing quartzites with intercalated grits, micaceous sandy shales and sericite quartzites	~100
(1) Feldspar-bearing grits and quartzites, more or less conglomeratic	~80
Unconformity	
Gneissose biotite granite	

In most localities in Katanga, the "Mine Series" group is bounded at the base by thrust faults, and even where its base is seen, the base of the Roan is not reached. This means that a precise correlation of the succession given in Table 12, representing the lower part of the Katangan, with that given in Table 11 is not yet possible. According to OOSTERBOSCH (1959), the most likely hypothesis is that the "Mine Series" overlies concordantly all or a part of the Lower Roan and might correspond to Members (4) and (5) of the succession given in Table 12. However, the possibility cannot be excluded that the Lower Roan is a neritic facies of the "Mine Series".

The Roan of the western and northern margins of southern Katanga

At the contact against the Kibaran, the rock sequences beneath the Great Conglomerate that belong to the Roan or have been assigned to it, crop out in several localities. The conglomerates of the Nzilo Massif were already mentioned (see p. 234), and they belong probably to the base of the Roan. Similar rocks occur farther in the northeast in the region of the Lufira Gorge, but here the conglomerates are sometimes overlain by grits and red shales.

Still farther in the northeast, on the eastern margin of the Upemba Rift, in a region bounded by Lat. 8° S. and Lat. 9° S., there is a long strip of arenaceous rocks, formerly attributed to the Kundelungu, but since shown to belong to the Roan (DUMONT, 1962). The stratigraphy of these rocks was discussed by RORIVE (1954), who called them the "Nonda System". However, we shall use here the name "Nonda Group" (see Table 13).

TABLE 13

Stratigraphy of the Nonda Group

Lithological description	Thickness, m
Upper formation (from top to bottom)	
More or less coarse-grained arkoses, quartzitic grits, and conglomerates containing arkose layers	>1,350
Lower formation (from top to bottom)	
Arkoses, shales, arkoses, and conglomerates	~1,175

The general succession of red and violet rocks remains the same despite variations in the thickness and facies of individual formations. The thickness of the group varies between 2,100 m and 3,000 m. The basal conglomerate begins always with a conglomerate breccia ("scree breccia"), and fills in an irregular, dissected surface.

In the south, these rocks merge into the Djipidi (CAHEN, 1954, p. 78) lying unconformably between the tillite of the Great Conglomerate and the Kibaran. The Kabele and Kabenga Conglomerates of the western margin of the Upemba Rift were almost certainly continuous with the Nonda of the eastern margin (see Fig. 21; CAHEN, 1954, pp. 257–258).

With respect to their facies and thickness, the Nonda Group, and the Kabele and Kabenga Conglomerates, have much in common with sequences B0 and B1 of the Bushimay (see pp. 252, 254), the Kabele and Kabenga Conglomerates acting as links between the Nonda Group and the Bushimay. At least a part of these rocks is of continental facies, but they do not display glacial or periglacial features.

Finally, farther in the northeast, between Mitwaba and Pweto (see Fig. 18), there is a succession investigated by DUMONT (1962) and summarized in Table 14.

Farther in the northeast, the Lufonzo Group (probably identical with the Mutendele Group) rests directly on the Kantanta Group (see pp. 237, 251).

Because of their stratigraphical position and lithological composition, the

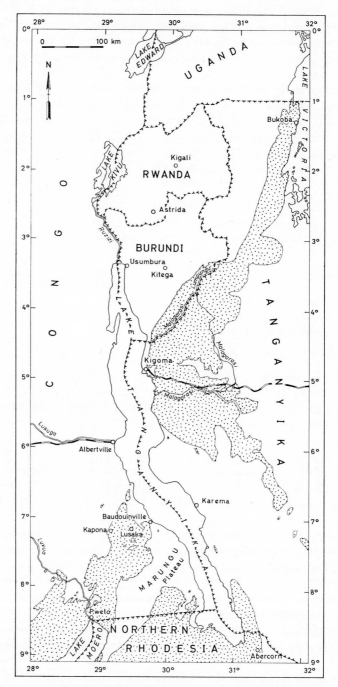

FIG. 18. Sketch map of the Katangan *sensu lato* of northeastern Katanga and Zambia, Tanzania, and Burundi.

TABLE 14

Stratigraphical succession in the region between Mitwaba and Pweto

Lithological description	Thickness, m
(3) Mutendele Group	
Grey or black shales, feldspar-bearing sandstones, quartzites	> 200
(2) Kitondwe Group	
Limestone breccias, stromatolitic limestones, partly silicified, black silicified oolite	total 50
Mica-bearing shales and coarse arkosic conglomerate	total less than 10
(1) Kantanta Group	
Silicified stromatolitic limestones with fine-grained white oolite	50–75
Red, gritty, feldspar-bearing conglomerate with large pebbles; intercalated grit and arkose	500–600

Mutendele and Lufonzo Groups must represent the Mwashya Sequence (see p. 238), the Kitondwe and Kantanta Groups representing all or a part of the Roan.

General succession of the Roan

In conclusion, there remain several unknowns and doubts about the Roan succession. At the present time, any attempt at subdivision other than on a lithological basis would be premature. The present state of knowledge suggests that there are at least two successive sequences. One of them would reach from the base of the Katangan to the top of the "Mine Series" Group, the other, or others, from the Dipeta and Mofya Groups to the silicified oolite. The Kantanta and Kitondwe Groups would be the northern representatives of these two sequences; the Kantanta Group resting unconformably on the Kibaran, while the Kitondwe Group rests either on the Kantanta Group or directly on the Kibaran.

The relationships between the Mwashya Sequence and the underlying strata

The Mwashya Sequence rests conformably or pseudoconformably on its basement. No angular unconformity has been observed, but the Mwashya "Conglomerate" has some of the lithological properties of a tillite and contains pebbles from the underlying Roan (silicified oolite, jasper, dolomite) and from the basement (granite, quartzite, schists, and greenstones), denoting at least an interruption of sedimentation, tectonic movements, and transgression. The conglomerate generally occurs within a group of macignos into which it passes, both upwards and downwards, by a progressive diminution in the grain size and quantity of the clastic material. Frequently it is separated from the top of the Roan only by a very thin layer of macigno. In the Copper Belt of southern Katanga, the Mwashya "Conglomerate"

seems to be absent and might be replaced by a pink shale containing chert
nodules.

The Mwashya Sequence

The Mwashya Sequence is known in the Katanga fold belt and farther in
the north, where it is intercalated between the Kundelungu and the Roan
or between the Kundelungu and the Kibaran basement (DUMONT, 1962).
Above the macigno complex that includes the conglomerate, the characteristic rocks of the unit are grey or black, often banded slates and shales
and feldspar-bearing quartzites, with an order of succession varying somewhat from region to region. In the north (see p. 251), the Lufonzo Group
consists (from top to bottom) of feldspar-bearing quartzites (thickness,
200 m); black shales with phthanites and cherts (300 m), and a conglomerate
with tillite horizons (25 m). The Mutendele Group displays the same general
stratigraphical succession, except that the base is not seen but is possibly
conglomeratic.

Relationships between the Great Conglomerate and the Mwashya Sequence

The Great Conglomerate and the Mwashya Sequence are generally
thought to pass continuously into each other, as several geologists, e.g.,
FRANCOTTE (1959), have proved. However, in certain localities the Mwashya
Sequence may be largely or entirely absent, and the Great Conglomerate
may rest directly on the top of the Roan, on various formations belonging
to the Roan, or on the Kibaran (see CAHEN, 1954, pp. 70–71).

These somewhat contradictory observations might well indicate that in
many regions there are, near the top of the Mwashya Sequence, rocks belonging to the periglacial phase of the Great Conglomerate glaciation. Consequently, some sections are continuous, while others suggest that the
Great Conglomerate is transgressive with respect to the underlying
Mwashya Sequence.

The Great Conglomerate and its relationships with the Lower Kundelungu

A description of the Great Conglomerate is given on p. 241. It is
sufficient here to say that it is a complex that in the Katangan fold belt
consists mainly of conglomerate and tillite, sometimes with intercalated
phyllites that may be banded, and quartzitic or arkosic sandstones, while
in the northern, subtabular margin of southern Katanga there is a tillite
overlain by a conglomeratic and arenaceous rock sequence which is grouped
with the tillite to form the Great Conglomerate complex, but which might be
equivalent to the Lower Kundelungu (see p. 239). In the Katangan fold belt,
the tillite of the Great Conglomerate is sometimes directly overlain by a
variable thickness of phyllites and calcareous phyllites, frequently blackish
and banded. Once again, they may make up a part of the glacial and periglacial group.

The Kakontwe formation is usually considered the base of the Lower

Kundelungu. North of Bunkeya, the Lower Kundelungu begins with a 240-m-thick sequence of red, feldspar-bearing grits and arkoses containing lenses of conglomerate (BEUGNIES, 1952). Only from here on can one talk of a basal conglomerate of the Lower Kundelungu which expands north-wards to be incorporated in the conglomerate group overlying the tillite, mentioned above.

Observations in the Bunkeya region suggest that there is a break between the Great Conglomerate and the Lower Kundelungu, or that, in any case, the passage from one to the other is marked by a change in the sedimento-logical and climatic conditions during the deposition.

The Lower Kundelungu

The Lower Kundelungu sequence is well developed in the southern part of Katanga and appears to reach a thickness of about 2,000 m in the Upper Lufira basin. Its thickness is reduced to about 1,000 m in the area of Kambove, near Jadotville; and farther north, in the external folds of the fold belt (Lukafu region), it decreases from 800 m in the Mwashya Anti-cline to 425 m in the Gombela Anticline. Still farther north, at the Kibaran border, the tillite of the Great Conglomerate is overlain by 200 m–300 m of conglomerate that might represent both the basal conglomerate and a lateral facies of the Lower Kundelungu.

The Lower Kundelungu is thus lenticular, as are its constituents, which are also very variable in lithology. The banded slates and calcareous phyllites, which probably form a part of the tillite complex of the Great Conglomerate, have sometimes been included at its base. Usually, the Lower Kundelungu is begun with a group called the "Kakontwe Limestone", con-sisting of calcitic and dolomitic limestones, and calcareous phyllites. Northwards, in the Mwadingusha and Bunkeya regions, the "Kakontwe Limestone" is absent, and the base is formed by sandstones or feldspar-bearing sandstones which, beyond Bunkeya, pass into conglomerates that clearly show that the Lower Kundelungu is distinct from the Great Con-glomerate (see p. 238).

The relationships between the Little Conglomerate and the Lower and the Upper Kundelungu

The field relationships demonstrate a fairly clear break separating the Little Conglomerate from the Lower Kundelungu. Broadly speaking, the Little Conglomerate takes on a tillite facies towards the north, and a marine conglomerate facies towards the south. The passage from one to the other occurs between Bunkeya and Kambove (near Jadotville; see Fig. 17). In the south, the Little Conglomerate contains pebbles of Lower Kundelungu rocks among which pebbles of the Kakontwe Limestone are most charac-teristic. In the Lukafu area, it contains pebbles of silicified oolite from the top of the Roan.

In view of the abundance, among the rolled pebbles, of Kakontwe Lime-stone located 2,000 m lower in the succession, the lithological composition of the Little Conglomerate in southern Katanga allows the conclusion that a tectonic phase exists, confirmed by the transgressive overlap of the Little Conglomerate over the Kibaran basement in the north. This overlap, at one time thought to be relatively minor (CAHEN and MORTELMANS, 1948), now seems to be rather important (DUMONT, 1962). The Little Conglomerate is always overlain by a probably lagoonal dolomitic limestone, the "Pink Limestone", which is the lowermost bed of the Upper Kundelungu. This succession seems to indicate progressive immersion.

The Upper Kundelungu

The Upper Kundelungu sequence is one of the most characteristic divisions of the Katangan. Its maximum thickness is reached in the external folds of the Katangan fold arc in the Gombela area, east of Mwashya (see Fig. 17). Towards both the north and the south its thickness decreases. However, the seeming independence of the Lower Group compared with the other two groups (CAHEN and MORTELMANS, 1948) now appears to be less important than previously thought (DUMONT, 1962) and does not justify the recognition of a Middle Kundelungu, as CAHEN and MORTELMANS had defined it.

The various formations that make up the Lower Group are well differentiated in the north of the type area, where they yield the succession quoted in Table 11. In the centre of the basin (southern Katanga), some of these formations are no longer separable, and the Lower Group seems to pass, with no apparent break, into the Middle Group, whose basal member, the Kyubo feldspar-bearing grit, does not seem to occur in this region.

A characteristic horizon that is relatively constant is the "Upper Kundelungu Chert", which is included in Formation B of the Middle Group and yields rare microfossils, especially traces of algae.

The break between the Middle Group and the Upper Group might be sharp.

6.2.4. Tillites

Three conglomerates without visible bedding have been described as tillites, namely, the Little Conglomerate, the Great Conglomerate, and the Mwashya Conglomerate.

SCHERMERHORN and STANTON (1963a) rejected the tillitic nature of these rocks on the basis of some dubious correlations. It is useful to recall here the main properties that allow them to be considered glacial formations (CAHEN, 1947; 1963a, b).

The Little Conglomerate, with a maximum thickness of 80 m, has a grey-green or grey-blue, calcareous–argillaceous or sandy–argillaceous matrix. It contains much clastic debris of variable size and lithological composition, angular fragments and splinters, among which are numerous shards of quartz. Scattered throughout this unbedded matrix are numerous pebbles and boulders that may reach a size of 1 m³. They range from subangular to subrounded and are often faceted; striated pebbles are locally abundant, and pebbles with percussion marks occur. Among the very varied assemblage of pebbles there are, in particular, granites that have been transported for a considerable distance.

The slates and phyllites that underlie the tillite are deformed in a way that may be attributed to the action of a glacier. No glacial pavements have been found. The subglacial topography is slightly irregular.

The Little Conglomerate extends over the whole of the Katangan type area and also northeast of Katanga. However, in the southern part of Katanga its facies is marine and the passage into the tillite facies occurs in the Kambove region (Fig. 19).

The Great Conglomerate is very similar to the Little Conglomerate. Large boulders (up to several cubic metres) occur, and striated pebbles appear to be more common. Its thickness reaches 200 m. The tillite facies is more characteristic in northern Katanga than in southern Katanga, where it is usually considered to be fluvioglacial, as is also the case in Zambia, where the Great Conglomerate also occurs. The main difference between the Little Conglomerate and the Great Conglomerate, apart from the much greater thickness of the second, is the frequent occurrence of definite varves in the Great Conglomerate, while only one dubious occurrence of varves has been reported in the Little Conglomerate (Fig. 20).

Both conglomerates rest on an erosion surface. This is not the case with the Mwashya Conglomerate, which passes gradually into the surrounding

FIG. 19. Little Conglomerate, or *Petit Conglomérat* (subaqueous, not glacial) at the base of the Upper Kundelungu. Near Luingila River, central Katanga. Photo, L. Cahen.

FIG. 20. Glacial varves with erratics in the Great Conglomerate complex of Katanga. Luingila River, central Katanga. Photo, G. Mortelmans.

rocks, which are of the same constitution as its matrix. For the rest, it looks like a tillite, but striated pebbles are rare, while faceted pebbles are abundant. It might, perhaps, be a glaciomarine deposit, but might also be a tilloid, containing reworked glacial material (CAHEN, 1963b). The Mwashya Conglomerate is much thinner and a more local occurrence than the other two; its thickness is less than 5 m in Katanga.

Traces of glacial activity have been reported from the base of the Roan (CAHEN, 1947). They have not been confirmed, and their existence is very problematical (CAHEN, 1963b).

6.2.5. Tectonics

The Katangan consists of a series of mutually concordant beds that rest with a major unconformity on their basement and are unconformably overlain by the Lukuga Sequence of Upper Carboniferous and Permian age (see Fig. 17). The folding that has affected the Katangan, or the Katangan Orogeny, consists of several phases, which are named after the rocks they affect, such as the Roanian and the Kundelungan. The last important Kundelungan phase is the main phase of folding that has affected the whole series. It was of such violence in the southern part of Katanga that it masks the earlier less marked movements, but their existence can be deduced from their sedimentological effects. Farther north, in the foreland, the beds are generally flat-lying or undulating, and the movements that occurred during the geological evolution of the Katangan Basin are more readily decipherable (CAHEN and others, 1961).

A first Roanian phase is distinguishable in southern Katanga by means of its sedimentological consequences. After the deposition of the "Mine Series" Group, it caused a deposition of clastic sediments, which form the lowermost member of the Dipeta Group. A second Roanian phase of movement followed by erosion is deduced from the lithological composition of the pebbles in the Mwashya Conglomerate (granites and other pre-Mwashya rocks). Two Roanian phases are also present in the north of the country, one of them between the Kitondwe and the Kantanta Groups (see p. 237), the first group being transgressive on to the Kibaran basement with respect to the second group; the other phase being indicated through the overlap of beds ascribed to the Mwashya Sequence with respect to the Kitondwe and Kantanta Groups and thus on to the Kibaran basement. Two phases have similarly been distinguished by means of studies in the Nonda area (see p. 235). The exact nature of these Roanian movements is badly known, and some movements should be considered "posthumous" Kibaran movements. It is not certain whether the later Roanian movements were closely related to later Kundelungan phases or were repercussions of a separate orogeny that affected mainly other regions.

There probably existed four Kundelungan folding phases of differing intensity. They are connected by the constancy of their effects, which caused, with the passage of time, the northward displacement of the zones of maximum subsidence and, after the main phase of folding, the northward overfolding of the folds and the northward displacement of the nappes.

The first Kundelungan phase occurred after the deposition of the Great Conglomerate and caused the marked subsidence of the Lower Kundelungu in southern Katanga (Elisabethville–Katanga–Rhodesia frontier). This episode is marked by a conglomerate, distinct from the tillite of the Great Conglomerate, along the northern and western margins of the basin of subsidence (see pp. 238, 239).

A second, particularly well-marked, phase is deduced from the lithological composition of the pebbles in the Little Conglomerate and from its marked transgressive overlap towards the north and the northeast (see p. 240). This phase was followed by another phase, about which little is known, that was placed between the Little Conglomerate and the Upper Kundelungu and marked the beginning of the Upper Kundelungu subsidence. The Upper Kundelungu subsidence may be divided in two, namely, the subsidence of the Lower Group, whose axis seems to have been located in an area near Elisabethville and north of the maximum subsidence of Lower Kundelungu time; and the subsidence of the Middle and Upper Groups, particularly evident in the external portions of the Katanga fold arc, e.g. at Gombela, which was again located north of the previous subsidences. Between these two periods of subsidence a phase of, perhaps, great importance probably existed, marked in the north by the formation of the Plateau Arkoses (see p. 240).

Finally, the third and main Kundelungan phase affected all or nearly all of the Upper Kundelungu. In the Kolwezi area (Western mines), thrust sheets of the "Mine Series" Group rest on a relatively high level of the Upper Kundelungu. In the subtabular foreland, on the Kundelungu Plateau, the uppermost unit, which is not, however, recognized in the southern fold belt, is slightly folded with a trend parallel to that of the folds that are better developed in southern Katanga. The thrust planes themselves are slightly refolded.

Along the fold arc, the tectonic intensity increases from the southeast towards the northwest. First there are folds overfolded to the northeast, eventually complicated by faulting, then anticlines with their southern flanks thrust towards the north or the northeast, and finally large nappes, completely separated from their roots. The resistance caused by the Nzilo Kibaran Massif was probably responsible for the shearing of beds that caused the formation of nappes with a displacement estimated as more than 30 km (FRANÇOIS, 1959). Transcurrent faulting along generally E.–W. directions was the last major tectonic event (DEMESMAEKER, FRANÇOIS, and OOSTERBOSCH, 1963).

Radial faults, contemporary with or postdating the folding are known from the subtabular part of Katanga.

6.2.6. Metamorphism

The degree of regional metamorphism increases from the north towards the south. Absent in the north, it successively attains the sericite zone, the chlorite zone, and, more rarely, the biotite zone towards the south. The following manifestations of nondynamic metamorphism are known from the southern part of Katanga (north of Solwezi in Zambia): rocks containing corundum and garnet are reported from the Lower Kundelungu, and a fairly general scapolization occurs in the Roan and Lower Kundelungu. A posttectonic formation of biotite and muscovite has been demonstrated (BELLIÈRE, 1961). The cause of the metamorphism is not known for certain.

6.2.7. Plutonic activity

A controversy that has for many years engaged those who favour and those who oppose the existence of granites in the Katangan of the Copper Belt of Katanga and of Zambia still remains to be settled. It has passed through three successive phases, namely, a first phase, during which the existence of a "young" granite intrusive in the Katangan and considered to be the source of the mineralization was nearly universally agreed; a second phase, during which many geologists, knowing of no intrusive granites, considered the mineralization syngenetic; and, finally, a third phase, which, in a slightly different form, reconsidered the first explanation. This means that there were not necessarily intrusive granites, but rather that metamorphism could continue as far as to a selective granitization of suitable rocks (DARNLEY, 1960; GYSIN, 1960; CAHEN and others, 1961; VAES, 1960, 1961, 1962). Recent age determinations support the idea that granite was re-mobilized during the Katangan time (SNELLING and others, 1964). In southern Katanga, some gabbros and dolerites, which are post-Lower Kundelungu in age and might reach the base of the Upper Kundelungu, are certainly intrusive. On the northern margin of the type Katangan, necks or sills of quartz dolerite or labradorite dolerite and associated sheets of amygdaloidal lavas are of post-Great Conglomerate and pre-Little Conglomerate age (CAHEN, 1954, p. 89).

6.2.8. Mineralization

The deposits of copper and associated metals in Katanga and Zambia have given rise to many descriptions in literature. OOSTERBOSCH (1960) published a synthesis of the pertinent problems.

The copper and uranium mineralizations of the Roan of Katanga are restricted to two sedimentary rock groups that differ in their stratigraphical succession, degree of metamorphism and tectonic structure. First, in southern Katanga, in the western mines (Kolwezi, Musonoi, Ruwe, etc.), the mines and old mines around Elisabethville (Ruashi, Etoile du Congo, etc.), and the Kambove, Fungurume, Shinkolobwe, and Luishya mines among others, the mineralization is restricted to the "Mine Series" Group (see Table 11 and p. 234). Second, the deposits of southeastern Katanga (Kinsenda, Musoshi, etc.), and their continuation in the Copper Belt of Zambia, lie in the Lower Roan (see Table 12 and p. 234).

Stratiform disseminated deposits with copper and cobalt mineralizations and vein deposits with stratiform appendages, and a uranium mineraliza-tion with associated nickel, cobalt, and copper, may be distinguished. No obvious genetic relationship has been observed between the mineralizations and known magmatic phenomena.

The data, especially relating to the copper and cobalt deposits of the "Mine Series" do not allow the identification of the origin of the mineraliza-tion as syngenetic or epigenetic; and many factors pertaining to a syn-genetic explanation are equally valid for a selective epigenetic interpreta-tion of the mineralization. This type of mineralization is always older than the main phase of folding.

By contrast, the uranium veins at Shinkolobwe, Swambo, Kalongwe, and other localities are definitely epigenetic and, in their present form, are later than the transcurrent faulting (see p. 244). If the fact is considered that the uraninites in some mines (Shinkolobwe, Kalongwe, Luishya, etc.) are older than those in other mines (western mines, Musoshi in Zambia), the conclusion follows that, despite great paragenetic similarities, the strati-form copper–cobalt deposits and the uranium veins do not necessarily belong to a single metallogenetic episode. OOSTERBOSCH (1960) quoted two hypotheses, as follows. Either there were two periods of mineralization, viz., a copper–cobalt mineralization before the folding or at its beginning, and another uranium mineralization during the folding; or there was only a single metallogenetic period prior to the main phase of folding that was followed by the remobilization of the uranium. OOSTERBOSCH favoured the first hypothesis.

To complete the picture, there is, in addition to the vein-type mineralization occurring in the mines mentioned above, a vein type other than uranium-bearing, viz., the Kipushi mineralization, which contains copper, zinc, lead, silver, cadmium, germanium, gallium, and several other metals. There are also deposits of "massive" type at Kengere (lead, zinc, silver, and copper), at Lombe (zinc, lead), at Lukela, Tantara, Sampwe, and Tenke (copper) which, like the Kipushi deposits, are situated in the Kakontwe Formation (see Table 11 and p. 239).

It seems that the following conclusions are valid.

(1) There was a stratiform, copper–cobalt mineralization that formed before the main Kundelungan phase of folding and whose origin, according to OOSTERBOSCH (1960), may be syngenetic or epigenetic. A uranium mineralization with an age of about 720 Myr in Swambo and partly in Shinkolobwe may belong here (CAHEN, 1963d).

(2) There were at least two periods of epigenetic uranium mineralization, at (620 ± 20) Myr and at (520 ± 20) Myr ago, the first postdating the main folding phase and the second entirely posttectonic. The older mineralization (at Shinkolobwe, Luishya, and Kalongwe) again contains copper and nickel in particular. The younger mineralization, at Musoshi, is, according to VAES (1961), accompanied by a markedly metasomatic metamorphism. The uranium mineralization in the Western mines and in some of the Rhodesian mines belongs here.

(3) There was a posttectonic Cu–Pb–Zn–Ag–Cd–Ge mineralization at Kipushi. The lead-isotope ages suggest that it was approximately contemporaneous with the second uranium mineralization (CAHEN, 1961a).

6.2.9. Summary of the Katangan of the type area

General setting

The Katangan succession consists of three thick, mainly subaqueous and marine groups (Roan, Lower Kundelungu, Upper Kundelungu) that indicate subsidence and are separated by at least two periods of mainly continental deposition (Mwashya–Great Conglomerate and Little Conglomerate). Together they make up an approximately 8,000-m-thick sequence. As a result, particularly, of tectonic complications, the outcrops of the Roan, which now are not very extensive, are difficult to correlate, and a number of problems about the history of the first part of Roan time still remain to be solved.

Roan time

In spite of a notable unconformity that separates the Roan from the Kibaran, on the one hand, and the Muva and the Lufubu "Systems", on the other hand, and in spite of its general concordance with the rest of the Katangan, the Roan, or at least its lower part, falls within the Kibaran Orogenic Cycle. The lowermost portions of the Lower Roan and its more northerly equivalents have a characteristic molasse facies, and it has been shown that in the vicinity of Lat. 9° S. and farther in the north, these formations form the filling of the fore-, intra-, and back-troughs of the Kibaran Orogeny (see p. 204).

The oldest Katangan rocks were thus deposited immediately after the main phase of the Kibaran orogeny. The present knowledge of the Precambrian geology of northern Katanga verifies this conclusion and contradicts the opinion expressed previously (CAHEN, 1954, p. 114).

A first Roanian tectonic phase might affect all the basins and seems to indicate a widespread rejuvenation. It did not give rise to an angular unconformity, but to a strong increase in erosion between the "Mine Series" and the Dipeta and Mofya Groups.

The little that is known of palaeogeographic conditions shows that, at least until the deposition of the "Mine Series", there was for the Roan of southeastern Katanga a subsiding area in the south and a shoreline in the north-northeast. For the Roan in the area of the western mines, the shore lay in the northeast and, perhaps, in the north (OOSTERBOSCH, 1959). However, conditions particularly brought about by thrust displacements do not allow an exact definition of the region of subsidence which might have been in the extreme south of Katanga or still farther south. A second Roanian phase marks the close of this period. It caused the emergence of some Roan deposits.

Mwashya and Great Conglomerate time

The Mwashya and Great Conglomerate time is marked by a more or less continuous tendency towards emergence, especially in the region north of Kambove. The first signs of this tendency may be found in the possibly glacial Mwashya deposits. Their deposition was followed by subsidence and, very rapidly, by renewed emergence marked by the tillite of the Great Conglomerate. South of Katanga the tendency to emerge may have been less marked, the conglomerates being less clearly tillitic. According to BEUGNIES (1953, p. 42), the tendency towards emergence was nearly continuous in the so-called Kalabi Ridge, about 15 km east of Mulungwishi. The period closed with the first Kundelungan phase, which caused renewed subsidence.

Lower Kundelungu time

The Lower Kundelungu time is marked by a distinct subsidence south of a region that included the so-called Kalabi Ridge. In this southern trough, the thickness of the Lower Kundelungu beds may reach 2,500 m in the southern part of the Tenke area and, perhaps, even more farther south in Zambia. The sedimentation began with the deposition of the calcareous and pelitic Kakontwe Formation, which is confined to this area. A second Kundelungan phase then began with uplift of the southern part of the country which is manifested by the deposition in the trough of flysch-type sediments (upper formations of the Lower Kundelungu). At the same time in the north arenaceous sediments were being deposited on the continental shelf. This period closed with a tendency towards emergence, marking the end of the second Kundelungan phase.

Little Conglomerate time

The trend towards emergence was accomplished by the arching of the hinterland so that the Little Conglomerate of southern Katanga presents a littoral facies and incorporates many pebbles of the Kakontwe calcitic and dolomitic limestone, while, in the northern part, approximately from the "Kalabi Ridge" onwards, it consisted of a continental tillite.

Upper Kundelungu time

A third Kundelungan phase is manifested by a tendency towards subsidence, clearly more marked to the north of the "Kalabi Ridge" than in the south, and by a distinct transgression in the north. At first, arenaceous and calcareous sediments were deposited in the northern trough. The intensification of crustal movements probably caused renewed transgression and the deposition of coarser-grained sediments. A new area of subsidence still farther in the north was the site of deposition of micaceous pelitic sediments followed by a thick group of arenaceous deposits; these, in turn, were, after a break, followed by deposition of arkoses derived from an already emerging area. The last phase of Kundelungan folding occurred at this time, affecting all the strata and causing the overfolding towards the north and, subsequently, the thrusting of parts of the southern trough towards or over the northern trough.

Summary

The southern trough is the oldest. It was the site of the only intrusions in the Katangan of the type area (see p. 230), of nondynamic metamorphism and, probably, of granitization. The northern trough is younger, and has no evidence of metamorphism. Only extrusive igneous activity is known (see p. 245). The Katangan is characterized by a distinct tectonic polarity from the south towards the north, and has a marked tendency towards subsidence. It seems reasonable to conclude that the type region of the Katangan was a geosyncline, at least during the Kundelungan phases of the orogeny. The evolution of the area during the Roan time cannot, however, be adequately summed up, in spite of the subsiding character of the southern trough during this time. It must not be forgotten that the Katangan geosyncline extends far into Rhodesia, and, without examining both countries, it is impossible to obtain an exact picture of this vast group of rocks.

6.3. *The Katangan of northeastern Katanga and of northwestern Katanga and Kasai*

6.3.1. Introduction

Immediately adjacent to the type region there are two areas where formations very similar to the Katangan of the type area exist. One of them, northwest of Katanga (see Fig. 21) is a basin that is nearly completely separated from the southern Katanga basin; in northeastern Katanga (see Fig. 18) less information is available than for the Katangan of the type area.

6.3.2. The Katangan of northeastern Katanga

Historical survey

The rocks of northeastern Katanga have been correlated with the Katangan of the type area, but have not been studied in such detail. More-

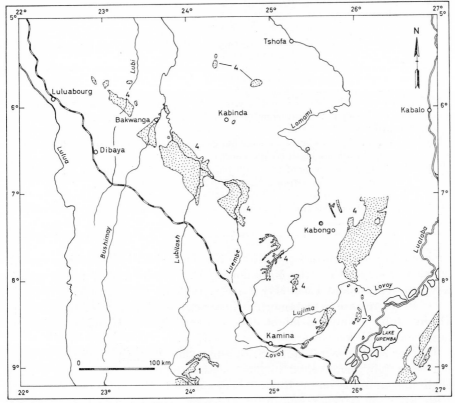

Fig. 21. Sketch map of the Bushimay in northwestern Katanga and southeastern Kasai. 1, Luamba. 2, Nonda. 3, Kabele and Kabenga Conglomerates. 4, Bushimay *sensu stricto*.

I

over, the most recent results are still unpublished. The geology of northeastern Katanga owes much to the investigations of E. GROSSE in 1918 and
of F. BEHREND in 1914; they established the stratigraphical basis and gave
many details of the tectonics and intrusions. The two geologists were in
agreement on the major features of the stratigraphical succession. In 1934,
I. DE MAGNÉE considerably modified the succession; after another journey
to the region, he (DE MAGNÉE, 1955) still held the same views. However,
DUMONT (1962) established the correlation of some of the stratigraphical
units of this area with the Katangan of the type area and confirmed the
validity of the major features of the stratigraphical column of GROSSE and
BEHREND. The account given here is based on CAHEN (1954, pp. 89–96) and
DUMONT (1962).

Stratigraphy

A section drawn from Lake Tanganyika through Baudouinville, Lusaka,
and Kapona (see Fig. 18) and parallel sections farther south, all with a
W.N.W.–E.S.E. orientation, shows the stratigraphical units presented in
Table 15.

TABLE 15

The W.–E. succession of the Katangan lithostratigraphical units in
northeastern Katanga

Lithological units	Thickness, m
(I) Arenaceous–pelitic group: shales with micaceous layers at the top, arkoses passing into conglomerates at the base (Mulobozi Group)	800
(II) Limestones, shales, cherts in thin banded beds (Lusaka lime-stones): locally, a basal conglomerate	300–400
(III) Group largely consisting of grey and black shales and mica- and feldspar-bearing sandstones. Just south of the Lusaka Mission, this group is overlain by a tillitic conglomerate	250–300
(IV) Group largely consisting of conglomerates, arkoses and grits; limestone horizon	>400

Group I overlies unconformably the Baudouinville diorite–gabbro massif,
which is younger than the Marungu rhyolite (ignimbrite?), which might
have an age of about 1,650 Myr (CAHEN, 1963a).

Group IV rests on a metamorphic basement and is separated from Group
III by faults. Group III might directly overlie Group II, which certainly
lies conformably on Group I.

Farther south, near Lat. 9° S. (see pp. 236, 237), the Lufonzo Group,
almost certainly equivalent to the Mwashya Sequence and resting with a
slight unconformity on the Roan, is very similar to Group III (see Table 15),
with which it is geographically continuous. The Lufonzo Group occurs
below the basal surface of the flat-lying Upper Kundelungu. The Upper
Kundelungu commences here, with its Lower Group (see Table 11) resting

on the Little Conglomerate. This Upper Kundelungu is continuous with Group IV (DUMONT, 1962).

The stratigraphical succession in northeastern Katanga, resulting from the data discussed, is presented in Table 16.

Table 16

Stratigraphical succession in northeastern Katanga

Lithological units	Thickness, m
Upper Kundelungu (Unit IV in Table 15)	>400
Little Conglomerate (Tillite facies)	
Unconformity	
Tillite (?). Where a tillitic conglomerate overlies the Lufonzo Group conformably, it might be the Great Conglomerate	
Lufonzo Group (Unit III in Table 15), probably belonging to the Mwashya Sequence	200–300
Marungu Group (Units II and I in Table 15), probably belonging to the Roan:	
(B) Lusaka limestones	300–400
(A) Mulobozi arkoses and conglomerates	800

Tectonics

Throughout the area the Upper Kundelungu beds are subhorizontal or gently undulating. By contrast, beds of the Marungu Group are much more disturbed, strongly inclined, or even folded. Tectonic axes in the Upper Kundelungu have essentially a N.N.E. trend, while those of the Marungu have a N.N.W.–N.W. trend. All beds are affected by radial faults.

Metamorphism

Apart from the contact metamorphism (see below), the Lusaka limestones are often recrystallized and display effects of epizonal metamorphism. The Upper Kundelungu is not metamorphosed.

Plutonic activity

The Mount Kalolo hornblende granite and olivine gabbro accompanied by pigeonite-bearing labradorite dolerite have been intruded into the Marungu beds, ascribed to the Roan (see Table 16). The hornblende granite and the olivine gabbro are related.

Relationships with adjacent areas

The importance of the Katangan of northeastern Katanga lies in the fact that it serves as a connecting link between the Katangan of the type area and the Malagarasian of Burundi, which is only a part of the Bukoban of Tanzania. The stratigraphical succession given in Table 17 and verified by DUMONT (1962) is compatible with the stratigraphy of the Malagarasian of southern Burundi.

Conclusions

It seems that during the deposition of the Marungu Group northeastern Katanga was characterized by an intracontinental trough filled with basin deposits. A more or less continental episode followed and subsequently transgressive shelf sediments of the Upper Kundelungu were deposited.

6.3.3. The Katangan of northwestern Katanga and Kasai

Geographical situation

In Lomami and southeastern Kasai a thick sedimentary group, the Bushimay, crops out and has been studied in some detail in an area extending from about Long. 26° E. to Long. 22° E. and from Lat. 5° S. to Lat. 9° S. (see Fig. 21). An isolated group, called the Luamba Group, cropping out on both sides of Long. 24° E. and of Lat. 9° S. was described by NINOVE (1954) and is comparable to the Bushimay.

Historical survey

The first studies on the Bushimay Group were made by J. CORNET in 1897, F. F. MATHIEU in 1912, R. KOSTKA in 1913 and E. RICHET in 1919. According to most of these geologists, and also to R. VAN AUBEL, who studied the group in 1927, the quartzitic and pelitic rocks of this group belong to the Kundelungu, while the calcareous rocks belong to the former Lubudi System of J. CORNET, which is older than the Kundelungu. E. POLINARD in 1925 and in 1949 determined the correct succession of these beds and excluded the possibility that the quartzites and pelites underlying the calcareous beds might belong to the Kundelungu if the calcareous beds were, as was originally thought, attributed to the Lubudi of CORNET. The present-day knowledge is based on the work of RAUCQ (1957) in Kasai and CAHEN and MORTELMANS (1947) in western Katanga. For western Katanga the observations of DUMONT (1950, 1962) added further details.

Stratigraphy

In the Bushimay, a calcareous–pelitic group of rocks overlies an arenaceous–pelitic group, divided into an extensive upper part and a lower part restricted to the immediate vicinity of the Kibaran Belt in the southeastern part of the Bushimay outcrop (see Fig. 21). There is thus a general threefold division, the lowermost sequence being more restricted in area than the other two. This stratigraphical scheme is still unpublished. The distinction between the two sequences, B2 and B1, is due to RAUCQ (1957), while the separation of sequence B1 from sequence B0 was suggested by CAHEN and MORTELMANS (1947). The notation used in Table 17 is that of RAUCQ or is adapted from the one he employed.

Table 17 lists only sequences and groups. RAUCQ (1957) subdivided the groups into a large number of formations.

In its type area, the Bushimay rests on pre-Kibaran rocks of the Kasai

TABLE 17

Stratigraphical succession of the Bushimay

Lithostratigraphical units	Lithological description	Thickness, m
Sequence B2		
Group B2e	Mainly calcitic limestones, often reef deposits, with stromatolites	>100
Group B2d	Mainly dolomitic limestones with various cherts	~400
Group B2c	Dolomitic limestones, usually reef deposits, with shaly intercalations, stromatolites	~290
Group B2b	Dolomitic limestones, calcareous shales, dolomitic shales, conglomerate with calcareous pebbles and cement	~125
Group B2a	Reef dolomitic limestones with stromatolites	~105
	Break in sedimentation	
Sequence B1		
Group B1e	Micaceous, feldspar-bearing, muddy grits, various shales, dolomitic shales, dolomitic limestones, micaceous dolomitic grit	~52
Groups B1d–a	In Kasai: micaceous muddy grit with calcareous cement towards the top, quartzitic towards the bottom	~405
	Basal conglomerate	
	In Katanga: fine-grained quartzites, some feldspar-bearing more or less micaceous shales. The basal conglomerate of Sequence B1 is here included in Group B0b of Sequence B0	800–1,000
Sequence B0[a]		
Group B0b	Conglomeratic arkoses and quartzites, conglomerates	~500
Group B0a	Red quartzites and shales with a horizon of pink chert	0–1,500

[a] Known only in western Katanga.

basement and is overlain by Cretaceous rocks. In Katanga, it rests unconformably on the Kibaran and is unconformably overlain by the Upper Carboniferous and Permian Lukuga Sequence. The discovery of Bushimay pebbles in the Kabele and Kabenga Conglomerates (see p. 254), that was subsequently attributed to the Great Conglomerate, cited in CAHEN and MORTELMANS (1947) and CAHEN (1954, p. 257), is, however, false. DUMONT (1962) found only Kibaran pebbles there and attributed, probably correctly, the Kabele and Kabenga Conglomerates to the Nonda (Roan) and the Bushimay (B0b).

The Luamba Group

NINOVE (1954) described a group of rocks that he called the Luamba Formation and that strongly resembles the Bushimay but is not definitely correlated with it. The succession of these beds, which crop out at the intersection of Long. 24° E. and Lat. 9° S., is, from top to bottom, sandstones and shales (thickness, ~ 10 m), silicified limestones with stromatolites (~ 350 m), micaceous sandstones, grits and shales, and quartzites, conglomerates, and cherts that are sometimes oolitic (~ 430 m).

The Luamba Group rests unconformably on a pre-Kibaran basement and is older than the Upper Carboniferous (Lukuga Sequence). It was deposited in a basin that is now isolated, and was, perhaps, also originally so, and forms a fairly simple syncline cut by radial faults. The lithological facies resembles closely that of the Bushimay, but no precise correlation is possible, even though the Luamba outcrops extend towards the north-northeast and then towards the northeast, a trend which occurs in the typical Bushimay outcrops in the Lovoy River area.

The Luamba has been equated not only with the Bushimay but also with the Lulua Complex (see CAHEN, 1954, pp. 242, 546). According to the present-day knowledge, the latter correlation appears less probable.

Correlation with the Katangan of the type area

The geologists who, during the past twenty years, have studied the Bushimay in the field and who know the Katangan of the type area agree that the Bushimay and the Roan are equivalents (CAHEN and MORTELMANS, 1947; RAUCQ, 1957; DUMONT, 1962). However, the Bushimay was deposited in a basin completely, or nearly completely, separated from the basin of deposition of the Katangan in its type area. If former connections existed between the basins, they were never important, and later epeirogenic movements caused them to disappear completely. Consequently, the arguments presented in favour of correlation must be considered. General arguments have been presented by RAUCQ (1957), and DUMONT (1962) has given more cogent reasons, viz., for lithological and geomorphological reasons the Kabele and Kabenga Conglomerates (see p. 253) are thought to belong to the Lower Bushimay. These conglomerates of the left bank of the Upemba depression must have previously formed a continuous sheet with the thick succession on the right bank (CAHEN and MORTELMANS, 1947). This conglomeratic group, described as the Nonda Group (RORIVE, 1954; see p. 235), underlies the tillite of the Great Conglomerate in the Lufira Valley (DUMONT, 1962), and its continuation towards the east forms the base of the Roan in northern Katanga.

Tectonics

In addition to the deformations of the basin that occurred during the course of sedimentation, the Bushimay has been affected by two tectonic phases whose relative age is not certain, namely, a folding giving rise to axes generally with a S.W.–N.E. trend and another, across the former, with generally S.E.–N.W.-trending axes. The most probable hypothesis is that the first phase preceded the second one (RAUCQ, 1957).

The folding with S.W.–N.E.-trending axes is approximately parallel to the Kibaran folding. It appears close to the Kibaran Belt as tight folds with a southeasterly vergence (the folds of the Kibaran have a northwesterly vergence), and farther west, in Kasai, as very open folds with the same S.W.–N.E. trend. The slight vergence of these undulations is towards the southeast. Flat-lying faults often separate the Bushimay sequence from the Kibaran (CAHEN and MORTELMANS, 1947; RAUCQ, 1957). The tectonic phase with a general S.E.–N.W. trend is represented by undulations with dips of a few degrees, and it is responsible for the generally synclinal appearance of the Bushimay (see Fig. 21). After the tectonic activity ceased, and, doubtless, before the Mesozoic, the region was cut by several faults with trends more or less parallel to the axes of the second system of undulations (RAUCQ, 1957).

Metamorphism

Even in the eastern, most strongly folded, part of the Bushimay basin there is no metamorphism. Detailed investigations by RAUCQ (1957) have only verified the existence of diagenesis that probably took place only a little after the deposition of the sediments.

Plutonic activity

The Bushimay has been the site of volcanic activity that has left its mark throughout the outcrop area (see Fig. 21). This, an amygdaloidal lava is an andesite. At the confluence of the Sankuru and the Bushimay Rivers it contains oligoclase–andesine or andesine (An_{27}–An_{30}), but elsewhere andesine (up to An_{40}). The pyroxene is pigeonite.

Besides the extrusive facies there is an intrusive facies with ophitic structure that may be interpreted as deriving from the vents of volcanoes or from volcanic fissures. All these rocks have undergone chloritization and silicification. The amygdaloidal rock at the Lujima River–Lovoy River confluence is cut by quartz veins containing epidote and chalcopyrite. In Kasai, the age of the effusive and intrusive rocks alike is post-Bushimay and pre-Lower Cretaceous. In fact, many pebbles of these rocks occur in the basal conglomerate of the Cretaceous cover in the region near the confluence of the Sankuru and Bushimay Rivers (MEYER DE STADELHOFEN and RAUCQ, 1960). In Katanga, one can narrow the limits, since all the Bushimay, including its intrusive and volcanic rocks, is unconformably overlain by Upper Carboniferous strata (CAHEN and MORTELMANS, 1947).

Mineralization

There is, particularly at the Lubi River, a stratified lead, zinc, copper, and silver mineralization. Only lead and zinc occur as sulphides, but copper occurs as carbonate and silicate, and silver is associated with the copper minerals. The deposits have been considered epigenetic disseminations (see RAUCQ, 1957, p. 105). At present it seems certain that at least the stratified galena mineralization in Group B1e (see Table 17) is syngenetic

(RAUCQ, 1957). Furthermore, RAUCQ's (1957) studies on the distribution of various minerals in the strata suggest that the mineralization may, in fact, be syngenetic and that its epigenetic appearance is caused by mobilization or concentration after the end of the tectonic activity that produced the faults in whose vicinity the deposits occur. Near the confluence of the Lujima and the Luembe Rivers there is a massive epigenetic deposit of galena. None of these deposits have been exploited.

Summary

With respect to the Kibaran Belt, the nearest part of the Bushimay constitutes a thick filling of molasse facies in its foredeep (see p. 206). The foreland of the Kibaran Belt (see p. 227) consists of the pre-Kibaran rocks of the "Kasai Basement" (see p. 174).

Sequence B0 (see Table 17), entirely confined to the Kibaran foredeep, constitutes nearly the whole of the molasse facies, with a thickness of about 2,000 m. This filling of the foredeep was succeeded by the deposition of shallow-water shelf sediments which similarly covered the foreland of the Kibaran Belt. The distribution of facies shows that the continental area that was the source of sequence B1 sediments (see Table 17) was located in the southeast and the south, while the basin deepened towards the northwest, where subsidence was especially marked towards the end of the deposition of sequence B1 and during the deposition of sequence B2. The local subsidence of the former Kibaran foredeep continued during part of the deposition of sequence B1.

Thus, as time passed, the influence of the Kibaran Belt on the Bushimay diminished. This fact also appears in the tectonics, because it is obvious that the movements causing the formation of tectonic units parallel to those of the Kibaran are the oldest and may be interpreted as posthumous movements of the Kibaran Belt, while the synclinal deformation with a S.E.–N.W. trend, feeble in intensity but wide in extent, is probably younger and might well be related to the Katangan movements.

6.4. *The Malagarasian*

6.4.1. Geographical location

In the southeastern portion of Burundi, in the valleys of the Upper Malagarasi River, the Lumpungu River, and of their tributaries, rocks analogous to those of the Katangan crop out. They form a part of a much larger sequence which stretches into Tanzania and is there called the Bukoban. The Malagarasian and the Bukoban are the northeastward continuations of the Katangan of northeastern Katanga, from which they are separated only by the Lake Tanganyika Rift (see Fig. 18).

6.4.2. Historical survey

In Burundi, the 1:200,000 map of DELHAYE and SALÉE (1928) and SALÉE's (1931) memoir gave the first data of Malagarasian stratigraphy.

CAHEN (1954, pp. 142–148), comparing the stratigraphy given by DELHAYE and SALÉE with their own maps, some scattered observations, and field work in Tanzania, reached the conclusion that important modifications were necessary. Present-day knowledge is based on WALEFFE (1965).

6.4.3. Stratigraphy

After his sufficiently detailed study of the Mosso region, WALEFFE (1965) abandoned most of the names given by DELHAYE and SALÉE and recognized, instead, four distinct units, which he called the Kibago, the Mosso, the Nkoma, and the Musindozi. The relationships between the Kibago, the Mosso, and the Musindozi are well established, while those between the Nkoma and the others have given rise to discussion (see Table 18).

TABLE 18

Summary of the stratigraphy of the Kibago, the Mosso, and the Musindozi (Malagarasian)

Stratigraphical units	Lithological description	Thickness, m
Kibago	Muddy and micaceous sandstones with shales and feldspar-bearing quartzites	~450
	Feldspar-bearing quartzites with shales and sandstones	~200
	Calcareous feldspar-bearing sandstones, sandy shales, quartzites	~200
	Conglomerates with pebbles of basalt, silicified limestone and Burundian rocks, with layers of mica-bearing shales	up to 15
	Disconformity	
Mosso	Basalts (local)	up to 30
	Silicified limestones, dolomitic limestones, interbedded with shales, stromatolites	50–100
	Basaltic amygdaloidal lavas	100–>300
	Unconformity	
Musindozi	Dolomitic limestones with intraformational breccia, silicified beds, stromatolites	200–390
	Shales and calcareous shales	up to 150
	Basalts (pillow lavas)	20–150
	Shales, sandstones, and quartzites	40–225
	Conglomerates with pebbles of quartzite and of Burundian rocks	12.5–130

The Mosso lies unconformably on the Musindozi, which, in its turn, lies unconformably on the Burundian. The Kibago is overlain by alluvium and lies unconformably on the Mosso, the Musindozi, and the Burundian. The Nkoma lies similarly unconformably on the Burundian. Its relationships with the other units have not been observed, but WALEFFE's (1965) map, examination of aerial photographs, and consideration of its possible relationship with the Musindozi all indicate that the Nkoma lies unconformably on the Musindozi. WALEFFE (1965) believes that the Nkoma is deposited in a trough during the period of erosion responsible for the unconformity between the Mosso and the Musindozi. The uppermost beds of the Nkoma may thus be correlated with the volcanism and the deposition of all or a part of the Mosso.

The Nkoma consists of about 750 m–1,000 m of light-coloured quartzites with intercalations of conglomerates and shales and, in its upper part, of altered volcanic rocks, some of which may have been originally amygdaloidal basaltic lavas. At the base there is a conglomeratic breccia containing angular fragments of Burundian rocks.

6.4.4. Tectonics

The Musindozi is folded, with a mean S.W.–N.E. strike. The Nkoma, the Mosso, and the Kibago show broad undulations with a northeasterly trend. Radial faults occur in the Nkoma, the Mosso, and the Musindozi.

6.4.5. Metamorphism

The metamorphism of the Musindozi, the Nkoma, and the Mosso is weak and epizonal; the Kibago is unmetamorphosed. Locally, effects of thermal metamorphism have been observed in the Nkoma.

6.4.6. Plutonic activity

Two principal basaltic eruption phases have been noted. One is local and occurs in the Musindozi, while the other, which appears to have been notable, belongs to the Mosso and consists of two episodes separated by the deposition of carbonate sediments. The volcanism of the upper part of the Nkoma might belong to the second phase.

Intrusive rocks consist of a doleritic gabbro at the Musindozi–Burundian junction. It postdates the basal beds of the Musindozi. In addition, there exist doleritic gabbro sills interstratified in the northeastern part of the Nkoma outcrop.

6.4.7. Relationships with Tanzania and Katanga

The Malagarasian corresponds to the Bukoban taken as a whole. The Bukoban is subdivided from top to bottom, as given in Table 19.

The Kibago is the exact equivalent of the Manyovu red beds which form its continuation. The Mosso continues as the Ilagala dolomitic limestones and the Gagwe amygdaloidal lavas. The Nkoma continues as the Bukoba sandstone.

Consequently, the Kibago and the Mosso together correspond to the Uha Group, and the underlying Musindozi must be an equivalent of the Kigonero flags and of a part of the Busondo Group.

The relationships between the Bukoba sandstone and the other units have not been elucidated in Tanzania. From WALEFFE's (1965) observa-

TABLE 19

Summary of the stratigraphy of the Bukoban of Tanzania.
According to HALLIGAN (1963)

Stratigraphical units	Lithological description	Thickness, m
Uha Group	Bukoba sandstone	
	Igamba sandstone	Local
	Manyovu red beds	600–900
	Ilagala dolomitic limestone	150
	Gagwe amygdaloid lavas	Up to 600
	Disconformity	
	Kigonero flags	150
	Disconformity	
Busondo Group	Malagarasi sandstone	Up to 300
	Nyanza shale	Up to 200
	Uruwira sandstone	Up to 600
	Slight unconformity	
Masontwa Group	Mkuyu sandstone	?
	Mokuba shales	?

tions in Burundi it is possible to infer that the Bukola sandstone would not be younger than the Manyovu red beds, but would probably have been deposited during the interval between the deposition of the Kigonero flags and the Uha Group.

The thickness of the corresponding units in Burundi and Tanzania is similar, with the exception that the lower formations of the Musindozi Group reach a thickness of 1,100 m in Tanzania and only 650 m in Burundi. It is not possible to state to what extent this is caused by the reduction of the thickness of all strata in Burundi or by the absence there of some units such as the Nyanza shale and the Uruwira sandstone. Likewise, the Masontwa Group is unknown in Burundi.

However, the Malagarasian and the Bukoban form the continuation of the Katangan of northeastern Katanga, from which they are separated only by the geologically young Tanganyika Rift. The correlations established by CAHEN (1954, p. 263) should be revised on the basis of new data in all areas concerned. At present, all that can be said is that the successions on both sides of the Tanganyika Rift are rather similar.

6.4.8. Summary

As for the Katangan of northeastern Katanga (see pp. 250–52), it seems that the Malagarasian was probably deposited in an intracratonic trough, this being the case at least for the Musindozi. This trough was presumably located in Tanzania, the beds acquiring a shelf facies towards Burundi. Both the Kibago and the Nkoma seems also to possess a shelf facies. The Nkoma sediments appear to have been deposited in a local tectonic trough (rift?).

6.5. *The Lindian and the Ubangian*

6.5.1. Geographical setting

The group of formations called the Lindian in the Ituri, Maniema, and
Uele, and the Ubangian, farther west in the Ubangi, cover an area in
eastern and northern Congo from about Lat. 4° S. to Lat. 4° N. and in
northern Congo from the area of the Rift Valleys in the east to the neighbourhood of the Ubangi River in the west (see Figs. 5 and 22). Their type

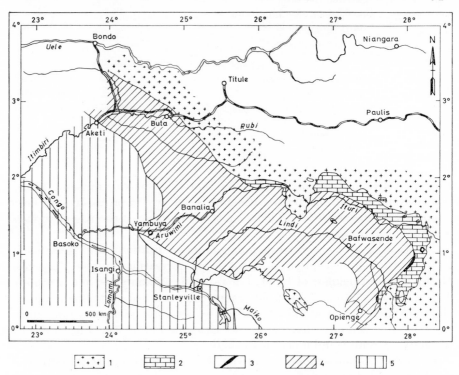

Fig. 22. Sketch map of the Lindian. 1, Mainly Kibalian and granite. 2, Lower Lindian.
3, Tillite. 4, Upper Lindian. 5, Mesozoic and Cenozoic deposits. Modified from
VERBEEK (1960).

area consists of the basins of the Ituri, Lindi, and Aruwimi Rivers (the true
name of Aruwimi River is Lohali River) and may extend as far as to the
Itimbiri River. Other areas, where observations are less detailed and
correlation more uncertain are Ubangi in the west, and Maniema in the
southeast.

6.5.2. Historical survey

By the end of the Nineteenth Century some observations had been made
by single travellers. Later, reconnaissance work by the *Compagnie des
Chemins de Fer du Congo Supérieur aux Grands Lacs Africains (C.F.L.)* and
the *Société Internationale Forestière et Minière du Congo (Forminière)* pro-

duced the first concrete data on the Lindian, then usually called the Kundelungu. The surveys culminated in the classic memoir of HENRY (1924), who divided the outcrops into two groups, namely, the "Kundelungu" mudstone group overlying the "Lubudi" limestone. In 1940–1941, M. SLUYS carried out field work and published the results in numerous papers (see, e.g., SLUYS, 1945). He confirmed the major features of the stratigraphy given by HENRY. These two geologists studied mainly the type area of the Lindian; its westward extension, the Ubangian, is known only from a few studies by ADERCA (1950, 1952). As for the continuation of the Lindian into Maniema, this was investigated by HENRY (1924) and SLUYS (1947). The present state of knowledge of the type area is reviewed in a paper of VERBEEK (1960), who based his account on results obtained by the *Syndicat pour l'Etude géologique et minière de la Cuvette congolaise* (1957–1959) and on all previous work, including numerous unpublished studies by the *Forminière*. While keeping the main features of the classification of HENRY and SLUYS he adjusted the stratigraphic position of several formations thought by HENRY and SLUYS to belong to the lower division. In fact, they belong to the upper division.

6.5.3. Stratigraphy of the type area

The stratigraphy of the Aruwimi (Lohali)–Ituri–Lindi Rivers sequence is summarized in Table 20.

TABLE 20

Stratigraphy of the Lindian of the type area
according to VERBEEK (1960)

Lithostratigraphical units	Lithological description	Thickness, m
	Banalia quartzitic sandstones	1,000–1,200
	Alolo shales with thin beds of dolomitic limestone	250–300
Schisto-gréseux sequence	Galamboge Rapids quartzites	100–150
	Kole and Mamungi shales and slates, with red calcitic limestones, often oolitic (C 6) and Edaye banded dolomitic limestone (C 5)	>350
	Basal "complex": conglomerates and breccias, shales	40–300
	Unconformity	
Continental formations	Lower Lenda tillite	(40–50)
	Opienge conglomerate	(8–10)
	Break in sedimentation	
Schisto-calcaire sequence	(C4) Asoso Formation: sandstones and shales, marls and chert	50
	(C3) Lenda calcitic and dolomitic limestones, particularly oolitic, and calcitic reef limestones with stromatolites	50–75
	(C2) Silicified limestones, often oolitic	30–50
	(C1 and C0) Arkoses (C1) and lenticular conglomerates (C0) of Penge-on-Ituri	40–50

In the type area, the Lindian is unconformably overlain by the upper Jurassic Stanleyville Series and probably by the Upper Carboniferous and Permian Lukuga Series. It rests on badly known basement of granites and mica schists (see p. 162) which notably includes the Kibalian.

The stratigraphy of the region between the Aruwimi (Lohali) and the Itimbiri Rivers is important because this little known area is transitional between the type region and Ubangi. According to VERBEEK (1960), who also made available important unpublished information, only the lower part of the *Schisto-gréseux* occurs there, and appears to be transgressive on a basement consisting of granite and mica schist.

6.5.4. Detached masses correlated with the Lindian

North and east of the type area there occur outliers of varying size that may be attributed to the Lindian, but whose exact position in its stratigraphy is sometimes open to discussion. The largest rock bodies occur at Niangara and at Mount Homa, the second definitely, the first one possibly, preserved between faults (CAHEN, 1954, pp. 178, 179).

The stratigraphic series of Mount Homa, with subtabular beds, recalls either the lower part of the *Schisto-gréseux* or the *Schisto-calcaire* of the Lindian. The Niangara area contains numerous units unknown in the type Lindian of the type area and is still more difficult to correlate with it; the succession, with a thickness greater than 100 m, is folded.

The Mount Homa massif is cut by galena veins yielding a conventional age of 750 Myr for their lead.

6.5.5. Stratigraphy of the Ubangian

In Ubangi, the present-day knowledge is based on the investigations of ADERCA (1950, 1952). The knowledge, which is still fairly rudimentary, is summarized as follows.

The Ubangian consists of an upper unit of sandstones, grits, and quartzites, with a basal conglomerate which is about 250 m thick, and a lower unit mainly consisting of shales and calcareous shales with banded argillaceous limestones and cherts. The thickness of the lower part is several hundred metres. The contact between the two units is at least transgressive. ADERCA regarded it as unconformable, but this conclusion has not been verified.

6.5.6. Correlation between the Ubangian and the Lindian

ADERCA (1950, 1952) correlated the upper and lower units with the *Schisto-gréseux* sequence and the *Schisto-calcaire* sequence, respectively, of the Lindian type area. According to the results of VERBEEK (1960), it would appear that the Ubangian as a whole corresponds to the *Schisto-gréseux* sequence. Nearly all the rock types of the lower unit are observed in the Mamungi shales and in the basal "complex", but it is still impossible to ascertain the position occupied by the upper unit of the Ubangian. Most likely, it corresponds to the siliceous rocks overlying the Mamungi shales, namely, the Galamboge quartzites or the Banalia quartzitic sandstones.

6.5.7. Relationships with formations in the Central African Republic

The Lindian–Ubangian and, in particular, the *Schisto-gréseux* sequence of the region between Banzyville and Yakoma continue uninterrupted into the Central African Republic as the Lower Kotto "System". The Lower Kotto is divided, from top to bottom, into the Fouroumbala sandstone and the cherts of the Kassa horizon (GÉRARD, 1958). An examination of the map of the area drawn by MESTRAUD (1953) suggests, however, that the Kassa horizon is not necessarily located at the base, but might, as in Ubangi, be interstratified with the lower part of the group. The Lower Kotto "System" is nearly everywhere preserved between faults.

6.5.8. The Lindian of Maniema

There is a fairly large number of partly isolated outcrops of red sandstones arkoses, or red conglomerates, and calcitic or dolomitic limestones, which lie unconformably on older folded rocks, Burundian among others (see CAHEN, 1954, p. 148). The majority of the outliers have been attributed to the *Schisto-gréseux* sequence or to the *Schisto-calcaire* sequence of the Lindian. This interpretation, virtually certain for the group as a whole and particularly for the northern part of Maniema, becomes less and less certain farther away from the type area. The outliers are of great theoretical importance because they form the connection between the Katangan in the south, the Malagarasian in the east, and the Lindian in the north. The broad distribution of the outliers and the Malagarasian with respect to the uplifted regions along the rift valleys is significant. The outliers classified as Lindian are abundant and occur in the low-lying areas of Maniema, but disappear in the uplifted areas of Kivu. The Malagarasian appears in the depressed region southeast of the Rwanda–Burundi high, which, again, itself succeeds the uplifted area of Kivu in the east. It is therefore probable that a more or less continuous sedimentary cover existed before the deformations that ended in the uplift of both sides of the Eastern Congo Rift Valley (Western Rift Valley).

6.5.9. Tectonics

The *Schisto-gréseux* sequence is certainly transgressive on the *Schisto-calcaire* and there is even a slight unconformity at places (CAHEN, 1954, p. 176). In any case, the stratigraphic revision shows that nearly all the deformations of any importance are attributable to a post-*Schisto-gréseux* tectonic phase, witnessed by folds and faults. The most obvious fold is the vast syncline of Banalia (see Fig. 22), which is asymmetrical with a vergence towards the northeast. The southwestern flank of the syncline is the northeastern limb of an asymmetrical anticline with the same vergence. In addition, the anticline is faulted. These two tectonic elements—the Yambuya anticline and the Banalia syncline—have a N.W.–S.E. trend and extend at least from the Aruwimi to Maiko (on the right bank of the Lualaba River, east of Stanleyville). East of the type region, folds with a northeasterly trend are also known, mainly in the *Schisto-calcaire* sequence.

In the Niangara outlier, 200 km north of the type area, there is strong deformation of variable trend with dips between 17° and 50°. The lack of sure stratigraphic correlation makes it impossible to say whether this deformation belongs to a post-*Schisto-calcaire* sequence phase or a post-*Schisto-gréseux* sequence phase.

In Ubangi, there is at least a transgressive overlap of the upper unit above the lower unit, that is, of a group that probably represents a high level in the *Schisto-gréseux* above a lower part of the same sequence. The angular unconformity between these two units recorded by ADERCA (1950) may exist, but the available data can also be interpreted as showing the juxtaposition by faulting of folded Lindian with subtabular Lindian. This point should be clarified by future detailed studies.

6.5.10. Metamorphism, plutonic activity, and mineralization

From the type area as far as to Ubangi, the Lindian is unmetamorphosed. Neither has any plutonic activity taken place except in the Ubangian, where the two units are penetrated by bosses of post-Ubangian gabbro and diabase. No mineralization of economic importance seems to occur in these rocks. Galena veins occur at Mount Homa (see p. 157) and in the Niangara outlier (A. MEYER, personal communication).

6.5.11. Summary

On a weathered, smoothed, and denuded crystalline substratum, an epicontinental sea deposited shelf sediments. After the slight subsidence during the deposition of the *Schisto-calcaire* sequence there was a more marked subsidence during the deposition of the *Schisto-gréseux* sequence. Known variations in facies and thickness show that subsidence was greater in the southwest than in the northeast. The only crustal movements of any importance were undulations of large radius with a generally N.W.–S.E. trend. Both the sedimentation and structure seem characteristic of deposition in a basin which must have extended far to the north (Niangara) and to the east (Mount Homa) and to have opened broadly towards the south.

6.6. *The West Congolian*

6.6.1. General Comments

At a variable distance, but scarcely exceeding 200 km, from the Atlantic Ocean, occur the first outcrops of a long belt running nearly parallel to the coastline from the Cameroons to Angola. The part of the belt that outcrops in the Lower Congo (formerly called the Western Congo Group, in part; see Fig. 23) is here called the West Congolian. This assemblage includes folded strata towards the Atlantic and flat-lying beds towards the interior. It is not directly connected to the rocks discussed in Sections 6.2 and 6.5, which succeed it from the south to the east and from the east to the north around the margin of the Congo Basin (see Fig. 26).

The Sansikwa is considered a part of the West Congolian "tectonostratigraphic" unit. This conclusion derives from the fact that the main tectonic disturbance affecting the Sansikwa was the West Congolian orogeny. On a regional scale, it is consequently certain that the Sansikwa belongs to the West Congolian by reason of the definitions given on p. 150. Nevertheless, there is an unconformity of some importance above the Sansikwa (see p. 224), and it seems possible that the Sansikwa is an approximate chronological equivalent of the Kibaran–Burundian; for this reason it was treated with the Kibaran–Burundian (see p. 228).

6.6.2. Historical survey

The first geological observations on the West Congolian are incorporated in the works of E. DUPONT published in 1889, of J. CORNET in 1897, and of V. BRIEN in 1910. However, F. DELHAYE and M. SLUYS, in 1924 and 1929, established the basis of the present-day knowledge of the West Congolian. Their works were subsequently revised by L. CAHEN in 1948, geologists of the *Syndicat de recherche minière au Bas et au Moyen Congo* (J. LEPERSONNE in 1948 and 1950; L. CAHEN in 1950; M. C. BRANDES in 1949; P. MATHIEU in 1952; unpublished reports; see CAHEN, 1954, pp. 209–236), and by those of the *Service géologique du Congo Belge* (SEKIRSKY, 1958; ANTUN, 1961a; unpublished reports). All this research makes the Lower Congo one of the geologically best-known regions of the Congo.

6.6.3. Stratigraphy of the West Congolian

The stratigraphy of the West Congolian, based on published and unpublished research, is summarized in Table 21. It differs from the previous stratigraphical schemes by the general subdivision of the major units. Formerly, the Inkisi, Mpioka, and Mfidi had the rank of series and were grouped together as "*Système Schisto-gréseux*". One could thus bring out the fairly abrupt change in sedimentation between the *Schisto-calcaire* sequence and the *Schisto-gréseux* sequence (CAHEN, 1954, p. 234). The new observations emphasize the fairly great importance of the sub-Inkisi unconformity and the at least local transition, by means of the Ngandu Group, from the underlying calcareous to the overlying red feldspar-bearing arenaceous facies, which make it preferable to adopt the subdivision given in Table 21.

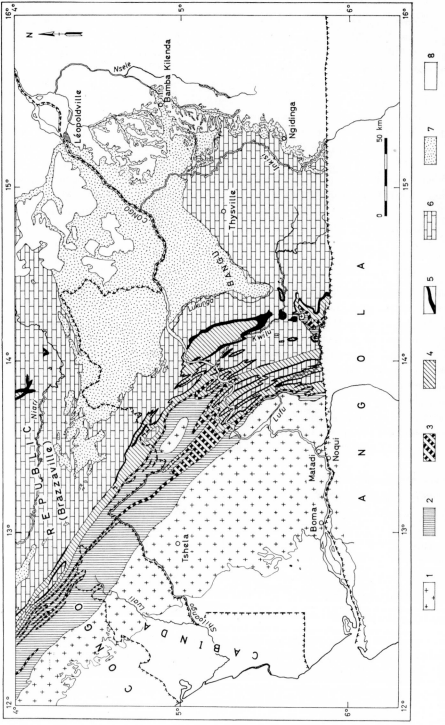

Fig. 23. Sketch map of the West Congolian. 1, Mayumbian. 2, Sansikwa. 3, Lower tillite with associated lavas. 4, Upper Shiloango—Louila. 5, Upper tillite. 6, *Schisto-calcaire*. 7, Mpioka and Inkisi. 8, Mesozoic and Cenozoic cover.

The contact between the Sansikwa and the Lower Tillite Complex

In the Sansikwa area an unconformity separating the Lower Tillite and the accompanying lavas from the Sansikwa is clear enough on maps (see p. 224). In addition, the strike of the tillite and its associated suite of volcanic rocks differs slightly from the strike of the Sansikwa.

The lithological properties of the tillite will be discussed on p. 272. Here, it is only necessary to give an account of the relationships between the lavas and the Tillite Complex. The lavas are microdolerites, basalts, and andesites. They are accompanied by agglomerates and tuffs and are interstratified in the Tillite Complex. The main mass of the tillite may lie either above or below the lavas. The tillite contains pebbles derived from the lava. Besides the lava proper there are some gabbroic rocks preserved in the Sansikwa and interpreted as the roots of the vents (see p. 224).

TABLE 21

Stratigraphical summary of the West Congolian

Lithostratigraphic units	Lithology	Thickness, m
Inkisi		>920
	Upper Group (I_{II})	>600
	Quartzite-shale formation(s), badly known, feldspar-bearing quartzites, and Luvumvu shales (I2c)	>300
	Zongo quartzitic arkoses (I2b)	>300
	Lower Group	
	Morozi quartzites and shales (I2a)	20–30
	Fulu arkoses (I_I)	300–400
	Mount Bidi conglomerate, with an arkosic matrix (I0)	Up to 15
	Unconformity	
Mpioka *sensu lato*		~1,000
	Mpioka Sequence (*sensu stricto*)	950–1,000
	Upper Group (P II)	550
	Liansama shales and quartzites (P 3)	300
	Kubuzi feldspar-bearing quartzites (P 2)	250
	Lower Group (P I)	400–450
	Vampa shales and quartzites (P 1)	400
	Conglomerate of Bangu and Niari (P 0)	Up to 40
	Hiatus	
	Mfidi Sequence	Up to 50
	Luvemba Group (F II). Feldspar-bearing quartzites, arkosic conglomerate at the base	
	Gidinga Group	
	Sandstones and grey or green calcareous shales, fine-grained quartzites	
	Basal conglomerate	
	Hiatus	

Continued on next page

TABLE 21 (*contd.*)

Lithostratigraphic units	Lithology	Thickness, m
Schisto-calcaire		~1,100
	Ngandu Group (C IV)	Up to 90
	Shales and calcareous shales, argillaceous limestones and dolomitic limestones	
	Bangu Group (C III)	Up to 300
	Magnesian limestones and dolomitic limestones, often dark and hydrocarbon-bearing	
	Kisantu oolites and pseudo-oolites, shales, locally a basal breccia. Stromatolites, indeterminate microfossils	
	Lukunga Group (C II)	~300
	Oolitic limestones, stromatolite limestones, shales, calcareous shales, calcareous sandstones, cherts	
	Kwilu Group (C I)	>480
	Luanza Formation: oolitic limestones, stromatolite limestones, calcareous shales and shales	155
	Bulu Formation: calcareous shales, mudstones, calcareous sandstones	>315
	Finely banded pink and grey dolomites	12
	Hiatus	
Upper tillite of the Lower Congo	Hiatus and slight unconformity	Up to 150
Upper Shiloango–Louila		700–1,000
	Sekelolo Group	
	Limestone breccia, stromatolite limestones in reefs, black argillaceous limestones, shales, feldspar-bearing quartzites	200–350
	Lesser Bembezi Group	
	Quartz phyllites, slates, calcareous grits, quartzites, and conglomerates	500–700
	Disconformity	
Lower tillite of the Lower Congo	Tillite, periglacial formations, and lavas (see p. 272)	Up to 400
	Unconformity	
Sansikwa (see p. 221)	Major unconformity (see p. 224)	

The Upper Shiloanga–Louila

The basal conglomerate contains material torn from the underlying lava and pebbles of shale, limestone, and quartz. The Lesser Bembizi Group seems to be fairly constant in thickness and facies throughout the region. The Sekelolo Group decreases in thickness from the west to the east. In its upper part some shaly members in the west decrease in thickness or are replaced towards the east by calcareous members unknown in the west (CAHEN, 1954, p. 216).

The Upper Tillite Complex

The Upper Tillite and its upper and lower contacts have been studied in detail. The tillite itself will be discussed on p. 272. It lies with a very slight unconformity on older strata, in particular on older beds of the Upper Shiloango–Louila in the west and on younger ones in the east. Some minor tectonic events, notably the formation of small faults, are of post-Upper Shiloango–Louila and pre-Tillite age. Some faults younger than the tillite but older than the *Schisto-calcaire* are also known to occur. In any case, there is scarcely any break between the pink dolomite at the base of the *Schisto-calcaire* and the Tillite Complex.

The Schisto-calcaire

The Kwilu Group begins with a probably lagoonal dolomite (see CAHEN, 1954, p. 220) which passes upwards, by gradation but fairly rapidly, into marine deposits. The group bears witness to a transgression and ends with limestones deposited in shallow water. An abrupt regression caused the terrigenous sedimentation of the Lukunga Group. This group appears to represent a complete cycle of sedimentation: pelitic and arenaceous sediments occur at the base, calcareous sediments in the middle, and pelitic

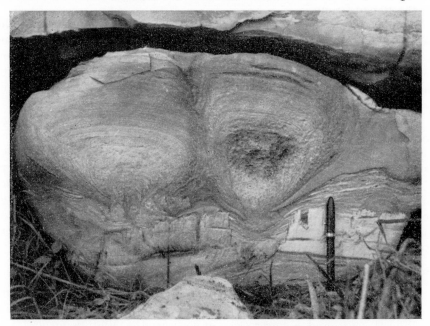

FIG. 24. Stromatolites of the Lukunga Group of the *Schisto-calcaire* (West Congolian of Lower Congo). Thysville. Photo, M. C. Brandes.

sediments again at the top (Fig. 24). The nature of the contact between the Lukunga and Bangu Groups is still unknown. The possibility of a slight unconformity cannot be excluded. The Bangu Group as a whole appears to indicate near-shore sedimentation, partly littoral and current-swept, partly, perhaps, lagoonal. The coastal influence appears to have continued during the deposition of the Ngandu Group, but terrigenous effects become more and more marked. Instead of being considered a separate group, the Ngandu Group might be regarded as comprising the upper formations of the Bangu Group. No definite break exists between the two groups, and their contact may be perfectly gradational.

The relationships between the Schisto-calcaire and the overlying beds

Both the Inkisi and the Mpioka may lie directly on the *Schisto-calcaire* (Fig. 25). Several types of contact are known, namely: (1) the conglomerate of Bangu and Niari lies practically conformably on the Ngandu Group which, again, lies conformably on the Bangu Group; (2) the conglomerate of Bangu and Niari lies with a very slight unconformity on the Bangu Group; (3) the conglomerate of Bangu and Niari lies with a definite unconformity on breccias that fill depressions in the downwarps of folded Bangu Group beds and erode the upwarps of these beds—the folds die out in depth; (4) the conglomerate of Bangu and Niari or only a part thereof lies with hiatus on the Mfidi sequence, which itself rests with hiatus on the Bangu group; (5) the Inkisi lies with a fairly clearly marked unconformity on the Bangu Group.

The movements that caused the change in sedimentation, justifying the name *Schisto-calcaire* and the formerly used name *Schisto-gréseux* (see p. 265), seem to have taken place fairly gradually, so that the deposition of the sediments marking the passage from one type of sedimentation to the other type either were followed by the main tectonic phase (contact of type 1), or were preceded and interrupted by it (contact of type 4).

The Ngandu Group, the breccias underlying the conglomerate of Bangu and Niari, and the Mfidi sequence occur only in places in different regions. Their relationships are open to discussion. The different types of contact listed above suggest that it is probable, as indicated in Table 21 and on p. 271, that the Mfidi sequence belongs to the Mpioka sequence *sensu lato*, and that the Ngandu Group belongs to the *Schisto-calcaire*, but it is still possible that these two sequences are contemporaneous, and that one of them or both might be coeval with the breccias that underlie the conglomerate of Bangu and Niari (contact of type 3).

The Mpioka

As used in this paper, the name "Mpioka" refers to a major stratigraphic unit consisting of two sequences, an upper, or the Mpioka, sequence in the traditional sense and a lower, less important, the Mfidi sequence. The Mpioka sequence generally begins with the conglomerate of Bangu and

FIG. 25. Contact between base of the Mpioka and the *Schisto-calcaire* (West Congolian of Lower Congo). South of Inkisi. Photo, P. Mathieu.

Niari and, in places, the Mfidi sequence is overlain by the conglomerate. The Mfidi sequence is lenticular and lies disconformably on various horizons of the Bangu Group. It is overlain by the eastern facies of the Mpioka sequence (see below). The thickness of the conglomerate of Bangu and Niari is greatest where the Mfidi sequence is absent or very thin.

The typical or the western facies of the Mpioka is presented in Table 21. The eastern facies occurs mainly on the right bank of the Inkisi River (see Fig. 23). With respect to the succession in the Bangu region, it has a reduced thickness, generally from 100 m to 225 m. In the north, at Bamba–Kilenda, it consists essentially of an alternating sequence of shales and fine-grained, feldspar-bearing quartzites, red and often micaceous, which follow a basal conglomerate of reduced thickness. In the south, at Ngidinga, the rocks are more feldspar-bearing and arenaceous. Rare shaly partings occur towards the base above the conglomerate.

The passage from the western facies to the eastern facies is sharp, and takes place across a notable zone of radial faults at most 10 km broad. A discussion of the correlation of the two facies was presented by CAHEN (1954, p. 233), and the most acceptable hypothesis seems to be that the Mpioka sequence was everywhere deposited with a thickness of the order of 1,000 m, that it was deformed by post-Mpioka, pre-Inkisi, movements (see p. 272) and that the pre-Inkisi erosion was responsible for part or all of the reduction of the thickness. As a consequence, the eastern facies should represent the lower part of the sequence.

With regard to the Mfidi sequence, the sediments of the Gidinga Group appear to have been deposited in a closed aquatic environment, a lake or a lagoon, and the Luvemba Group represents littoral deposition with a shore line in the south or the southeast. Similarly, the material of the Mpioka sequence seems to have been derived, at least partly, from the south or the southeast.

The Inkisi–Mpioka contact

The contact between the Inkisi and the Mpioka is slightly unconformable. In places, the Inkisi rests, with a basal conglomerate, on either facies of the Mpioka described on p. 271, whereas at Bamba Kilenda it forms an anticline whose southern flank overlies a thickness of 225 m of Mpioka, while 3.5 km towards the north the other flank of the same anticline lies on the Bangu Group of the *Schisto-calcaire*. Here, the angular discordance is of the order of 5°; at the Bangu Plateau, it is from 1° to 2°.

The Inkisi

The Inkisi, whose uppermost units have not been studied with the same care as its other units, seems to consist of sediments derived, at least partly, from the north-northeast and, probably, from the east.

6.6.4. Comments on tillites

The tillites consist largely of two thick conglomerate units. As their glacial nature was denied by SCHERMERHORN and STANTON (1960, 1963a), it is useful to summarize the various properties witnessing to their glacial origin.

The Upper Tillite, which does not exceed 150 m in thickness, has a calcareous–argillaceous matrix with much clastic debris of varying size and type, particularly fragments of quartz. It is generally light grey-green and unstratified. The pebbles and boulders may reach 1 m³ in size and are scattered at random. The inclusions are subangular or subrounded. The proportion of pebbles in the matrix is variable but never very great. Striated pebbles occur, but, it seems, only in places. By contrast, faceted pebbles are very common, as are crushed pebbles. Many of the pebbles have been transported for long distances. Before the deposition of the Tillite Complex an emergence took place; and after the deposition, a gradual submergence (CAHEN, 1954). The occurrence of glacial varves is not certain, even though there exist banded sediments at the contact of the tillite.

The Lower Tillite is very similar to the Upper Tillite, with which it has for a long time been confused and with which it shares most of the lithological properties. Its matrix is darker grey, often blackish, and its boulders reach several cubic metres in volume. No striated pebbles have been observed. By contrast, varves carrying sparsely distributed pebbles are known.

The Lower Tillite, like the Upper Tillite, but in greater abundance, contains rocks (loess sandstones) indicating aeolian action. The Lower Tillite is accompanied by lavas devoid of pillow structure (see CAHEN, 1947, 1954, 1963b).

The lithological properties mentioned above are observed virtually throughout Lower Congo. No change of facies is known in this small area, although some changes occur both north and south of Lower Congo.

6.6.5. Tectonics

After the period of erosion that followed the Mayumbian folding the Sansikwa beds were deposited and were affected by tectonic activity of some importance which might be, in Lower Congo, the feeble representative of an orogeny more prominent elsewhere (see p. 154). The preceding account permits a number of tectonic episodes to be listed, all of slight importance except the one that took place between the Mpioka and the Inkisi, and the main episode following the Inkisi. The main West Congolian phase is certainly of post-Mpioka and probably of post-Inkisi age, because in the slightly folded regions of the Bangu and the Cataracts Plateau and at Bamba Kilenda the Inkisi follows the style of the Mpioka and of the *Schisto-calcaire* sequence in spite of the slight unconformity (maximum observed, 5°) which separates them. The folds of the West Congolian Orogeny have a S.S.E.–N.N.W. trend, broadly parallel to the Atlantic Ocean coastline and are overturned towards the east-northeast; they decrease from the west towards the east. In the western zone of outcrops, the West Congolian strata are inverted and overlain by Mayumbian rocks. It is probable that thrusts occur in this zone. Farther in the west, the older rocks are greatly affected by the West Congolian folding. The degree of metamorphism increases from the east towards the west.

In the eastern part of Lower Congo, the beds only undulate, and the folds with a great radius trend from the southwest to the northeast (the "Combian" trend of Niari), doubtless controlled by the original trend of the basement of the West Congolian (see p. 194).

The main phase of folding was followed by notable radial movements, viz., the post-Inkisi faulting with frequently a general trend from the west-southwest to the east-northeast, and the undulations mentioned above. The occurrence of post-Mpioka and pre-Inkisi faults is likely.

6.6.6. Metamorphism

Metamorphism has not affected the rocks along the eastern margin of the belt, but it passes gradually into an epizonal metamorphism in the Upper Shiloango and Sansikwa at their contact with the Mayumbian. The metamorphism of the Mayumbian increases from the east to the west and is at least partly caused by the West Congolian Orogeny (see p. 195).

6.6.7. Plutonic activity

Apart from the gabbros and dolerites of the Sansikwa (see p. 224), considered to be connected with the doleritic, basaltic, and andesitic lavas associated with the Lower Tillite, no intrusive rock is known at the contact of the West Congolian rocks. Quartz veins are numerous there, especially in the western zone, where the oldest rocks crop out. Nevertheless, quartz veins are known to occur in all West Congolian, and barite veins occur in the Mpioka and Inkisi rocks.

In the Matadi region, a posttectonic hyperalkalic granite containing riebeckite and aegirite, called the Noqui granite, cuts the Matadi–Palabala sequence (see p. 196), forming a structure that is a part of a large tectonic unit overlying inverted West Congolian. The structure is consequently caused by the West Congolian orogeny, and the Noqui granite is thus younger than the main phase of the West Congolian Orogeny. This conclusion should be considered with respect to the ages obtained on pegmatites and migmatites of Boma that date from the West Congolian Orogeny (see p. 195).

6.6.8. Mineralization

Copper and lead veins are known to occur in the Upper Shiloango–Louila, the Upper Tillite, and the lower part of the *Schisto-calcaire* sequence. They have no economic importance, but seem to be connected with economically more important mineralizations in the large post-Inkisi faults or adjacent to them. The most notable of these, at Bamba Kilenda, is a fault containing chalcocite or sphalerite, pyrite, and argentian galena, chalcopyrite, bornite, and various vanadium sulfate and arsenate minerals. In places, the minerals occur in the fault, elsewhere in adjacent rocks, and, preferentially, at the top of the *Schisto-calcaire* sequence and in the Lower Inkisi. Other, less important, mineralizations are layered and thereby resemble the Niari mineralizations in Congo–Brazzaville, emplaced in some beds of the *Schisto-calcaire* sequence, but almost always near sizable radial faults.

The lead mineralizations of Bamba Kilenda and Niari have been analysed with respect to the isotopic constitution of their lead. A conventional age of about 740 Myr (see p. 156) was thereby obtained. An epigenetic mineralization consisting of veins and veinlets of argentian galena in the Sansikwa, the Upper Shiloango, and the *Schisto-calcaire* sequence yielded a conventional age of 440 Myr–460 Myr (see p. 156).

6.6.9. Summary

Between a badly defined western craton that must have been located west of the present-day Boma (see p. 194) and have been formed, at least partly, of Lower Mayumbian rocks, and an eastern craton comprising the du Chaillu Massif and the basement of the Kwango, there was an area of subsidence that became the West Congolian geosyncline. The first sediments to be involved in the West Congolian orogenic cycle yielded the Sansikwa rocks and were deposited in an elongated basin with a north-northwest trend. It is possible that the cycle whose beginning was marked by the Sansikwa sedimentation might have been interrupted, and that the Sansikwa, after its initial evolution, might have become affected by a later orogenic cycle. This, then, would explain the relative tectonic independence of the Sansikwa from that of the overlying beds (see p. 224).

After a period of emergence, the West Congolian subsidence continued during the deposition of the Upper Shiloango–Louila strata as four main phases, each separated by hiatuses or disconformities caused by emergence. The data available are insufficient to define the origin of the sediments of the Upper Shiloango–Louila beds, the Upper Tillite and of most of the *Schisto-calcaire*. However, the terrigenous sediments of the Mpioka sequence include a source in the east or the southeast, and the Inkisi has sources in the northeast and the east. These easterly sources denote a rejuvenation of the eastern craton after tectonic events postdating the *Schisto-calcaire* sequence. In the eroded western regions of Lower Congo, folding must have assumed some importance soon after the deposition of the Mpioka sediments forming ridges, the erosion of which could have contributed material towards the formation of the Inkisi, which, in some respects, is molasse-like.

To sum up, the West Congolian Orogeny was a very important geologic event that strongly affected the older rocks (see p. 195). The West Congolian geosynclinal axis must have passed through the region west of Matadi (see p. 194). In fact, only the external part of this geosyncline is known, and it may, during a late stage, have been connected with an area of subsidence on the foreland by means of a strait between the du Chaillu Massif and the Kwango (see p. 276).

6.7. *The bottom of the Congo Basin*

6.7.1. Introduction

The rocks dealt with in Sections 6.2 and 6.6 crop out around the margin of the Congo Basin. This section deals with what is known of the basement of the basin. Two diamond drill holes, located at Samba and Dekese (see Fig. 2), have pierced the Mesozoic and Late Palaeozoic cover, and a seismic survey permits some extrapolation of the pertinent data.

6.7.2. Geological data

In the drill hole at Samba on the Maringa River, in the northern part of the Congo Basin, red, feldspar-bearing arkosic quartzites, very fine-grained and containing micaceous and argillaceous beds, had a thickness of almost 900 m, extending from 1,168 m to 2,038 m below the surface. The quartzites display properties, such as ripple marks and cross-bedding, showing that they were deposited in a shallow basin; this very thick and uniform sequence indicates marked subsidence. The base of the formation was not reached, and the beds observed were horizontal (CAHEN and others, 1959).

At Dekese on the Lukenie River, in the southern part of the Congo Basin, an almost identical but slightly coarser-grained sequence was found at a depth of 1,680 m–1,856 m. Here also, the base was not reached. The beds dip at about 30°, probably because of a post-Permian flexure (CAHEN and others, 1960).

At the time of drilling at Samba, no similar rocks of comparable thickness were known to crop out. Since then, it has been found that the Banalia quartzitic sandstone, the upper part of the *Schisto-gréseux* sequence of the Lindian (see p. 261) has an almost identical facies over a thickness of at least 1,000 m–1,200 m. All these beds are virtually fossil-free (only a few doubtful spores have been observed).

6.7.3. Geophysical data

In the two drill holes mentioned and in certain Lindian outcrops, the red, quartzitic sandstones are characterized by seismic refraction, yielding velocities of about 4,200 m sec^{-1}–4,600 m sec^{-1} (EVRARD, 1960). An isobath map showing the distribution of the 4,200 m sec^{-1} refractor (EVRARD, 1960, Appendix 2) suggests that similar strata floor a large part of the basin. Seismic reflection surveys show that these beds are generally subhorizontal. The top of the red quartzitic sandstone in the Samba drill hole is followed with continuity to similar outcrops in the Banalia syncline which might indicate that the erosion surface forming the contact between cover rocks and the feldspar-bearing quartzite is a regular surface with a dip of 3.6 m km^{-1}, that is, with an inclination of about one-fifth of a degree. Furthermore, the 4,200 m sec^{-1} refractor in the southwestern corner of the Congo Basin tends to run along the Congo River towards Léopoldville, rising in this direction by 2 m km^{-1}. Unfortunately, the seismic survey ends about 200 km from Léopoldville. If one extrapolated with the same gradient, Léopoldville would be reached at an altitude between 200 m and 300 m above the sea level. Now, at Léopoldville–Kalina, the Inkisi of the West Congolian crops out at an altitude of about 270 m and disappears under the Mesozoic strata with a slight northeastwardly dip. Everywhere else, an extrapolation of the seismic data towards the margins of the basin is still impossible.

Seismic reflection surveys have shown that, at various points in the basin, the thickness of subhorizontal or gently undulating sedimentary rocks might reach several thousand metres (EVRARD, 1960, p. 77).

6.7.4. Conclusions

The account presented on the previous pages allows no definite conclusions, but suggests that for the largest part of the basin the rocks underlying the Mesozoic or Upper Palaeozoic cover belong to a single sequence

which, over a vast area, is lithologically similar to the upper part of the
Schisto-gréseux sequence of the Lindian and seems to link up with it towards the north and the northeast. It may also be continuous with the
Inkisi towards the southeast. Moreover, the lithofacies of the beds underlying the basin is very similar to that of the Banalia quartzitic sandstones
and of the imperfectly known Luvumvu shales of the Inkisi (see Table 21).

6.8. *Summary*

6.8.1. General correlation

The Katangan, the Bushimay, the Malagarasian, and the Lindian of
Maniema all rest unconformably on the Kibaran or its equivalent, viz., the
Burundian (see Fig. 26). This conclusion may be valid also for the Lindian
of the type locality in the basement of which tin-bearing granites of Burundian type crop out, and, similarly, for the Ubangian, which is a continuation
of the Lindian towards the west. Thus, all the rocks mentioned above have
the same older age limit, the Kibaran Orogeny, the syntectonic phases of
which have been dated at about 1,250 Myr. The older age limit of the West
Congolian, including the Sansikwa, is the Upper Mayumbian folding with
an age estimated at more than 1,500 Myr. However, the Katangan has
(620 ± 20) Myr as its younger age limit. It contains lead and uranium
mineralizations dated at or about 480 Myr, 520 Myr, 620 Myr, and 720 Myr
(see p. 156).

The Lindian and the West Congolian similarly contain lead mineralizations with a conventional age of 740 Myr. The age of the West Congolian
folding is about 625 Myr, and its posttectonic episodes have ages of about
525 Myr and 465 Myr (see p. 156).

Finally, the Katangan is almost completely continuous with the Malagarasian, and the Lindian with the Ubangian. The Lindian seems to be
connected with the West Congolian under the Congo Basin, and there is
scarcely any doubt that prior to the erosion of the uplifted East Congo–
Rwanda–Burundi zone the Lindian was more or less continuous with the
Malagarasian.

It is thus almost certain that the sequences studied above are chronologically comparable; the beginnings and ends of these sequences were,
however, not necessarily exactly coeval.

6.8.2. The Katangan of the Congo, seen as a whole

Among the assemblages cropping out southeast of the Kibaran–Burundian Belt, viz., the Katangan of the type locality, the Katangan of northeastern Katanga, and the Malagarasian, the first-named was deposited
in a geosyncline and the others in intracratonic troughs (see pp. 248, 252,
and 259). By contrast, the assemblages exposed to the northwest of the
Kibaran–Burundian Belt, namely, the Bushimay and the Lindian, are
shelf deposits, formed in subsiding basins (see pp. 256 and 264). To the

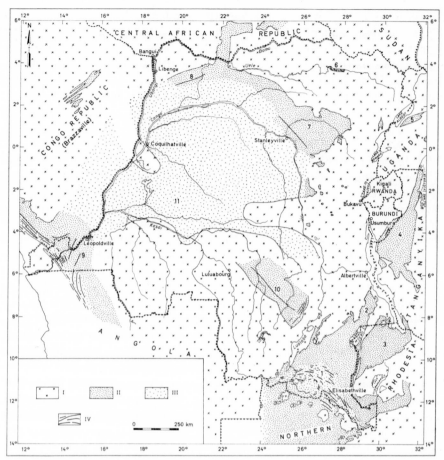

FIG. 26. The Katangan, general view. (The Upper Palaeozoic–Recent cover is not indicated.) I, Pre-Katangan basement. II, Katangan outcrops. III, Katangan beneath thick Upper Palaeozoic–Recent cover. 1, Katangan geosyncline with platform facies towards the north. 2, Northeastern Katanga (intracontinental basin).
3, Plateau Series (platform facies). 4, Bukoban and Malagarasian (intracontinental
basin and platform facies). 5, Bunyoro glaciogenic deposits; attribution to
Katangan uncertain. 6, Lindian of Niangara, folded; attribution to Katangan
uncertain. 7, Lindian (platform facies). 8, Ubangian (platform facies). 9, Lower
Congo geosyncline with platform facies towards the east. 10, Bushimay (platform
facies). 11, Congo basin (basin of subsidence). Heavy lines indicate principal areas
of folding.

west, the folded West Congolian probably connects across the foreland with
the flat-lying beds under the Congo Basin.

It consequently appears that there was an old craton, partly occupying
the site of the present-day Congo Basin and bordered from the east to the
southeast and from the southwest to the west by less stable zones, namely,
geosynclines in the west and in the southeast and intracratonic troughs in

the east. The central part of the craton, which coincided with the Congo Basin, subsided more than its marginal parts and there then existed a true basin of subsidence. The facies variations of the Bushimay and comparison of the Bushimay and Luamba facies show that without doubt the subsidence took place already during the Roan time. The facies and thickness of the feldspar-bearing quartzites of the central basin, probably to be correlated with the Upper Inkisi and the top of the Upper Lindian, both of which are correlated with the Upper Kundelungu, show that the subsidence continued during the Upper Kundelungu time.

During the Upper Kundelungu time the basin of subsidence must have extended significantly towards the north, beyond the present-day limits of the Lindian.

7. Rocks of dubious age, perhaps Lower Palaeozoic. Relationships between the Precambrian and the cover rocks

7.1. *Introduction*

Nowhere in the Congo, Rwanda, or Burundi are the Katangan and its equivalents, dealt with in Section 6, overlain by rocks older than Upper Palaeozoic. Like the Lindian of Maniema, and perhaps of the type area, the Katangan is unconformably overlain by the Lukuga Series whose lower part belongs to the Upper Carboniferous. The Lindian of the type area and the West Congolian are overlain by Upper Jurassic strata, and the Katangan of northwestern Katanga and Kasai, and the Ubangian by Lower Cretaceous strata. The analogous sequences of the Congo Basin are overlain by Upper Jurassic strata in the north and Upper Carboniferous rocks in the south.

Upper Carboniferous and younger rocks form a generally unfolded cover that everywhere unconformably overlies the basement discussed in Sections 3–6. Furthermore, no rocks that indubitably belong to the Cambrian are known in Central Africa.

The Precambrian age of the youngest basement rocks does not, therefore, rest on stratigraphic evidence. This situation has given rise to much discussion, and the youngest Kundelungu strata (Katangan) have been assigned a Devonian age, without palaeontological proof (ROBERT, 1956).

7.2. *The Precambrian–Cambrian boundary in Central Africa*

There is still no world-wide agreement as to where the base of the Cambrian should be put. The boundary between the Cambrian and the Precambrian poses a particular problem because it does not form the boundary between two assemblages of fossil animals or plants, in spite of some recent attempts to define the top of the Precambrian palaeontologically.

Recourse to geochronology is rendered difficult by the absence of a precise boundary between the Cambrian and the Precambrian. Nevertheless,

Lower Cambrian rocks appear to be younger than 600 Myr–620 Myr while older rocks contain no characteristic Cambrian fossils or are even almost entirely fossil-free (see HOLMES, 1960; CAHEN, 1961b). An age such as (600 ± 20) Myr seems, at the present time, a convenient geochronological datum for the boundary between the Precambrian and the Cambrian. However, while using this age it must be regarded as approximate and provisional.

The Katangan of Katanga is older than (620 ± 20) Myr (see pp. 155 and 246). However, some strata at the top of the Kundelungu, which are not present in the folded region on which the datings were made, might be a little younger, but this is not probable (CAHEN and others, 1961). It may thus be concluded that the greater part of the Katangan belongs definitely to the Precambrian, but it cannot be ruled out that the top might reach the base of the Lower Cambrian. Similarly, the West Congolian (see p. 156) is also older than the provisional age set above for the boundary between the Precambrian and Cambrian, although, as in Katanga, some beds at the top are not found in the intensely folded area from which the dated rocks and minerals were collected. It therefore seems proper to generalize for all the formations described in Section 6 (the Katangan and its equivalent) the conclusions reached for the Katangan of the type area.

7.3. *Rocks of dubious age*

7.3.1. Introduction

Apart from the top of the Katangan, for which some doubt remains, there are two sequences of uncertain age which may belong to the Palaeozoic, namely, the Bilati Group of northern Kivu and the Mount Nongo Formation in the Upper Ituri. They will be briefly discussed in the following paragraphs.

7.3.2. The Bilati Group

The Bilati Group ("Upper Formations II of Bilati") includes a folded series of slates and phyllites, arkosic grits, quartzites, and conglomerates which rest unconformably either on rocks that are imprecisely correlated with the Burundian or older rocks that have lithological features in common with the Ruzizian (see CAHEN, 1954, p. 185). The beds are of palaeontological interest because they have yielded two fossils described as cephalopods. The first of them resembles, at least superficially, Ordovician cephalopods, while some doubt remains about the biogenic origin of the second, which was found *in situ*; the first was found on the washing table of a gold works on the Bilati River. Nevertheless, its derivation from the black, pyrite-bearing phyllites of the Bilati Group seems to be the only possibility. In spite of some search, no other fossils have been discovered (CAHEN, 1954, p. 185). Provisional geochronological information favours an Upper Precambrian age for the Bilati Group.

7.3.3. The Mount Nongo formation

The Mount Nongo Formation, which is preserved between faults, is very similar in facies and lithology to the *Schisto-gréseux* sequence of the Lindian. It is a fairly fine-grained red sandstone with a feldspar-bearing matrix, and contains lenses of conglomerate with angular pebbles of red or pink grit, and of shales. The beds are gently folded and cut by a dolerite dyke. The formation has an area of 4 km², and it contains fragments of fossils, perhaps Palaeozoic, which unfortunately have been lost (see CAHEN, 1954, p. 181). This discovery has not been confirmed by later investigations. The Palaeozoic age of the Mount Nongo Formation must therefore be considered doubtful.

7.4. *Various Palaeozoic events older than Upper Carboniferous*

7.4.1. Lower Palaeozoic plutonic activity

Even though Palaeozoic rocks older than the Lukuga sequence are both rare and of doubtful age, there are many plutonic rocks that have been dated as Lower Palaeozoic.

Some pegmatites of post-Katangan age in southern Kivu have been dated at about 550 Myr (MONTEYNE-POULAERT and others, 1963), and others in the Lower Congo are nearly 525 Myr old (CAHEN and others, 1963). These pegmatites and metasomatic metamorphism in southeastern Katanga which, according to VAES (1961, 1962), is connected with a uranium mineralization with an age of 520 Myr (CAHEN and others, 1961), belong to the Cambrian.

7.4.2. Lower Palaeozoic mineralizations

Mineralizations that may or may not be connected with the above-mentioned plutonic events are common.

In Rwanda and in southern Kivu, veins containing uranium minerals have yielded an age of about 550 Myr (MONTEYNE-POULAERT and others, 1963). An epigenetic uranium mineralization affecting the Katangan of Katanga and of Zambia took place about 520 Myr ago (CAHEN and others, 1961; see p. 155). These mineralizations are generally not workable.

Several lead mineralizations, sometimes containing only lead, sometimes also other metals, are Palaeozoic. In southern Katanga, a lead mineralization with an age of about 520 Myr may have formed a part of the sulfide mineralization at Kipushi, and in Zambia a younger mineralization has an age between 460 Myr and 480 Myr. These lead mineralizations would thus be Cambrian and Ordovician, respectively.

Lead veins with a conventional age of similar magnitude, about 440 Myr–460 Myr, have affected the West Congolian and older rocks of the Lower Congo. This mineralization is thus of Ordovician age (see p. 156).

K

7.5. *Summary*

The only rocks in the Congo, Rwanda, and Burundi that might be Lower Palaeozoic are the extreme top of the Katangan and its equivalents, for which a Lower Cambrian age cannot be excluded, and the Bilati Group and the Mount Nongo Formation, whose ages are uncertain.

However, pegmatites and mineral veins formed repeatedly during the Cambrian and the Ordovician and seem to be, at least partly, posttectonic features belonging to the Katanga Cycle.

Bibliography

ADERCA, BERNARD (1950). Etude pétrographique et carte géologique du district du Congo-Ubangi (Congo belge). *Mém. Inst. Roy. Colonial Belge, Classe Sci. Nat. Méd., Collection in 8°*, **18**, Fasc. 4.

ADERCA, BERNARD (1952). Contribution à la connaissance pétrographique et géologique de la partie occidentale du Bas-Uele (Congo belge) et à la métallogénie des gisements aurifères de la région. *Mém. Inst. Roy. Colonial Belge, Classe Sci. Nat. Méd., Collection in 8°*, **20**, Fasc. 5.

AGASSIZ, JEAN-FRANCOIS (1954). Géologie et pegmatites stannifères de la région Mumba-Numbi, Kivu (Congo belge). *Comité Nat. Kivu* [N.S.] **7**.

ALDRICH, L. THOMAS, WETHERILL, GEORGE W., DAVIS, GORDON L., and TILTON, GEORGE R. (1958). Radioactive ages of the micas from granitic rocks by Rb–Sr and K–A methods. *Trans. Am. Geophys. Union*, **39**, 1124.

ANCION, CHARLES et CAHEN, LUCIEN (1952), Les minerais de fer du Congo belge. *Congr. Géol. Intern., Compt. Rend., 19e, Algiers, 1952, Symp. sur le Fer*, 83.

ANONYMOUS (1957). *Ann. Rept. Geol. Surv. Uganda, 1956*, 6.

ANONYMOUS (1958). *Ann. Rept. Geol. Surv. Uganda, 1957*, 4.

ANONYMOUS (1959). *Ann. Rept. Geol. Surv. Uganda, 1958*, 4.

ANONYMOUS (1960). *Ann. Rept. Geol. Surv. Uganda, 1959*, 4.

ANTUN, PAUL (1961a). Observations préliminaires sur le massif cristallophyllien de Kimuaka (Bas-Congo). *Ann. Soc. Géol. Belg.*, **84**, B229.

ANTUN, PAUL (1961b). Rapport succinct d'activité scientifique, 1960. Unpublished.

BELLIÈRE, JACQUES (1961). Manifestations métamorphiques dans la région d'Elisabethville. *Publ. Univ. Etat Elisabethville*, **1**, 175.

BERTOSSA, ANTONIO et THONNART, PIERRE (1957). Etude géologique de la région de Matadi–Inga–Monolithe accompagnée d'une carte à l'échelle du 1/100.000e. *Bull Serv. Géol., Congo Belge Ruanda-Urundi*, **7**, No. 5.

BESSOLES, BERNARD, COSSON, JEAN, GRASSAUD, JEAN et ROQUES, MAURICE (1956). Age apparent de la diorite quartzique des Saras dans le Mayombe (Afrique équatoriale française). *Compt. Rend. Soc. Géol. France*, 6e Sér., **6**, 86.

DE BETHUNE, PIERRE et MEYER, ANDRE (1956). Les carbonatites de la Lueshe (Kivu, Congo Belge). *Compt. Rend.*, **243**, 1132.

BEUGNIES, ALPHONSE (1952). La tectonique kundelunguienne. *Acad. Roy. Belg., Classe Sci., Mém., Collection in 8°*, **27**, 8.

BEUGNIES, ALPHONSE (1953). Le complexe des roches magmatiques de l'entre Lubilash/Lubishi (Katanga). *Mém. Inst. Roy. Col. Belge, Classe Sci. Nat. Méd., Collection in 8°*, **23**, Fasc. 1.

DE BOURNONVILLE, DIDIER (1961). Conglomérat sous le col de la route Nyanza–Lac Makamba. Unpublished Report.

CAHEN, LUCIEN (1947). Les glaciations anciennes pré-Karroo du Bassin du Congo et de l'Afrique australe. *Bull. Soc. Belge Géol., Paléontol., Hydrol.* **56**, 109.

CAHEN, LUCIEN (1948a). Etude d'échantillons "d'itabirites" (banded ironstones) du socle ancien de l'Entre-Luembe-Lubilash (Katanga). *Ann. Serv. Mines Com. Spéc. Katanga*, **XII, XIII**, *1947–1948*, 93.

CAHEN, LUCIEN (1948b). Les formations anciennes, antérieures à la Tillite du Bas-Congo. (Le Groupe des Monts de cristal). *Bull. Soc. Belge Géol., Paléontol., Hydrol.*, **57**, 77.

CAHEN LUCIEN (1954). *Géologie du Congo Belge*. Liège.

CAHEN, LUCIEN (1961a). Review of geochronological knowledge in middle and northern Africa. *Ann. N.Y. Acad. Sci.*, **91**, 535.

CAHEN, LUCIEN (1961). L'échelle des temps géologiques. Summer Course on Nuclear Geology, Varenna 1960 (Lecture 12), 402.

CAHEN, LUCIEN (1963a). Grands traits de l'agencement du soubassement de l'Afrique centrale. Esquisse tectonique au 1/5,000,000. *Ann. Soc. Géol. Belg.*, **85**, B183.

CAHEN, LUCIEN (1963b). Glaciations anciennes et dérive des continents. *Ann. Soc. Géol. Belg.*, **86**, B19.

CAHEN, LUCIEN (1963c). Tectoniques superposées au Bas-Congo (République du Congo, Léopoldville). *Ann. Soc. Géol. Belg.*, **86**, B213.

CAHEN, LUCIEN (1964). Eléments géochronologiques relatifs à la corrélation des terrains précambriens terminaux du Bas-Congo et du Katanga (Congo). *Musée Roy. Afr. Centr., Sect. Géol., Minéral. Paléontol. Rappt. Ann. 1963*, 96.

CAHEN, LUCIEN, DELHAL, JACQUES, LEDENT, DOLLY et REINHARZ, MAX (1963). L'âge des migmatites de Boma et de l'orogenèse Ouest-congolienne. Indications préliminaires sur l'âge des formations mayumbiennes et antérieures. *Ann. Soc. Géol. Belg.*, **86**, B229.

CAHEN, LUCIEN, DELHAL, JACQUES et MONTEYNE-POULAERT, GINETTE (1965). Contribution à l'étude pétrographique et géochronologique de granites kibariens (Katanga central et septentrional). *Musée. Roy. Afr. Centr., Sect. Géol., Minéral. Paléontol., Rappt. Ann. 1964*, 89.

CAHEN, LUCIEN, EBERHARDT, PETER, GEISS, JOHANNES, HOUTERMANS, FRIEDRICH GEORG, JEDWAB, JACQUES and SIGNER, PETER (1958). On a correlation between the common lead model age and the trace-element content of galena. *Geochim. Cosmochim. Acta*, **14**, 134.

CAHEN, LUCIEN, FERRAND, JEAN-JACQUES, HAARSMA, MARINUS J. F., LEPERSONNE, JACQUES et VERBEEK, THEO (1959). Description du sondage de Samba. *Ann. Musée Roy. Congo Belge, Sér. in 8°, Sci. Géol.*, **29**.

CAHEN, LUCIEN, FERRAND, JEAN-JACQUES, HAARSMA, MARINUS J. F., LEPERSONNE, JACQUES et VERBEEK, THEO (1960). Description du sondage de Dekese. *Ann. Musée Roy. Congo Belge, Sér. in 8°, Sci. Géol.*, **34**.

CAHEN, LUCIEN et LEPERSONNE, JACQUES (1956). Lexique stratigraphique international, **IV**, 7a, Congo belge. Centre Nat. Rech. Sci., Paris.

CAHEN, LUCIEN et MORTELMANS, GEORGES (1947). Le système de la Bushimaie au Katanga. *Bull. Soc. Belge Géol., Paléontol., Hydrol.*, **56**, 217.

CAHEN, LUCIEN et MORTELMANS, GEORGES (1948). Le groupe du Katanga. Evolution des idées et essai de subdivision. *Bull. Soc. Belge Géol., Paléontol., Hydrol.*, **57**, 459.

CAHEN, LUCIEN, PASTEELS, PAUL, LEDENT, DOLLY, BOURGUILLOT, EDGARD, VAN WAMBEKE, LEOPOLD et EBERHARDT, PETER (1961). Recherches sur l'âge absolu des minéralisations uranifères du Katanga et de Rhodésie du Nord. *Ann. Musée Roy. Afr. Centr., Sér. in 8°, Sci. Géol.*, **41**.

COMBE, A. D. (1932). The geology of south-west Ankole. *Mem. Geol. Surv. Uganda*, **2**.

COMMISSION DE GÉOLOGIE DU MINISTÈRE DES COLONIES (1935). *Légende de la carte géologique de Congo belge au 500,000e*. (2nd Ed.) Brussels.

CORIN, FRANCOIS (1946). Contribution à l'étude géologique des régions de Boma et de Matadi. *Bull. Soc. Belge Géol., Paléontol., Hydrol.*, **55**, 212.

CORIN, FRANCOIS (1948). Note sur la géologie des environs de Matadi. *Ann. Soc. Géol. Belg.*, **71**, B 71.

COSSON, JEAN (1953). Etat des travaux sur la coupure géologique Pointe-Noire. *Rappt. Ann. Serv. Géol. Afrique Equatoriale Française, 1953*, 162a.

COSSON, JEAN (1955). *Notice explicative sur les feuilles Pointe-Noire et Brazzaville Gouv. Gén. Afrique Equatoriale Française*, Paris.

CRUYSSAERT, JAN (1962). Petrographische waarnemingen in het overgangsgebied tussen het granietbatholiet van noord-oost Congo en de West-Nijl-Formatie. *Natuurw. Tijdschr. (Ghent)*, **44**, 29.

DARNLEY, A. G. (1960). Petrology of some Rhodesian Copperbelt orebodies and associated rocks. *Trans. Inst. Mining Met.*, **69**, 157.

DE DYCKER, RAYMOND (1949). Les caractéristiques géologiques des gisements miniers du Ruanda. *Nouveaux Mém. Soc. Belge Géol., Paléontol., Hydrol.* [N.S.], **3**.

DELHAL, JACQUES (1957a). Les massifs cristallins de la Lulua et de Lueta (Kasai). *Mém. Inst. Géol. Univ. Louvain*, **20**, 211.

DELHAL, JACQUES (1957b). Massif charnockitique au Kasai (Congo belge). *Bull. Soc. Belge Géol., Paléontol., Hydrol.*, **66**, 10.

DELHAL, JACQUES (1958a). Les roches charnockitiques du Kasai (Congo belge). *Commission Tech. Co-op. Africa S. of Sahara*, **44**, 271.

DELHAL, JACQUES (1958b). Etude pétrographique d'un complexe de roches vertes dans le Sud-Kasai. *Bull. Serv. Géol. Congo Belge Ruanda-Urundi*, **8**, No. 3.

DELHAL, JACQUES (1958c). Excursion dans les migmatites des environs de Boma. *Commission Tech. Co-op. Africa S. of Sahara.* [Stencilled].

DELHAL, JACQUES (1959). Sur le volcanisme ancien dans le Sud-Kasai (Congo belge). *Bull. Soc. Belge Géol., Paléontol., Hydrol.* **67**, 179.

DELHAL, JACQUES (1963). Le socle de la région de Luiza (Kasai). *Ann. Musée Roy. Afr. Centr. Sér. in-8°, Sci. Géol.*, **45**.

DELHAL, JACQUES (1964a). Etudes en relation avec des travaux de géologie régionale. 1. Bas-Congo. *Musée Roy. Afr. Centr., Sect. Géol. Minéral. Paléontol., Rappt. Ann. 1963*, 80.

DELHAL, JACQUES (1964b). Etudes en relation avec des travaux de géologie régionale. 2 Région nord-orientale et du Rwanda. *Musée Roy. Afr. Centr., Sect. Géol. Minéral. Paléontol., Rappt. Ann. 1963*, 81.

DELHAL, JACQUES et FIEREMANS, CARLOS (1964). Extension d'un grand complexe charnockitique en Afrique centrale. *Compt. Rend.*, **259**, 2665.

DELHAL, JACQUES et LEDENT, DOLLY (1961). Nouveaux résultats sur des roches du socle du Kasai. *Musée Roy. Afr. Centr., Sect. Géol. Mineral. Paléontol., Rappt. Ann. 1963*, 91.

DELHAL, JACQUES et LEDENT, DOLLY (in press). Quelques résultats géochronologiques relatifs aux formations du socle de la région de Luiza, Kasai. *Bull. Soc. Belge Géol., Paléontol., Hydrol.*

DELHAL, JACQUES et LEGRAND, ROBERT (1957). Le groupe de la Lulua. *Bull. Soc. Belge Géol., Paléontol., Hydrol.*, **66**, 20.

DELHAL, JACQUES, LEPERSONNE, JACQUES et RAUCQ, PAUL (in press). Le complexe sédimentaire et volcanique de la Lulua (Kasai) *Ann. Musée Roy. Afr. Centr. Sér., in 8°, Sci. Géol.* in press. A summary, under the same title, was published in *Musée Roy. Afr. Centr. Sect. Géol. Minéral. Paléontol., Rappt. Ann. 1963*, 48. Tervuren, 1964.

DELHAYE, FERNAND et SALÉE, ACHILLE (1928). Carte géologique de l'Urundi et du Ruanda au 200.000e. Brussels, 1928.

DEMESMAEKER, GEORGES, FRANCOIS, A. et OOSTERBOSCH, R. (1963). La tectonique des gisements cuprifères stratiformes du Katanga. In: *Stratiform copper deposits in Africa.* Symposium, 2nd part. Tectonics. Association of African geological surveys, Paris, 47/115.

DENAEYER, MARCEL-ÉMILE (1959). Les syénites métasomatiques de Kirumba. Contribution à la lithogenèse des volcans du Kivu (Congo belge). *Acad. Roy. Sci. Coloniales, Classe Sci. Tech., Mém., Collection in 8°* [N.S.], **9**, fasc. 2.

DÉVIGNE, JEAN-PIERRE (1959). Le Précambrien du Gabon occidental en Afrique Equatoriale Française et régions limitrophes. *Afrique Equator., Haut Comm. Rép., Bull. Dir. Mines Geol.*, **11**.

DUHOUX, PAUL V. (1950). La pétrogenèse et la métallogenèse du domaine minier de Kilo-Moto. *Ann. Soc. Géol. Belg.*, **73**, M171.

DUMONT, PAUL (1952). Contribution à l'étude des couches du Lubudi (Kibara supérieur) dans la vallée du Moyen Lubudi (Katanga). *Univ. Libre Bruxelles, Lab. Géol.* (Unpublished).

DUMONT, PAUL (1962). Renseignements inédits. Thesis in preparation.

DURAND, GEORGES L. et LAY, CLAUDE (1960). Détermination de l'âge de quelques galènes de la vallée du Niari (Moyen Congo). *Compt. Rend.*, **251**, 750.

EMMONS, WILLIAM H. (1937). Gold deposits of the world. New York.

EVRARD, PIERRE (1960) Sismique. *Ann. Musée Roy. Congo Belge, Sér. in 8°, Sci. Géol.*, **33**.

FIEREMANS, CARLOS (1959). Le "compartiment Kasadi-Sadi" du groupe de la Lulua. Relations stratigraphiques et tectoniques avec les régions Luiza–Lueta et le Nord-Est de la Lunda (Angola). *Bull. Soc. Belge Géol., Paléontol., Hydrol.*, **67**, 232.

FLYNN, K. F. and GLENDENIN, L. E. (1959). Half-life and beta spectrum of Rb 87. *Phys. Rev.*, **116**, 744.

FOGLIERINI, FRANCOIS et MESTRAUD, JEAN-LOUIS (1958). Notice explicative sur la feuille Bangui-Est. *Carte géologique de reconnaissance à l'échelle du 1/500.000.* Gouv. gen. Afrique Equatoriale Française. Paris.

FRANÇOIS, A. (1959). Excursions effectuées les 4, 5 et 6 juillet 1959, dans les terrains du systéme du Kundelungu. *Bull. Géol. Congo Belge Ruanda-Urundi*, **1**, 23.

FRANCOTTE, JEAN (1959). Excursions effectuées les 10, 11 et 12 juillet 1959, dans les terrains du faisceau de Mwashya. *Bull. Géol. Congo Belge Ruanda-Urundi*, **1**, 26.

FRIEDLAENDER, CARL (1942). Sur les gisements aurifères de la région de Musefu (Congo belge). *Bull. Suisse Minéral., Pétrol.*, **22**, 248.

GAZEL, JACQUES, HOURCQ, VICTOR et NICKLÈS, MAURICE (1956). Carte géologique du Cameroun au 1/1,000,000. Notice explicative. *Terr. Cameroun, Bull. Dir. Mines Géol.*, **2**.

GÉRARD, GEORGES (1958). Carte géologique de l'Afrique équatoriale française, au 1/2,000,000. Notice explicative. Gouv. Gen. Afrique Equatoriale Française., Dir. Mines et Géol., Paris.

GÉRARD, GEORGES et JEAN et HUGÉ, JACQUES (1951). Etudes géologiques dans l'Ubangi. *Intern. Geol. Congress, 18th, London, 1948*, **XIV**, 247.

GÉRARDS, JACQUES et LEPERSONNE, JACQUES (1964a). Géologie du Nord-Est du Rwanda et stratigraphie du Burundien. *Musée Roy. Afrique Centr., Sect. Géol., Minéral., et Paléontol., Rappt. Ann. 1963*, 58.

GÉRARDS, JACQUES et LEPERSONNE, JACQUES (1964b). La stratigraphie du Burundien dans le Nord-Est du Rwanda et les régions avoisinantes. *Bull. Serv. Géol. Rép. Rwandaise*, **1**, 13.

GYSIN, MARCEL (1960). L'existence de granites "jeunes" à la frontière du district cuprifère Nord-rhodésien. *Arch. Sci. (Geneva)*, **13**, 103.

HALLIGAN, R. (1963). The Proterozoic rocks of western Tanganyika. *Geol. Surv. Tanganyika, Bull.*, **34**.

HENRY, JOSUE (1924). Etude géologique au Congo belge dans la contrée comprise entre Basoko–Stanleyville à l'Ouest, le Lac Albert et la Semliki à l'Est. *Ann. Soc. Géol. Belg., Publ. Congo Belge*, **XLVI**, C49/C310.

HEPWORTH, J. V. (1962). The geology of southern West Nile, Uganda, with particular reference to the charnockites and to the development of the Albertine Rift (Ph.D.

thesis, University of Leeds). *Research Institute of African Geology, 6th Ann. Rept., Sci. Results,* 29.

HEPWORTH, J. V. (1964). Explanation of the geology of Sheets 19, 20, 28 and 29 (southern West Nile). *Geol. Surv. Uganda, Rept.,* **10**.

HERMAN, PIERRE et RAUCQ, PAUL (1961). Données complémentaires sur les chromites du Kasai (Congo). *Bull. Soc. Belge Géol., Paléontol., Hydrol.,* **70**, 336.

HOLMES, ARTHUR (1960). A revised geological time-scale. *Trans. Edinburgh Geol. Soc.,* **17**, 183.

HOLMES, ARTHUR et CAHEN, LUCIEN (1957). Géochronologie africaine 1956. *Acad. Roy. Sci. Coloniales (Brussels), Classe Sci. Nat., Méd., Mém., Collection in 8°,* **5**, Fasc. 1.

KORPERSHOEK, H. K. (1960). North Angolan Precambrian. Notes on the proposed stratigraphical scale of the second edition of the international geological map of Africa. *Commission Tech. Co-Op. Africa S. Sahara,* **44**, 63.

DE KUN, NICOLAS (1954). Les pegmatites du Nord Lugulu. *Ann. Soc. Géol., Belg.,* **78**, Fasc. spéc., M27.

DE KUN, NICOLAS (1959). Les gisements de cassitérite et de columbo-tantalite du Nord Lugulu, Kivu, Congo belge. *Ann. Soc. Géol. Belg.,* **82**, M81.

LEDENT, DOLLY et CAHEN, LUCIEN (1964). Quelques données géochronologiques inédites relatives au Nord-Est et à l'Est de la République du Congo. *Musée Roy. Afr. Centr., Sect. Geol., Minéral Paléontol., Rappt. Ann. 1963,* 94.

LEDENT, DOLLY, LAY, CLAUDE et DELHAL, JACQUES (1963). Premières données sur l'âge absolu des formations anciennes du "socle" du Kasai (Congo méridional). *Bull. Soc. Belge Géol., Paléontol., Hydrol.,* **71**, 223.

LEDOUX, AUGUSTE (1913). Les roches cristallines du Kasai, 1ère série. Roches granitiques. *Ann. Soc. Géol. Belg., Publ. Congo Belge,* **40**, C177.

LEGRAND, ROBERT (1955). Premiers résultats du levé de la feuille de Luiza (Congo belge). *Bull. Soc. Belge Géol., Paléontol., Hydrol.,* **64**, 387.

LEGRAND, ROBERT, LOHEST, ALEX et RAUCQ, PAUL (1958). Occurrence de chromite dans le massif ultrabasique de la Lutshatsha (Kasai). *Bull. Soc. Belge Géol., Paléontol., Hydrol.,* **67**, 259.

LEGRAND, ROBERT et RAUCQ, PAUL (1957). La faille de la Malafudi et son cadre géologique (Kasai). *Bull. Soc. Belge Géol., Paléontol., Hydrol.,* **66**, 109.

LEGRAYE, MICHEL (1940). Grands traits de la géologie et de la minéralisation des régions de Kilo et de Moto (Congo belge). *Mém. Inst. Roy. Colonial Belge, Classe Sci. Tech., Collection in 8°,* **24**, Fasc. 3.

LENK-CHEVITCH, PANTALEON (1948). Sur la stratigraphie du Système de l'Urundi au Kivu et au Ruanda–Urundi. *Bull. Soc. Belge Géol., Paléontol., Hydrol.,* **57**, 554.

LEPERSONNE, JACQUES (1941). Notes sur la géologie de la région de la Lulua. (Unpublished.)

LEPERSONNE, JACQUES (1951). Données nouvelles sur la stratigraphie des terrains anciens du Bas-Congo. *Bull. Soc. Belge Géol., Paléontol., Hydrol.,* **60**, 169.

LEPERSONNE, JACQUES (1956). Les aplanissements d'érosion du Nord-Est du Congo belge et des régions voisines. *Acad. Roy. Sci. Coloniales (Brussels), Classe Sci. Tech., Mém. Collection in 8°,* **4**, Fasc. 7.

LHOEST, ALBERT (1946). Une coupe remarquable des couches de base de l'Urundi dans l'Itombwe (Congo belge). *Ann. Soc. Géol. Belg.,* **69**, B250.

LHOEST, ALBERT (1957a). Les différents types de filons de la concession Somuki à Rutongo (Ruanda). *Ann. Soc. Géol. Belg.,* **80**, B503.

LHOEST, ALBERT (1957b). Note préliminaire sur la géologie de la région Kigali–Rutongo dans le Ruanda. *Bull. Soc. Belge Géol., Paléontol., Hydrol.,* **66**, 190.

LHOEST, ALBERT (1958). Contribution à l'étude du microplissement. *Ann. Soc. Géol. Belg.,* **81**, B255.

LHOEST, ALBERT (1961). A propos des couches de Miovi (Ruanda) assise supérieure de l'Urundi. *Ann. Soc. Géol. Belg.*, **84**, 617.

LHOEST, ALBERT (1964). Précisions sur la stratigraphie des couches de base du Système de l'Urundi dans la partie nord du synclinal de l'Itombwe. *Ann. Soc. Géol. Belg.*, **86**, B557.

LORMAND, JACQUES (1955). Rapport sur la géologie du Bas-Uélé. (Unpublished.)

McCONNELL, RICHARD B. (1959). The Buganda group, Uganda, East Africa. *Congr. Geol. Intern., 20th, Mexico 1956, Assoc. Serv. Geol. Afr.*, 163.

MACGREGOR, A. M. (1951). Some milestones in the Precambrian of Southern Rhodesia. *Trans. Geol. Soc. S. Africa*, **54**, XXVII.

DE MAGNÉE, IVAN (1955). Les chutes supérieures de la Luvua. *Bull. Acad. Roy. Sci. Col.* [N.S.], **1**, 1193.

DE MAGNÉE, IVAN et ADÉRCA, BERNARD (1960). Contribution à la connaissance du tungsten-belt ruandais. (Aspects géologiques, géochimiques, métallogéniques). *Acad. Roy. Sci. Outre–Mer (Brussels), Classe Sci. Tech., Mém in 8°*, **11**, Fasc. 7.

MARCHANDISE, HUBERT (1958). Le gisement et les minerais de manganèse de Kisenge (Congo belge). *Bull. Soc. Belge Géol., Paléontol., Hydrol.*, **67**, 187.

MESTRAUD, JEAN-LOUIS (1953). Notice explicative sur la feuille Bangassou-Ouest. *Carte géologique de reconnaissance à l'échelle du 1/500,000.* Gouvernement Genéral de l'Afrique Equatoriale Française. Paris.

MESTRAUD, JEAN-LOUIS (1957). Coupure Bangui-Est. *Bull. Dir. Mines Géol., Afr. Equator. Franç.*, **8**, 87.

MEYER DE STADELHOFEN, CAMILLE et RAUCQ, PAUL (1960). Discussion sur l'âge et la signification de la dolérite de Tshala. *Bull. Géol. Congo Belge Ruanda–Urundi*, **2**, 45.

MINÉTAIN (SOCIÉTÉ DES MINES D'ETAIN DU RUANDA-URUNDI) (1958). Carte géologique du Ruanda-Urundi d'aprés Salée et documents de prospection. Echelle 1:500,000. (Unpublished.)

MONTEYNE-POULAERT, GINETTE et CAHEN, LUCIEN (1964). Ages de granites, pegmatites et filons de la chaîne kibarienne au Katanga. *Musée Roy. Afr. Centr., Sect. Géol., Minéral., Paléontol., Rappt. Ann. 1963*, 88.

MONTEYNE-POULAERT, GINETTE, DELWICHE, ROBERT et CAHEN, LUCIEN (1963). Age de minéralisations pegmatitiques et filoniennes du Rwanda et du Burundi. *Bull. Soc. Belge Géol., Paléontol., Hydrol.*, **71**, 210.

MONTEYNE-POULAERT, GINETTE, DELWICHE, ROBERT, SAFIANNIKOFF, ALEXANDRE et CAHEN, LUCIEN (1963). Age de minéralisations pegmatitiques et filoniennes du Kivu méridional (Congo oriental). Indications préliminaires sur les âges de phases pegmatitiques successives. *Bull. Soc. Belge Géol., Paléontol., Hydrol.*, **71**, 272.

MOORBATH, S. (1959). Isotopic composition of lead from British mineral deposits. *Nature*, **183**, 595.

MORELLI, BRUNO et RAUCQ, PAUL (1961). Lambeaux d'une série métamorphique manganésifère entre Mwene Ditu et Luputa (Kasai). *Bull. Acad. Roy. Sci. Outre-Mer (Brussels)*, **7**, 908.

MORELLI, BRUNO et RAUCQ, PAUL (1962). "Quartzites" ferrugineux de Kanda-Kanda (Kasai, Congo). *Ann. Soc. Géol. Belg.*, **85**, B123.

MORTELMANS, GEORGES (1939). Les formations du Kibara dans le coin nord-ouest de la feuille Mokabe-Kasari, au Katanga. *Bull. Soc. Belge Géol., Paléontol., Hydrol.*, **49**, 163.

MOUREAU, ANDRÉ L. (1960). Le Kibara inférieur et moyen dans le sud-ouest katangais. *Bull. Géol. Congo Belge Ruanda–Urundi*, **2**, 1.

MURATA, KIGUMA J., ROSE, H. J. JR., CARRON, M. K., and GLASS, JEANNETTE J. (1957). Systematic variation of rare-earth elements in cerium-earth minerals. *Geochim. Cosmochim. Acta*, **11**, 141.

NINOVE, GREY (1954). Observations géologiques le long du 24e méridien, entre les parallèles 8° et 9° 30' Sud. *Ann. Serv. Mines Serv. Géogr. Géol. Comité Spécial du Katanga.* **17**, 93.

OOSTERBOSCH, ROBERT (1959). La série des mines du Katanga. *Bull. Géol. Congo Belge Ruanda–Urundi*, **1**, 3.

OOSTERBOSCH, ROBERT (1960). Les minéralisations dans le Système de Roan au Katanga. Summary in: *Chronique des Mines d'Outre-Mer et de la Recherche minière*, **28**, 5.

PATTERSON, CLAIRE C. (1956). Age of meteorites and the earth. *Geochim. Cosmochim. Acta*, **10**, 230.

PATTERSON, CLAIRE C., GOLDBERG, EDWARD D., and INGHRAM, MARK G. (1953). Isotopic compositions of Quaternary leads from the Pacific Ocean. *Bull. Geol. Soc. Am.*, **64**, 1387.

PEETERS, LEO (1952). Observations géomorphologiques et géologiques au Sud-Ouest de Costermansville (Kivu). *Ann. Musée Roy. Congo Belge, Sér. in 8°, Sci. Géol.* **10**.

PEETERS, LEO (1955). Coupe du synclinorium de l'Itombwe dans la région de Lubumba (Haute-Ulindi). *Bull. Acad. Roy. Sci. Coloniales (Brussels)*, **1**, 268.

PEETERS, LEO (1956). Contribution à la géologie des terrains anciens du Ruanda–Urundi et du Kivu. *Ann. Musée Roy. Congo Belge, Ser. in 8°, Sci. Géol.*, **16**.

PHILLIPS, W. J. (1959). Explanation of the geology of Sheet 87 (Rakai). *Geol. Surv. Uganda, Rept.* **2**.

POCKLEY, R. P. C. (1961). *Longer lead model age table V* (mimeographed). Department of Geology and Mineralogy, Oxford.

POLINARD, EDMOND (1934). Constitution géologique de l'Entre Lulua-Bushimaie, du 7e au 8e parallèle. *Inst. Roy. Colonial Belge, Classe. Sci. Nat. Méd., Mém. in 8°*, **11**, Fasc. 5.

POLINARD, EDMOND (1935). Contribution à l'étude des roches éruptives et des schistes cristallins de la région de Bondo. *Inst. Roy. Colonial Belge, Classe Sci. Nat. Méd., Mém. in 4°*, **4**, Fasc. 2.

QUENNELL, A. M. and HALDEMANN, EDUARD G. (1960). On the subdivision of the Precambrian. *Intern. Geol. Congr., 21st, Copenhagen, 1960, Rept. Session Norden*, **IX**, 170.

QUENNELL, A. M., McKINLAY, A. C. M., and AITKEN, W. G. (1956). Summary of the geology of Tanganyika. Pt. 1: Introduction and stratigraphy (Pre-Karroo). *Geol. Surv. Tanganyika, Mem.*, **1**.

RAUCQ, PAUL (1957). Contribution à la connaissance du Système de la Bushimay (Congo belge). *Ann. Musée. Roy. Congo Belge, Sér. in 8°, Sci. Géol.*, **18**.

RAUCQ, PAUL (1961). Note préliminaire sur les massifs ultra-basiques du Kasai central et certains de leurs constituants métalliques. *Ann. Soc. Géol. Belg.*, **84**, B591.

REECE, ALAN (1960). The stratigraphy, structure and metamorphism of the Pre-Cambrian rocks of North-West Ankole, Uganda. *Quart. J. Geol. Soc. (London)*, **115**, 389.

ROBERT, MAURICE (1940). Contribution à la géologie du Katanga. Le système du Kundelungu et le système schistodolomitique (1ère partie). *Inst. Roy. Colonial Belg., Classe Sci. Nat. Méd., Mém. in 4°*, **6**, Fasc. 2.

ROBERT, MAURICE (1956). *Géologie et géographie du Katanga*. Bruxelles.

RORIVE, RAYMOND (1954). *Le Système des Kibara aux Monts Kibara*. Thesis, Faculté Polytechnique de Mons. (Unpublished.)

RUSSELL, R. D. and FARQUHAR, RONALD M. (1960). *Lead isotopes in geology*. New York and London.

SAFIANNIKOFF, ALEXANDRE (1950). Les systèmes de l'Urundi et de la Ruzizi, au Kivu, et les intrusions granitiques. *Ann. Soc. Géol. Belg.*, **73**, M87.

SAFIANNIKOFF, ALEXANDRE (1954). Classification des pegmatites du Congo belge et du Ruanda–Urundi. *Ann. Soc. Géol. Belg.*, **78**, Fasc. spéc., M57.

SALÉE, ACHILLE (1931). Carte géologique de l'Urundi méridional. *Mém. Inst. Géol. Univ. Louvain*, **V**, 167/174.

SCHAAR, GEORGES (1959). Les mines d'or du 5e parallèle. *Acad. Roy. Sci. Coloniales (Brussels), Classe Sci. Tech., Mém., Collection in 8°*, **4**, Fasc. 1.

SCHERMERHORN, LODEWIJCK J. G. (1960). Sedimentary cycles and orogenies in the Precambrian of northern Angola. *Commission Tech. Co-op. Africa S. of Sahara*, **44**, 49.

SCHERMERHORN, LODEWIJCK J. G. and STANTON, WILLIAM I. (1960). Tilloids of Angola. *Proc. Geol. Soc.* (*London*), **1573-1582**, 117.

SCHERMERHORN, LODEWIJCK J. G. and STANTON, WILLIAM I. (1963a). Tilloids in the West Congo geosyncline. *Quart. J. Geol. Soc.* (*London*), **119**, 201; with discussion, 234.

SCHERMERHORN, LODEWIJCK J. G. and STANTON, WILLIAM I. (1963b). The geology of degree sheet Sul B-33 (Bembe). *Bol. Serv. Geol. Min. Angola*, **7**, 5.

SEKIRSKY, BORIS (1958). Contribution à la carte géologique de la région comprise entre la rive gauche du fleuve Congo et Lufu (Bas Congo). *Bull. Serv. Géol. Congo Belge Ruanda–Urundi*, **8**, No. 1.

SLUYS, MAURICE (1945). La géologie de l'Ituri. Le Groupe de la Lindi. *Bull. Serv. Géol. Congo Belge Ruanda–Urundi*, **1**, 95.

SNELLING, NORMAN J. (1963). Age determination unit. *Overseas Geol. Surv., Ann. Rept., 1962*, 30.

SNELLING, NORMAN J. (1964). Age determination unit. *Overseas Geol. Surv., Ann. Rept., 1963*, 30.

SNELLING, NORMAN J., HAMILTON, E. I., DRYSDALL, A. R., and STILMAN, C. J., (1964). A review of age determination from Northern Rhodesia. *Econ. Geol.*, **59**, 962.

SOROTCHINSKY, CONSTANTIN (1953). Les roches des gisements aurifères de Kilo-Moto. *Mém. Inst. Géol. Univ. Louvain*, **17**, 19.

STEENSTRA, BENVENUTO (1954). Geology and petrography of the Kilo region (N.E. Belgian Congo). Thesis. 's-Gravenhage.

STHEEMAN, H. A. (1932). The geology of southwestern Uganda with special reference to the stanniferous deposits. Thesis. The Hague.

STIEFF, LORIN R., STERN, THOMAS W., OSHIRO, SEIKI and SENFTLE, FRANK E. (1959). Tables for the calculation of lead isotope ages. *U.S. Geol. Surv., Profess. Papers*, **334-A.**

STOCKLEY, G. M. and WILLIAMS, G. J. (1938). Explanation of the geology, Degree Sheet n° 1 (Karagwe Tinfields). *Bull. Geol. Surv. Tanganyika*, **10**.

THONNART, PIERRE (1955). Un poudingue au contact des quartzites et des roches vertes à Matadi. *Ann. Soc. Géol. Belg.*, **78**, B121.

THONNART, PIERRE (1956). Le conglomérat de Yelala. Sa contribution à l'étude stratigraphique et tectonique de la région de Matadi. *Bull. Serv. Géol. Congo Belge Ruanda–Urundi*, **6**, No. 6.

THOREAU, JACQUES (1935). Les gisements d'or dérivent-ils de magmas basiques? *Congr. Intern. Mines, Mét., Géol. Appl., 7e Paris 1935*, **1**, 3.

THOREAU, JACQUES (1956). Le granite à riebeckite de la région du Kahusi (Kivu). *Bull. Acad. Roy. Sci. Coloniales* (*Brussels*), **2**, 408.

THOREAU, JACQUES (1960). Le socle granitique du degré carré de Dibaya (Kasai). *Colloque Géochim. Liège, 1960, Centre. Nat. Rech. Géochim.*, Publ. 2 [Stencilled].

THOREAU, JACQUES, ADERCA, BERNARD et VAN WAMBEKE, LÉOPOLD (1958). Le gisement de terres rares de la Karonge (Urundi). *Bull. Acad. Roy. Sci. Coloniales* (*Brussels*), **4**, 684.

THOREAU, JACQUES et SAFIANNIKOFF, ALEXANDRE (1957). Triphylite, lithiophilite et phosphates associés du Congo belge et du Ruanda. *Bull. Acad. Roy. Belg., Classe Sci.*, **43**, 324.

VAES, JEAN F. (1960). Discussion of "Petrology of some Rhodesian orebodies and associated rocks". *Trans. Inst. Mining Met.*, **69**, 392.

VAES, JEAN F. (1961). L'uraninite dans les sédiments du Roan à Musoshi (Katanga sud-oriental). *Ann. Musée. Roy. Afr. Centr., Sér. in 8°, Sci. Géol.*, **41**.

VAES, JEAN F. (1962). A study of the metamorphism of the Roan sediments at the Musoshi copper deposits and its consequences. *Ann. Musée Roy. Afr. Centr., Sér. in 8°, Sci. Géol.*, **43**.

VAN DE STEEN, JEAN (1959). Le système des Kibara. *Bull. Géol. Congo Belge Ruanda-Urundi*, **1**, 8.

VAN DE WALLE, MARC (1960). Le stratigraphie du Kibara au Nord du 9ème parallèle. *Bull. Géol. Congo Belge Ruanda-Urundi*, **2**, 35.

VANDEN BRANDE, PIERRE (1937). Essai de division stratigraphique des formations primaires du Katanga méridional. *Bull. Soc. Belge Géol., Paléontol., Hydrol.*, **68**, 9.

VARLAMOFF, NICOLAS (1949). Relations entre les faciès des cristaux de cassitérite de la région de Kalima (Congo belge) et la géologie de leurs gisements. *Ann. Soc. Géol. Belg.*, **72**, B289.

VARLAMOFF, NICOLAS (1950). Granites et minéralisation au Maniema (Congo belge). *Ann. Soc. Géol. Belg., Mém.*, **73**, 111.

VARLAMOFF, NICOLAS (1953). Géologie des gisements stannifères de Symétain (Maniema, Congo belge). *Mém. Inst. Roy. Coloniale Belge, Classe Sci. Nat. Méd., Collection in 8°*, **22**, Fasc. 2.

VARLAMOFF, NICOLAS (1954). Matériaux pour l'étude des pegmatites du Congo belge et du Ruanda-Urundi. *Ann. Soc. Géol. Belg.*, **78**, Fasc. spéc. M1.

VARLAMOFF, NICOLAS (1957). Considérations sur la zonéographie et le zonage interne des pegmatites africaines. *Commission Tech. Co-op. Afr. S. Sahara, 2nd Meeting, Tananarive, 1957*, 95.

VARLAMOFF, NICOLAS (1958a). Succession des minéralisations stannifères et wolframifères du Maniema. *Ann. Soc. Géol. Belg.*, **81**, B275.

VARLAMOFF, NICOLAS (1958b). Les gisements de tungstène au Congo belge et au Ruanda-Urundi. Matériaux pour l'étude de leur géologie et de leur classification. *Acad. Roy. Sci. Coloniales (Brussels), Classe Sci. Tech., Mém. Collection in 8°*, **8**, Fasc. 2.

VARLAMOFF, NICOLAS (1959). Zonéographie de quelques champs pegmatitiques de l'Afrique centrale et les classifications de K. A. Vlassov et de A. I. Guinsburg. *Ann. Soc. Géol. Belg.*, **82**, B55.

VERBEEK, THEO (1960). Geologie en lithologie van de Groep van de Lindi (Noord-Oost Kongo). Thesis, Universiteit Gent. (Unpublished.)

WALEFFE, ARMAND (1965). Etude géologique du Sud-Est du Burundi (Régions du Mosso et du Nkoma). *Ann. Musée Roy. Afr. Centr., Sér. in 8°, Sci. Géol.*, **48**.

WEIS, GEORGES (1959). Le pays d'Uvira. Etude de géographie régionale sur la bordure occidentale du lac Tanganyika. *Acad. Roy. Sci. Coloniales (Brussels), Classe Sci. Nat., Méd., Mém., Collection in 8°*, **8**, Fasc. 5.

WOODTLI, ROBERT (1954). Contribution à l'étude géologique et pétrographique de la région orientale des mines de Kilo (Congo belge). *Mém. Inst. Géol. Univ. Louvain*, **19**, 1.

WOODTLI, ROBERT (1955). Une hypothèse sur l'origine des itabirites (note préliminaire). *Compt. Rend. Soc. Géol. France* [6], **5**, 52.

WOODTLI, ROBERT (1957a). L'origine des venues aurifères aux mines de Kilo (Congo belge). *Bull. Soc. Vaudoise Sci. Nat.*, **66**, 321.

WOODTLI, ROBERT (1957b). La structure de Kilo. Contribution à l'étude des fossés africains. *Acad. Roy. Sci. Coloniales (Brussels), Classe Sci. Tech., Mém., Collection in 8°*, **6**, Fasc. 2.

WOODTLI, ROBERT (1959). Description de quelques sondages dans les itabirites au N.-E. du Congo belge. *Congr. Intern. Geol., 20th, Mexico 1956, Ass. Serv. Geol. Afr.*, 469.

WOODTLI, ROBERT (196). Iron ore resources of the northeastern Congo. *Econ. Geol.*, **54**, 1385.

AUTHOR INDEX [1]

[1] Page numbers in *italics* refer to Bibliographies.

SUBJECT INDEX